College Geometry

ALSO BY LAWRENCE A. RINGENBERG
Informal Geometry (1967)

COLLEGE GEOMETRY

LAWRENCE A. RINGENBERG

Dean, College of Letters and Science
Eastern Illinois University

John Wiley and Sons, Inc.   New York   London   Sydney

To VI and
    RICH, JODY, and JOHN

Preface

A generation ago school geometry included some work with mensuration formulas in the upper grades of the elementary schools and one or two courses in geometry in the high schools. The college geometry course in those days typically was a course in advanced Euclidean geometry. The geometrical superstructure created in such a course rested on a foundation which had changed very little since the time of Euclid. Such courses reflected the genius of Euclid as well as some of the flaws and weaknesses in his development of geometry.

Today geometry permeates school mathematics from kindergarten through grade twelve. At the elementary school level the approach to geometry is largely informal. At the high school level an important objective is to develop Euclidean geometry as a formal system or structure. The modern high school geometry course is based on an improved version of Euclid, the improvements resulting from the work of Lobachevsky, Bolyai, Gauss, Hilbert, Birkoff, and a host of mathematicians and teachers who have been a part of the mid-twentieth century revolution in school mathematics.

This text was written as a flexible text for modern college geometry courses, to follow a high school level course, whether old fashioned or modern. This book is designed to help students review elementary geometry, to provide students with a solid modern foundation for

Euclidean geometry, and to extend the structure of Euclidean geometry beyond that normally achieved in high schools.

Chapter 1 begins with a discussion of formal versus informal geometry; it is for the most part informal plane geometry. Its purpose is to help students review elementary geometry and to experience the rediscovery of geometry through measurement, observation, intuition, and inductive reasoning. Appendix 1 may be considered an extension of Chapter 1. It is informal solid geometry.

Beginning with Chapter 2 the development is formal. It is a modern development using the point set approach. Space is considered as the set of all points. Lines and planes are sets of points satisfying certain incidence postulates. Rays, segments, angles, and triangles are defined as sets of points satisfying certain properties. The ruler and protractor postulates play key roles in the development. Coordinates are introduced early and are used extensively throughout large portions of the book. Distance and coordinates on a line are closely related in this development; the same is true of angle measure and ray-coordinates. Distance relative to a pair of points (which may be thought of as providing the unit of distance) is an important feature. The relationship among various coordinate systems on a line is developed early and is used in developing parametric equations. Parametric equations appear repeatedly in the development of the geometry of a line, of a plane, and of space.

The parallel postulate is introduced with a discussion of Euclidean and non-Euclidean geometries. A sequence of theorems in neutral geometry is designed to impress upon the student the common part of the geometries of Euclid and Lobachevsky as well as various equivalent ways in which their essential difference may be expressed.

Chapters 11 to 14 contain a modern treatment of several topics found in traditional college geometry texts.

This book may be used for courses suitable for students with a variety of backgrounds. It is particularly suited for prospective secondary school teachers, or teachers who wish to update their preparation in geometry. For students with weak backgrounds a course of 35 to 45 lessons based on Chapters 1 to 6 and Appendix 1 would be appropriate. An appropriate alternate course could be based on Chapters 1 to 10. To achieve a suitable pace it might be desirable to omit the proofs of the theorems in Chapters 8 and 10.

For students with a better background Chapter 1 might be omitted or assigned for independent study. A one-term course could be based on

Chapters 2 to 9, with a selection of topics from the remaining chapters. The entire text, including Appendix 1, may be used as a text for a two-course sequence totaling 60 to 90 lessons.

Appendix 2, *Computing with Approximate Data*, is designed for use as reference material or as regular text material. It should be helpful in creating a sensible attitude with regard to the number of digits retained in answers to numerical problems.

Appendix 3, *The Language and Symbols of Sets,* is included as reference material. Although the language of sets is a part of the background of many students, it is expected that some students will need to be introduced to unions, intersections, and subsets.

I served as a member of the SMSG Geometry With Coordinates (GW) writing team in 1961 and 1962. I am indebted to the School Mathematics Study Group for permission to use materials from the GW text. It should be noted, however, that SMSG has made no endorsement of *College Geometry*.

It is with great pleasure that I express my appreciation to those who have helped or encouraged me in writing this book. I am particularly indebted to the editorial staff of John Wiley and Sons and to several consultants, anonymous to me, who suggested improvements in the manuscript.

Lawrence A. Ringenberg

Charleston, Illinois

Foreword to the Student

I assume you are enrolled in a course for which this is the official text. My best wishes to you for an enjoyable and stimulating intellectual experience!

If you have not done so, go back and read the Preface. This will give you an overview of the book. This will help you to see how elementary geometry, foundations of geometry, and advanced topics of geometry fit into the pattern of this book.

Depending upon the time available and the specific objectives of your course, it may be that Chapter 1 and Appendix 1 on elementary geometry will be a part of your course, or they may be omitted from your course. If they are omitted, I urge you to read them anyway. If you have a good background, you will read them rather quickly, and the hasty review will be good for you. You will want to read more carefully those sections in which the ideas seem unfamiliar. You should work at least a few exercises in each list. If they seem easy for you, then a few is probably enough. If they seem not so easy, then you ought to read the text again and work more exercises.

Paper and pencil should be at hand when reading geometry—for doodling. Of course, there are some figures in the book. But you should draw many more. When you read, "Let L be a line and let A and B be two distinct points on L," draw a picture before you read any more.

A successful student of geometry must be able to think big, and he must be able to think little. He should look at the forest, at the trees, and even at the leaves on the trees. For example, suppose you have studied thoroughly Chapter 1 and Appendix 1, over a four-week period of time. You have looked at lots of trees in a forest. Do you appreciate the forest? You will see it a lot more clearly if you go back and reread all of this material in one afternoon or evening.

In studying a chapter for the first time it is a good idea to attempt to get the big picture first, then to chew on the details, and then to look at the whole again. Reviewing a week's work, or a month's work, with an honest effort to understand the big ideas, is important for mastery and understanding and as preparation for proceeding to new ideas.

L.A.R.

Contents

College Geometry

Elementary Geometry

1.1 *Introduction*

What is geometry? Geometry is a branch of knowledge with origins in antiquity. It includes our great heritage of knowledge regarding those properties of space and objects which have to do with the form, shape, and size of things. Geometry has its roots in man's experiences with physical objects. Modern geometries are abstract structures created by man in his efforts to organize geometrical facts and to create more geometry.

Primitive man had his first experience in geometry outside a classroom. He observed geometric figures in the heavenly bodies and in mineral crystals and snowflakes; in the leaf arrangement of plants and the structure of fruits and vegetables; in the spider's web, the bird's nest, and the bee's honeycomb. The universal existence of geometric form in nature led Plato to declare that "God eternally geometrizes." The conscious development of form was enhanced by man's esthetic nature and by the practical necessities of life. Through the manual activities needed in making clothing and rugs and building shelters and homes, man learned much about shape, size, and position. Geometric figures were favorite ornaments among nearly all primitive peoples. They were used in jewelry and in the architecture and decoration of the temples. In the early pottery of Egypt, Babylon, and other countries we can trace the progressive development of the appreciation of the beauties of geometric form by early peoples. Thus in a sense an appreciation of the artistic led to an appreciation of the geometric.

The ancient Egyptians and Babylonians made considerable progress in geometry. They developed the art of measuring land in connection with agriculture and irrigation. Apparently they knew how to compute the area of a trapezoid. In working with the circle they used, as did the early Hebrews, the value $\pi = 3$. The building of the pyramids between 3000 and 2400 B.C. required the application of several geometric principles. Extensive irrigation projects in Egypt were executed about 2200 B.C. Each year the ancient Egyptians resurveyed their farms. Last year's boundary markers would shift or disappear as a result of the flooding of the Nile River. This is the basis of the statement that "geometry is the gift of the Nile." Indeed, geometry literally means earth measurement. The prefix "geo," meaning earth, is found in such words as geology and geography, and "metry," meaning measure, appears in such words as metric, meter, and thermometer.

The idea of proving a rule or proposition by logical reasoning was unknown before the Greek civilization. The Greeks must have obtained their first taste for geometry from the Egyptian priests. But the philosophical debating societies of Greece were not content merely to accept the rules of practical geometry. The time was ripe for men of intelligence to organize the practical geometry of the Egyptians into a sequence of proved theorems. The list of Greek scholars important in the history of geometry includes Thales (born about 600 B.C.), Plato (429–348 B.C.), and Eudoxus (born about 400 B.C.).

In 322 B.C. Alexander the Great built the city of Alexandria at the mouth of the Nile. This city, inhabited by Egyptians and Greeks, became the center of literature, philosophy, science, and mathematics for the next thousand years. The founder of the mathematical school at the University of Alexandria and its most important teacher was Euclid, who lived around 300 B.C. Little is known of Euclid's life, though it is believed he studied in Athens under Plato.

Euclid's greatest work, the *Elements*, contains thirteen books:

Book 1. Rectilinear figures   Book 5. Proportion

Book 2. Geometric algebra, area   Book 6. Similar figures

Book 3. Circles, chords, and tangents   Books 7–10. Theory of numbers

Book 4. Polygons and circles   Books 11–13. Solid geometry

We do not know how much of the *Elements* is original with Euclid. It is certain that he made use of the work of mathematicians who preceded him. Euclid's great achievement was in systematizing the mass of material which had accumulated for three centuries since the time of Pythagoras. No writer in any branch of knowledge has exerted such an influence on his subject as has Euclid on elementary geometry. The *Elements* has been the most widely used text the world has ever produced. It has dominated the teaching of geometry for twenty-three centuries.

As a school subject, geometry has two purposes: one is to teach the facts of geometry, and the other is to teach the nature of proof. Geometry may be classified according to these two purposes as *informal* geometry and *formal* or *demonstrative* geometry. The basis of informal geometry is the physical world. Informal geometry is developed through intuition, experimentation, observation, and inductive reasoning. A formal geometry is developed as an abstract mathematical system. The basis of formal Euclidean geometry is also the physical world. It is our ultimate source of all ideas regarding shape and size. But a formal geometry is a self-contained logical system. It includes undefined terms, postulates (sometimes called axions), definitions, and theorems.

In a formal mathematical system a definition is a statement which explains the meaning of one word in terms of the meanings of other words, and a theorem is a statement derived from other statements by logical reasoning. In his *Elements* Euclid defined a point as "that which has no part." Such a definition is of little if any value in building geometry as a formal structure. Actually, Euclid did not use this definition in his proofs. The only properties of a point which he uses in his proofs are the relationships of points to other basic elements such as lines and planes, relationships which are stated in the postulates.

In building a modern mathematical system we stand on the shoulders of giants—giants who learned that the only possible way to build an acceptable abstract system is to leave some terms undefined and some statements unproved. In modern Euclidean geometry we consider points, lines, and planes as the primitive concepts, the most basic of all the objects under consideration. We do not define them. We consider them as abstractions with properties derived from objects and from the relationships among objects in space. We formulate the most basic of these relationships as statements which we call postulates. These statements we accept without proof. If P and Q are any two points, there is exactly one line containing them. This is a basic relationship of points and lines.

We accept it without proof in formal Euclidean geometry. Although Euclid's *Elements* contains a number of basic unproved statements called axioms and postulates, it was Hilbert (1862–1943) who first clearly recognized the necessity for undefined terms in a logical system and who first (1899) gave a suitable system of axioms for Euclidean geometry.

The objects in a formal geometry are abstractions. They have no physical substance. Their only properties we can use in developing a formal geometry are the properties which they have because of the postulates or properties that have been proved in theorems. The theorems in formal geometry are true statements. They derive their truth through logical reasoning. In proving theorems we can use only statements previously established. These include theorems, definitions and postulates. A mathematical structure is created by defining terms (each term is defined in terms of words previously defined or words which are left undefined) and by proving theorems (each theorem is derived solely from preceding theorems, postulates, or definitions). The postulates and the undefined terms are the foundation stones of the system. The definitions and the theorems are the superstructure.

What about the figures in a geometry text? Does the presence of figures which can be seen mean that the text is a text on informal geometry? Not necessarily. It is customary to draw figures to suggest situations or mutual relationships which exist in our minds. If the printed text is a record of geometry developed logically so that each item in the chain of reasoning has preceding results and/or axioms as its basis, then the geometry is a formal one. In a formal geometry one may get ideas by drawing pictures, by observing many cases, by making constructions and measurements; but those ideas are not admitted into the system as an integral part of the formal geometry unless they are stated as axioms or are proved to be logical consequences of preceding statements in the system.

Geometry as a school subject has both characteristics, the formal and the informal. In elementary and junior schools the informal approach predominates. At the senior high school level the main objective of the geometry course is to develop elementary geometry as a formal system.

The approach in Chapter 1 and Appendix 1 is largely informal. In several instances there are short chains of theorems obtained by deductive reasoning. For the most part, however, the theorems are motivated by experiences with physical objects or pictures and are stated without proof.

The purpose of Chapter 1 and Appendix 1 is to help students review and extend their understanding of the facts and formulas of elementary geometry.

In Chapters 2 to 14 the formal approach is predominant. In Chapters 2 to 10 a formal structure suitable for the needs of modern elementary geometry is developed. Chapters 11 to 14 treat several topics not usually included in a secondary school level course.

1.2 *Sets of Points and Measures*

Geometry is concerned with space and the size and shape of things that occupy space. To facilitate the study of geometric properties of objects it is convenient to study abstractions which have these geometric properties but do not have such irrelevant properties as weight, color, flexibility, strength, and radioactivity. These abstractions are geometric figures, or what amounts to the same thing, sets of points. Intuitively every point looks like every other point. Two distinct points are different in their position or location. We think of a point as something very small. By comparison, a tiny dot which we use to represent a point is very large. We think of a point as the smallest of the various geometrical abstractions, something with neither size nor shape. What really counts with a point is its position; that is all that matters. Two points are distinct if and only if their positions are distinct. Of course, this is not a profound observation. What we really are saying is that, at least in our geometry, point and position are synonymous. Elsewhere, in a variety of contexts, one may find statements about a "moving point," for example, a point P moves so as to generate a circle. From our point of view we would regard the letter P used in this way as a variable, that is, as a symbol to which various values or replacements are assigned. The set of all these replacements is a set of points. Precisely, it is the circle which might be described as generated by P.

It is interesting to think of a point as the intersection of two distinct intersecting lines. Regardless of the angles formed by these lines, their

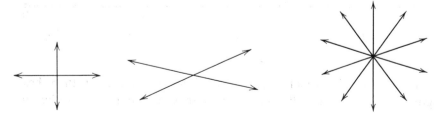

intersection is a set consisting of one point. A point may be the intersection of infinitely many lines, or of infinitely many planes, or of a plane
and a line. A point may be the vertex of an angle or the common vertex
of infinitely many angles. A set of points may be a line, or a plane, or an
angle, or a right triangle. We proceed to examine these ideas more carefully.

Modern Euclidean geometry begins with space considered as a set of
points, with certain subsets of space called lines, and with other subsets
called planes. Every line is a set of infinitely many points. Every plane is
a set of infinitely many points. Two points determine a line. More precisely,
if A and B are two distinct points, there is exactly one (sometimes we say
a unique line, or one and only one line) line which contains A and B. We
might assign a name to a line, for example, line L. Sometimes it is convenient to use a name which shows the names of two distinct points on it.
The unique line determined by two distinct points A and B is denoted by
$\overleftrightarrow{AB}$.

A *segment* (or line segment if you prefer) is a subset of a line which
consists of two distinct points of a line, called the *endpoints* of the segment,
and all of the points of the line between those two points. If A and B are
distinct points, $\overline{AB}$ denotes the segment with endpoints A and B. Since
there are infinitely many points between every two distinct points of a
line, it follows that every segment is an infinite set of points.

A *ray* is a subset of a line which consists of a point called the *endpoint*
of the ray, say point A; a point of the line distinct from A, call it B; all
of the points P which lie between A and B; and all of the points Q such
that B lies between A and Q. If A and B are distinct points of a line, $\overrightarrow{AB}$
denotes the ray which has endpoint A and which contains B. Since every
ray contains a segment, it follows that every ray is an infinite set of points.
Every point of a line is the endpoint of two distinct rays, called *opposite*
rays, which are subsets of that line. The intersection of these rays is their
common endpoint. The union of two opposite rays is the line which
contains them.

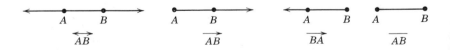

If there is a line which contains all of the points of a set, then these
points are said to be *collinear*; otherwise they are said to be *noncollinear*.

Three noncollinear points determine a plane. More precisely, if A, B, C are three noncollinear points, then there is exactly one plane which contains them. The unique plane which contains three noncollinear points A, B, C, is sometimes called plane ABC. We think of lines as being straight and planes as being flat. Every line looks like every other line, and every plane looks like every other plane. Segments of a line may differ in size, but they all have the same shape. The flatness property of a plane and the straightness property of a line are related in the following interesting way. If A and B are any two distinct points of a plane P, then the entire line $\overleftrightarrow{AB}$ is a subset of P. Have you ever seen a concrete finisher or a cabinetmaker test the flatness of a surface using a straightedge?

A subset of a plane is sometimes called a *plane figure*. If A, B, C are noncollinear points, then the set which consists of these points is a plane figure. Do you see why? Suppose D, E, F are distinct collinear points. Is the set which consists of D, E, F a plane figure? Let P be any plane that contains the line which contains the points D, E, F. Then P contains D, E, and F; hence the set consisting of D, E, and F is a plane figure.

One of the most familiar plane figures in elementary geometry is an angle. An *angle* is the union of two rays which have a common endpoint. If the two rays are opposite rays, we have a special case. Such a plane figure is sometimes called a *straight angle*. Sometimes we consider the special case in which the "two" rays are the same ray. This might be thought of as the zero-angle. The rays whose union is an angle are called the *sides of the angle*.

$\angle ABC$ denotes the angle which is the union of the rays $\overrightarrow{BA}$ and $\overrightarrow{BC}$. The point B is called the *vertex* of the angle.

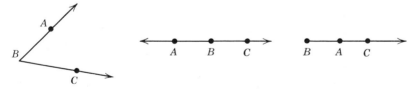

Another familiar plane figure in elementary geometry is a triangle. A *triangle* is a set consisting of three noncollinear points and the three segments determined by them. More precisely, if A, B, and C are three noncollinear points, then the union of the three segments $\overline{AB}, \overline{BC}, \overline{CA}$ is a triangle. This triangle is denoted by $\triangle ABC$. Each of the segments $\overline{AB}, \overline{BC}, \overline{CA}$ is called a *side* of the triangle. Each of the angles $\angle ABC, \angle BCA, \angle CAB$ is called *an angle of the triangle*.

A triangle is a special case of a polygon. A triangle is a three-sided polygon. A triangle is also a special case of a simple closed curve, that is,

A simple closed curve

A curve that is closed but not simple

A curve that is simple but not closed

A curve that is neither simple or closed

a curve with no endpoints that does not cross itself. A simple closed curve bounds a portion of the plane called its *interior*, and all of the points not in the interior of the curve or on the curve itself are said to be in the exterior of the curve. Thus a triangle separates the plane in which it lies, forming an exterior set, an interior set, and the triangle itself. Similarly,

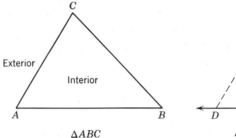
△*ABC*

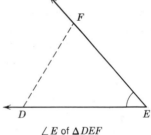
∠ *E* of △*DEF*

every polygon is a plane figure which separates the plane which contains it. Every polygon has an interior and an exterior (or an inside and an out-side if your prefer). Every polygon is the union of a set (three or more) of segments called the sides of the polygon. The endpoints of these sides are the vertices of the polygon. Four-sided polygons are called quadri-laterals. Five-sided polygons are called pentagons. Do you know the meaning of hexagon, octagon, heptagon, decagon, dodecagon, nonagon, 23-gon?

The *distance* between two points is a combination of a number and a unit of measure, for example, 3.1 feet. The *measure of an angle* is a combina-tion of a number and a unit of measure, for example, 135°. In this chapter we shall suppose that a unit for measuring distances has been fixed (you may think of feet if you wish) and that degrees are used throughout for measuring angles. Usually we shall not indicate the unit when recording distances or angle measures. The degree measure of ∠ *ABC* is denoted by

$m\angle ABC$. The statement $m\angle ABC = 60$ means that the degree measure of $\angle ABC$ is 60. If we speak of a 30° angle or if we mark an angle as 30° in a figure, we mean that the degree measure is 30.

If A and B are points, then AB is the distance between A and B. Thus $AB = 15$ is a short way of saying that the distance from A to B (or B to A) is 15. The *length* of a segment $\overline{AB}$ is the distance between its endpoints.

A useful idea in elementary geometry is the concept of a *number line.* Each point of a number line is considered to be matched with a number in such a way that the distance between any two points of the line may be obtained by subtracting the numbers which are matched with the points, subtracting the smaller from the larger so as to get a positive number for the difference. Thus if R and S are matched with -5 and -3, respectively, we may subtract the smaller number, -5, from the larger number, -3, to verify that $RS = 2$. The points of a number line have the same between-ness relations as the numbers which are matched with them. Thus if points A, B, C are matched with numbers a, b, c, respectively, on a number line, then B is between A and C if and only if b is between a and c. For A, P, Q in the preceding illustration, do you see that $AP = PA = a - p$? Note also that $q - p - (q - a) + (a - p)$, which agrees with the fact that $PQ = QA + AP$.

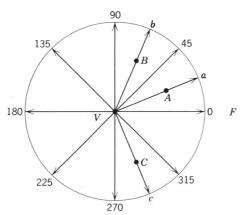

Another useful idea in elementary geometry is the concept of a *number wheel.* This might be thought of as a 360° protractor in a plane F and with center V. Each ray in F and with endpoint V is matched with a number

from 0 to 360, 0 included and 360 excluded, in such a way that the measures
of angles in F with vertex V may be computed using the numbers which
are matched with the sides of the angle. If $\overrightarrow{VP}$ and $\overrightarrow{VQ}$ are matched with
the numbers p and q, respectively, and if $p > q$, then $m\angle PVQ = p - q$
or $360 - (p - q)$, whichever is smaller. For the preceding illustration do
you see that $m\angle AVB = b - a$, $m\angle AVC = 360 - (c - a)$, and $m\angle BVC$
$= 360 - (c - b)$?

Every angle (not the zero angle) separates the plane that contains it.
A straight angle separates a plane which contains it into three components,
itself and two sets called *halfplanes*. An angle other than a zero angle or
a straight angle separates the plane which contains it into three components: itself, a set called the interior of the angle, and a set called the
exterior of the angle.

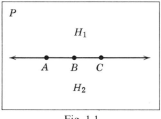
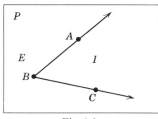

Fig. 1.1   Fig. 1.2

Figure 1.1 suggests a plane P containing a straight angle, $\angle ABC$. All
the points of P not on $\angle ABC$ make up two halfplanes, H_1 and H_2.
Figure 1.2 suggests a plane P containing an angle, $\angle ABC$, not a straight
angle or a zero angle. All the points of P not on $\angle ABC$ make up two sets
of points, one labeled I called the interior of the angle and one labeled E
called the exterior of the angle.

Two coplanar angles with a common side and whose interiors do not
intersect are called *adjacent angles*. Two coplanar angles (not straight
angles) whose union is the union of two lines, and which are not adjacent
angles, are called *vertical angles*. Angle A and angle B, distinct or not, are
called *supplementary* angles, and each is called the *supplement* of the other,
if and only if the sum of their measures is 180. Angle A and angle B,
distinct or not, are called *complementary angles*, and each is called the
complement of the other, if and only if the sum of their measures is 90. A
right angle is an angle whose measure is 90. An *obtuse* angle is an angle
whose measure is greater than 90. An *acute* angle is an angle whose measure
is less than 90. Two lines are *perpendicular* if their union contains a right
angle, or equivalently, if their union is the union of four distinct right

angles. A triangle is a *right triangle* if and only if one of its angles is a right angle. A triangle is an *obtuse triangle* if and only if one of its angles is an obtuse angle.

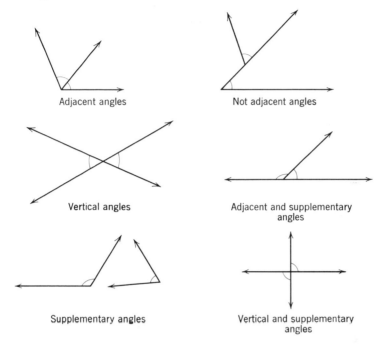

Adjacent angles	Not adjacent angles
Vertical angles	Adjacent and supplementary angles
Supplementary angles	Vertical and supplementary angles

Another familiar plane figure is a circle. A *circle* is the set of all points in a given plane at a given distance from a given point in the plane. More precisely, if C is a point in a plane P, and if r is a positive number, then the set of all points in P which are at a distance r from C is a circle. The point C (which is not part of the circle) is called the *center* of the circle. The number r is called the *radius* of the circle. Sometimes a segment which joins the center of a circle to a point of the circle (in other words, the center is one endpoint and a point of the circle is the other endpoint) is called a *radius* of the circle. A circle has one and only one radius, when radius is used in the sense of a number. A circle has infinitely many radii, when radius is used in the sense of a segment. A circle is an example of a simple closed curve. It separates the plane which contains it. It has an interior and an exterior.

A familiar space figure is a sphere. A *sphere* is the set of all points at a fixed distance from a given point. More precisely, if C is a point and if r is a positive number, then the set of all points which are at a distance r

from C is a sphere. The point C is called the *center* of the sphere and the number r is called the *radius* of the sphere. Sometimes a segment joining the center to a point of the sphere is called a *radius* of the sphere. A sphere is an example of a simple closed surface. It separates space, forming three components: itself, its interior, and its exterior.

We think of congruent figures as those which have the same shape and size. In the world of physical objects we see congruent figures every day: objects built to the same specifications on an assembly line or objects which are carbon copies of the same object. In geometry we consider all segments to have the same shape, and we agree that they have the same size if their lengths are the same. We also agree that two angles have the same shape and size if they have the same measure. Our formal definitions are as follows.

Definition. Two segments, distinct or not, are *congruent* if and only if their lengths are equal.

Definition. Two angles, distinct or not, are *congruent* if and only if their measures are equal.

In symbols, if $\overline{AB}$ and $\overline{CD}$ are segments, then $\overline{AB} \cong \overline{CD}$ if and only if $AB = CD$. Similarly, $\angle ABC \cong \angle DEF$ if and only if $m\angle ABC = m\angle DEF$.

A fundamental property of measure is the additive property which may be stated roughly as follows. *The measure of the whole is the sum of the measures of its parts.* In higher mathematics the conditions under which this property holds are examined critically. For segments and angles it works as one would expect it to work when thinking of the number line and the number wheel. More precisely, it works as we describe in the next paragraph.

If A, B, C, D, E are collinear points arranged as indicated in the following figure then $AE = AB + BC + CD + DE$, $AC = AB + BC$, $AC = AD - CD$, and so on. If $\overrightarrow{FH}$ is a ray between the two sides $\overrightarrow{FG}$ and $\overrightarrow{FI}$ of $\angle GFI$ then $m\angle GFI = m\angle GFH + m\angle HFI$.

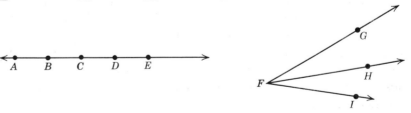

In modern mathematics an equation such as $A = B$ is considered to be a true statement if and only if "A" and "B" are names for the same thing.

Thus $3 + 4 = 7$ is a true statement since "$3 + 4$" and "7" are two names for the same number. Similarly, the equation $\overleftrightarrow{AB} = \overleftrightarrow{CD}$ means that "$\overleftrightarrow{AB}$" and "$\overleftrightarrow{CD}$" are names for the same line; $\angle ABC = \angle DEF$ means that "$\angle ABC$" and "$\angle DEF$" are names for the same angle; $AB = CD$ means that "AB" and "CD" are names for the same number; and $m\angle ABC = m\angle DEF$ means that "$m\angle ABC$" and "$m\angle DEF$" are names for the same number.

Exercises 1.2

1. If A, B, C are three noncollinear points, which of the following statements are true?

$$\overleftrightarrow{AB} = \overleftrightarrow{BA}, \quad \overleftrightarrow{AB} = \overleftrightarrow{AC}, \quad A = B, \quad \angle ABC \cong \angle ABC, \quad \angle ABC = \angle BAC,$$
$$\overrightarrow{AB} = \overrightarrow{BA}, \quad \overrightarrow{AB} = \overrightarrow{BA}, \quad \overline{AB} \cong \overline{BA}.$$

2. If A, B, C are three collinear points with B between A and C, which of the following statements are true?

$$\overleftrightarrow{AB} = \overleftrightarrow{AC}, \quad \overrightarrow{AB} = \overrightarrow{AC}, \quad AB = AC, \quad AB = BA, \quad AB + BC = AC,$$
$$AC + CB = AB, \quad \overline{AB} \cong \overline{BC}.$$

3. If $\overline{AB} = \overline{CD}$, which of the following statements are true?

$$\overline{AB} \cong \overline{CD}, \quad A = C \quad \text{or} \quad A = D, \quad AB + CD = 2 \cdot AB, \quad AB - CD = 0.$$

4. If A, B, C are three collinear points with B between A and C, which of the following statements are true?

$$\overline{AB} \supset \overline{BC}, \quad \overrightarrow{AB} \supset \overrightarrow{BC}, \quad \overrightarrow{AB} \supset \overrightarrow{BA}, \quad \overrightarrow{AB} \supset \overrightarrow{AC}, \quad \overrightarrow{AB} \supset \overrightarrow{BC}, \quad \overrightarrow{AB} \supset \{A, B\}.$$

5. In the figure $\overrightarrow{AC}, \overrightarrow{AE}, \overrightarrow{AG}$ are noncollinear, concurrent rays; $AC = AE = AG$ and B, D, F are the midpoints of the segments $\overline{AC}, \overline{AE}, \overline{AG}$; $m\angle BAD = m\angle DAF = 30$. Which of the following statements are true?

$$\angle BAD = \angle DAF, \quad \angle BAD = \angle CAE, \quad \overrightarrow{AD} = \overrightarrow{AE}, \quad \overline{AC} = \overline{AE}, \quad AC = AE,$$
$$AB = FG, \quad AG = AD + BC, \quad m\angle BAG = m\angle BAD + m\angle DAG,$$
$$m\angle CAG > m\angle CAD, \quad \angle CAG \supset \angle CAD, \quad \angle BAG = \angle BAD + \angle DAF.$$

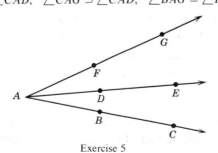

Exercise 5

6. If P is the plane determined by three noncollinear points A, B, C, which of the following statements are true?

$$P = \{A, B, C\}, \quad P \supset \{A, B, C\}, \quad P \supset \overleftrightarrow{AB}, \quad P \supset \angle ABC, \quad P \supset AB.$$

7. If A, B, C, D are the angles formed by two intersecting lines, as in the figure, then A and B are one pair of supplementary angles, and A and C are one pair of vertical angles. Prove that A and C are congruent.

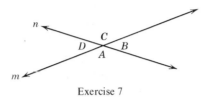

Exercise 7

8. On a number line, points A, B, C, D are matched with 5, 3.72, 1.5, and 6.2, respectively. Compute the following distances:

$$AB, \quad AC, \quad AD, \quad BC, \quad BD, \quad CD.$$

9. On a number wheel, rays $\overrightarrow{VA}, \overrightarrow{VB}, \overrightarrow{VC}, \overrightarrow{VD}$ are matched with 0, 37.3, 78, and 200, respectively. Compute the measures of the following angles:

$$\angle AVB, \quad \angle AVC, \quad \angle AVD, \quad \angle BVC, \quad \angle BVD, \quad \angle CVD.$$

10. On a number wheel, rays $\overrightarrow{VA}, \overrightarrow{VB}, \overrightarrow{VC}, \overrightarrow{VD}, \overrightarrow{VE}, \overrightarrow{VF}$ are matched with 0, 90, 180, 270, 300, and 330, respectively. Draw this wheel, marking these rays and the numbers matched with them. Identify two straight angles in the figure. Identify two pairs of vertical angles in the figure. Identify several pairs of complementary angles in the figure. Identify several pairs of supplementary angles in the figure. Identify several right angles in the figure.

11. Draw pictures of a right triangle with two congruent sides, a quadrilateral with two short adjacent sides which are congruent and two long adjacent sides which are congruent, a pentagon $ABCDE$ such that $ABCD$ is a square, two rays which do not intersect, two rays whose intersection is an endpoint of one of them but not of the other, two rays whose union is an angle, and four segments $\overline{AB}$, $\overline{BC}$, $\overline{CD}$, $\overline{DA}$ whose union is not a quadrilateral.

12. Given complementary angles A and B. If x is a real number such that $m\angle A = 3x + 5$ and $m\angle B = 2x + 15$, find x.

1.3 *Triangles*

To test whether two cardboard triangles have the same size and shape it is natural to put one on top of the other and to move it around a bit, perhaps turn it over, to see if it can be made to fit. In modern geometry we consider a triangle as a set of points, as defined earlier in this chapter, and we check to see if triangles are congruent by checking $\cong$ to see if their parts can be matched so that matched parts are congruent. The concept of a one-to-one correspondence is fundamental in this development.

In modern elementary mathematics we teach the concept of cardinal number using one-to-one correspondences between sets. Thus if A, B, C are three distinct objects, if D, E, F are three distinct objects, and if $S = \{A, B, C\}$, $T = \{D, E, F\}$, then S and T have the same cardinal number since it is possible to establish a one-to-one correspondence between these two sets. Indeed, we can match A with D, B with E, and C with F as suggested by the following symbols, $A \leftrightarrow D$, $B \leftrightarrow E$, $C \leftrightarrow F$, or more briefly by the symbol $ABC \leftrightarrow DEF$. Two one-to-one correspondences are considered the same if the matched pairs are the same. Thus $ABC \leftrightarrow DEF$ and $BAC \leftrightarrow EDF$ describe the same one-to-one correspondence between the two sets S and T, whereas $ABC \leftrightarrow DEF$ and $ABC \leftrightarrow EDF$ describe two different one-to-one correspondences between the sets S and T.

Consider triangles $\triangle ABC$ and $\triangle DEF$, not necessarily distinct. Then $ABC \leftrightarrow DEF$ denotes one of the six different one-to-one correspondences between the set of vertices of $\triangle ABC$ and the set of vertices of $\triangle DEF$. (Can you fill the blank in the sentence "$ABC \leftrightarrow$ _____" in five different ways so that each resulting statement denotes another one-to-one correspondence between the two sets of vertices?) Every time we match these vertices we establish six pairs of corresponding parts as in the following definition: If $ABC \leftrightarrow DEF$, then there are three pairs of *corresponding sides* and three pairs of *corresponding angles* as follows:

$$\overline{AB} \leftrightarrow \overline{DE}, \quad \overline{AC} \leftrightarrow \overline{DF}, \quad \overline{BC} \leftrightarrow \overline{EF},$$
$$\angle ABC \leftrightarrow \angle DEF, \quad \angle BCA \leftrightarrow \angle EFD, \quad \angle CAB \leftrightarrow \angle FDE.$$

The following definition provides a basis for the meaning of "same size and shape" as applied to triangles.

Definition. Given triangles $\triangle ABC$ and $\triangle DEF$, a one-to-one correspondence between their vertices, $ABC \leftrightarrow DEF$, is a *congruence* if each pair of corresponding parts are congruent.

If $ABC \leftrightarrow DEF$ is a congruence, then we write $\triangle ABC \cong \triangle DEF$, which is read "triangle ABC is congruent to triangle DEF." Sometimes we say that two triangles are congruent without specifying which parts correspond. Such a statement means that there is a one-to-one correspondence (perhaps more than one) between their vertices which is a congruence. To say that $\triangle ABC$ and $\triangle DEF$ are congruent means that at least one of the following six correspondences is a congruence: $ABC \leftrightarrow DEF$, $ABC \leftrightarrow DFE$, $ABC \leftrightarrow EDF$, $ABC \leftrightarrow EFD$, $ABC \leftrightarrow FDE$, $ABC \leftrightarrow FED$, whereas the statement $\triangle ABC \cong \triangle DEF$ is true if and only if $ABC \leftrightarrow DEF$ is a congruence.

Exercises 1.3.1

1. Given four points, A, B, C, D such that

$$AB = BC = BD = 40, \quad AD = AC = DC = 40\sqrt{2},$$

$$m\angle ABD = m\angle ABC = m\angle CBD = 90,$$

$$m\angle BAD = m\angle BDA = m\angle BAC = m\angle BCA = m\angle BCD = m\angle BDC = 45,$$

$$m\angle ADC = m\angle DCA = m\angle CAD = 60.$$

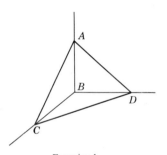

Exercise 1

Which of the following statements are true?

$$\triangle ABC = \triangle ABD, \quad \triangle ABD = \triangle DBA, \quad \triangle BCD = \triangle ACD, \quad \triangle ACD = \triangle CDA,$$

$$\triangle ABC \cong \triangle ABD, \quad \triangle ABD \cong \triangle DAB, \quad \triangle BCD \cong \triangle ACD, \quad \triangle ACD \cong \triangle CDA.$$

2. If $\triangle ABC$ is a triangle which is both equilateral (three congruent sides) and equiangular (three congruent angles), then which of the following statements are true?

$$\triangle ABC \cong \triangle ABC, \quad \triangle ABC \cong \triangle ACB, \quad \triangle ABC \cong \triangle BAC, \quad \triangle ABC \cong \triangle BCA,$$

$$\triangle ABC \cong \triangle CAB, \quad \triangle ABC \cong \triangle CBA.$$

3. Given $\triangle ADE$ with B and C the trisection points of $\overline{AD}$ and with segment and angle measures as marked. Which of the following statements are true?

$$\triangle ABE \cong \triangle DCE, \quad \triangle DBE \cong \triangle CAE, \quad \triangle DBE \cong \triangle ACE,$$

$$\triangle AED \cong \triangle EDA, \quad \triangle EBC \cong \triangle BCE, \quad \triangle AEB \cong \triangle EDC.$$

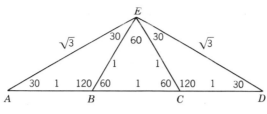

Exercise 3

4. Using a ruler marked in centimeters and a protractor marked in degrees draw two triangles $\triangle ABC$ and $\triangle DEF$ such that $m\angle A = m\angle D = 50$, $m\angle B = m\angle E = 55$, $AB = DE = 5.7$. Then measure the other sides and angles of these triangles and record the results.

$$m\angle C = \underline{\hspace{1cm}}, \quad m\angle F = \underline{\hspace{1cm}}, \quad AC = \underline{\hspace{1cm}},$$

$$DF = \underline{\hspace{1cm}}, \quad BC = \underline{\hspace{1cm}}, \quad EF = \underline{\hspace{1cm}}.$$

5. Draw two triangles $\triangle ABC$ and $\triangle DEF$ such that $m\angle A = m\angle D = 37$, $AB = DE = 5.3$, $AC = DF = 4.7$. Then measure the other sides and angles and record the results.

$$m\angle B = \underline{\hspace{1cm}}, \quad m\angle E = \underline{\hspace{1cm}}, \quad m\angle C = \underline{\hspace{1cm}},$$

$$m\angle F = \underline{\hspace{1cm}}, \quad BC = \underline{\hspace{1cm}}, \quad EF = \underline{\hspace{1cm}}.$$

6. Using a ruler and a compass draw two triangles $\triangle ABC$ and $\triangle DEF$ such that $AB = DE = 3.5$, $AC = DF = 4.7$, $BC = EF = 5.6$. Then measure the angles and record the results.

$$m\angle A = \underline{\hspace{1cm}}, \quad m\angle D = \underline{\hspace{1cm}}, \quad m\angle B = \underline{\hspace{1cm}},$$

$$m\angle E = \underline{\hspace{1cm}}, \quad m\angle C = \underline{\hspace{1cm}}, \quad m\angle F = \underline{\hspace{1cm}}.$$

7. Write the three theorems of elementary geometry which are suggested by Exercises 4, 5, and 6.

8. Cut out a paper triangle ABC as in the figure. Mark the midpoints, D and E, of $\overline{AC}$ and $\overline{BC}$. Make three folds so that A, C, B all fall on one point X between A and B.

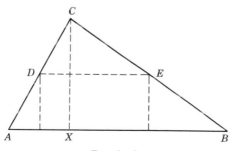

Exercise 8

9. Draw several triangles of different sizes and shapes. Measure the angles and record the measures and the sum of the measures for the angles of each triangle.

10. What theorem of elementary geometry is suggested by Exercises 8 and 9?

On the basis of the definition of a triangle congruence a statement such as $\triangle ABC \cong \triangle DEF$ is logically equivalent to six congruence statements involving corresponding parts. As suggested by Exercises 1.3.1 the truth of several of these six statements seems to imply the truth of the rest of them. The following three statements are fundamental in Euclidean geometry. In a formal development they would appear as postulates and/or theorems. In informal geometry they are accepted as true statements based on measurement evidence. We shall refer to them by their familiar names, S.A.S., A.S.A., and S.S.S. In each case we assume as given a one-to-one correspondence between the vertices of one triangle and the vertices of another triangle. The triangles need not be distinct.

S.A.S. If two sides and the included angle of one triangle are congruent to the corresponding parts of the second triangle, then the correspondence is a congruence.

A.S.A. If two angles and the included side of one triangle are congruent to the corresponding parts of the other triangle, then the correspondence is a congruence.

S.S.S. If the three sides of one triangle are congruent to the corresponding sides of the other triangle, then the correspondence is a congruence.

For example, if $ABC \leftrightarrow DEF$ is a one-to-one correspondence between the vertices of $\triangle ABC$ and the vertices of $\triangle DEF$, if $\angle A \cong \angle D$, if $\overline{AB} \cong \overline{DE}$, and if $\overline{AC} \cong \overline{DF}$, then $\triangle ABC \cong \triangle DEF$ (S.A.S.). Similarly, if $\angle A \cong \angle D$, $\angle B \cong \angle E$, and if $\overline{AB} \cong \overline{DE}$, then $\triangle ABC \cong \triangle DEF$ (A.S.A.). Also, if $\overline{AB} \cong \overline{DE}$, $\overline{AC} \cong \overline{DF}$, and $\overline{BC} \cong \overline{EF}$, then $\triangle ABC \cong \triangle DEF$ (S.S.S.).

Another basic statement of elementary geometry is suggested by measurement evidence, as in Exercise 9 of 1.3.1. This statement is a theorem in formal Euclidean geometry.

Triangle Angle Measure Sum. The sum of the measures of the angles of any triangle is 180.

Using this statement we may easily see that the measures of two angles of a triangle determine the measure of the third.

Exercises   1.3.2

1. In each pair of triangles like markings indicate congruent parts. Which pairs
of triangles could be proved congruent using the basic congruence statements?
In each case of congruence, label the vertices of the triangle, write the congruence
statement in symbols, and identify which congruence statement (S.A.S., A.S.A.,
S.S.S.) is the basis for your statement.

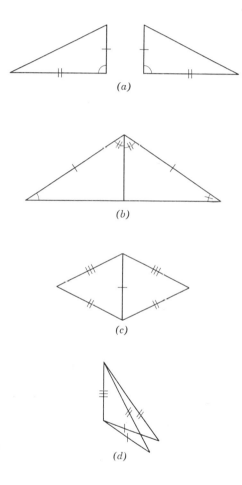

(a)

(b)

(c)

(d)

2. Supply the missing reasons in the following proof.

If $ABC \leftrightarrow DEF$ is a correspondence between the vertices of two triangles, if

$\overline{AB} \cong \overline{DE}$,   if $\angle B \cong \angle E$,   if $\angle C \cong \angle F$,   then $\triangle ABC \cong \triangle DEF$.

Proof:

1. $\angle B \cong \angle E$. $\angle C \cong \angle F$.	1. Hypothesis.
2. $m\angle B = m\angle E$. $m\angle C = m\angle F$.	2. If two angles are congruent, then they have equal measures.
3. $m\angle B + m\angle C = m\angle E + m\angle F$.	3. Step 2 and addition.
4. $m\angle A + m\angle B + m\angle C = 180$. $m\angle D + m\angle E + m\angle F = 180$.	4.
5. $m\angle A + m\angle B + m\angle C = $ $\quad\quad\quad m\angle D + m\angle E + m\angle F$.	5.
6. $m\angle A = m\angle D$.	6.
7. $\overline{AB} \cong \overline{DE}$.	7.
8. $\triangle ABC \cong \triangle DEF$.	8. Steps 1, 6, 7, and A.S.A.

3. In the figure, A, B, C, D are coplanar points, $AB = BC$ and $AD = DC$. Prove that $\triangle BAD \cong \triangle BCD$.

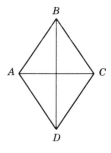

Exercise 3

4. Draw two triangles $\triangle ABC$ and $\triangle A'B'C'$ not congruent to each other and such that $AB = A'B'$, $m\angle A = m\angle A'$, $BC = B'C'$.

5. Given $\triangle ABC$ with $\overline{AB} \cong \overline{AC}$. Complete the following proof that $\angle B \cong \angle C$.

Proof: Consider the correspondence $ABC \leftrightarrow ACB$. The corresponding sides are $\overline{AB}$ and $\overline{AC}$, $\overline{BC}$ and $\overline{CB}$, $\overline{AC}$ and $\overline{AB}$.

1. $\overline{AB} \cong \overline{AC}$.	1.
2. $\overline{BC} \cong \overline{CB}$.	2.
3. $\overline{AC} \cong \overline{AB}$.	3.
4.	4.
5. $\angle B \cong \angle C$.	5. If two triangles are congruent, then their corresponding parts are congruent.

6. Given $\triangle ABC$ with $\angle B \cong \angle C$. Prove that $\overline{AB} \cong \overline{AC}$.

7. Given △*ABC* with exterior angle ∠*DBC*. (This means that *A*, *B*, *D* are collinear and arranged in the order named.) Prove that *m*∠*DBC* = *m*∠*BAC* + *m*∠*BCA*.

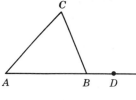

Exercise 7

8. Which of the following statements are true?

The measure of every angle of every triangle is less than 90.

The measure of one angle of a triangle may be greater than 90.

If one angle of a triangle has a measure of 90, the sum of the measures of the other two is 90.

If the three sides of a triangle are equal in length, then the measures of the angles of that triangle are equal.

If a triangle is equiangular, then it is also equilateral.

9. Given the figure with *AB* = *BC* and ∠*ABD* ≅ ∠*CBD*. Prove that *AD* = *DC*.

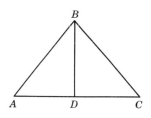

Exercises 9, 10, 11, 12

10. Given the same figure with *AB* = *BC* and *AD* = *DC*. Prove that ∠*ABD* ≅ ∠*CBD*.

11. Given the same figure with ∠*ABD* ≅ ∠*CBD*, ∠*CDB* ≅ ∠*ADB*. Prove that *AB* = *BC*.

12. Given the same figure with *AD* = *DC*, ∠*ADB* ≅ ∠*BDC*. Prove that *AB* = *BC*.

The following two theorems are important and are honored with names.

The Isosceles Triangle Theorem. If two sides of a triangle are congruent, then the angles opposite the sides are congruent.

Proof. Exercise 5 of 1.3.2.

Converse of the Isosceles Triangle Theorem. If two angles of a triangle are congruent, then the sides opposite these angles are congruent.

Proof. Exercise 6 of 1.3.2.

The numbers in an ordered set (a, b, c, d) are *proportional* to the numbers in a second ordered set (e, f, g, h) if there is nonzero number k such that $a = ke, b = kf, c = kg$, and $d = kh$. We understand $(a, b, c, d) \underset{p}{=} (e, f, g, h)$ to mean that a, b, c, d are proportional to e, f, g, h, and we call it a *proportionality*. The number k is called the *constant of proportionality*. There may be any number, two or more, of numbers in the two ordered sets.

Examples

$(2, 4) \underset{p}{=} (3, 6)$ since $2 = \frac{2}{3} \cdot 3$ and $4 = \frac{2}{3} \cdot 6$.

$(5, 10, 15) \underset{p}{=} (1, 2, 3)$ since $5 = 5 \cdot 1, 10 = 5 \cdot 2, 15 = 5 \cdot 3$.

Exercises 1.3.3

1. If $(5, 7, 12.5) \underset{p}{=} (3, x, 7.5)$, find x.

2. If $(x, y) \underset{p}{=} (c, d)$, prove that $(x, x + y) \underset{p}{=} (c, c + d)$.

3. Draw $\triangle ABC$ and $\triangle DEF$ with $AB = 4.0$, $BC = 5.3$, $AC = 6.7$, $DE = 3.0$, $EF = 4.0$, $DF = 5.0$. Measure the angles of these two triangles and record the results.

4. Draw $\triangle ABC$ and $\triangle DEF$ with $AB = 5.0$, $AC = 8.0$, $m\angle A = 60$, $DE = 6.0$, $DF = 9.6$, $m\angle D = 60$. Measure the other sides and angles of the two triangles and record the results. Solve $(AB, AC, BC) \underset{p}{=} (DE, x, y)$ for x and y. Compare x and y with DF and EF.

5. Draw $\triangle ABC$ and $\triangle DEF$ with $AB = 4.7$, $m\angle A = 70$, $m\angle B = 80$, $DE = 3.9$, $m\angle D = 70$, $m\angle E = 80$. Measure the other sides and angles of these triangles and record the results. Solve $(AB, AC, BC) \underset{p}{=} (DE, x, y)$ for x and y. Compare x and y with DF and EF.

Two objects have the same shape if their points can be matched so that measures of angles determined by corresponding points are equal and the lengths of segments joining corresponding points are proportional. In the case of geometrical figures we say that the figures are *similar* if their corresponding angles and segments satisfy these requirements.

Definition. A correspondence $ABC \leftrightarrow DEF$ is a *similarity* between $\triangle ABC$ and $\triangle DEF$, and we write $\triangle ABC \sim \triangle DEF$, if corresponding angles are congruent and if lengths of corresponding sides are proportional.

In other words $\triangle ABC \sim \triangle DEF$ if and only if $\angle A \cong \angle D, \angle B \cong \angle E$, $\angle C \cong \angle F$, and $(AB, BC, AC) \underset{p}{=} (DE, EF, DF)$.

As in the case of triangle congruences we need not establish all that is stated in the definition of a triangle similarity in order to establish the similarity. Evidence based on measurements supports the following similarity statements. In each case we assume as given a one-to-one correspondence between the vertices of one triangle and the vertices of a second triangle. The triangles need not be distinct.

S.A.S. If the lengths of two sides of one triangle are proportional to the lengths of the corresponding sides of the other triangle and if the angles included between these sides are congruent, then the correspondence is a similarity.

S.S.S. If the lengths of the three sides of one triangle are proportional to the lengths of the corresponding sides of the other triangle, then the correspondence is a similarity.

A.A. If two angles of one triangle are congruent to the corresponding angles of the other triangle, then the correspondence is a similarity.

Exercises 1.3.4

1. In the figure ABC is a right triangle with D a point between A and B; $\angle ACB$, $\angle ADC$, $\angle BDC$ are all right angles. Prove that $\triangle ADC \sim \triangle ACB \sim \triangle CDB$.

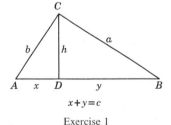

$$x+y=c$$

Exercise 1

2. For the figure in Exercise 1 complete the following statements:

$(AC, CB, AB) \underset{p}{=} (CD, \underline{\hspace{1cm}}, \underline{\hspace{1cm}}) \underset{p}{=} (AD, \underline{\hspace{1cm}}, \underline{\hspace{1cm}})$,

$(b, a, c) \underset{p}{=} (\underline{\hspace{1cm}}, \underline{\hspace{1cm}}, a) \underset{p}{=} (\underline{\hspace{1cm}}, \underline{\hspace{1cm}}, b)$,

$\dfrac{a}{?} = \dfrac{c}{a}, \quad \dfrac{b}{?} = \dfrac{c}{b}$,

$a^2 + b^2 = \underline{\hspace{1cm}} \cdot c + \underline{\hspace{1cm}} \cdot c = (\underline{\hspace{1cm}}) \cdot c = c^2$.

3. In the figure suppose $a^2 + b^2 = c^2$. We wish to prove that $\angle C$ is a right angle. Let $\triangle DEF$ be a triangle with $FE = a$, $DF = b$, $m\angle F = 90$. Then using the result of Exercise 2 we know that $x^2 = \underline{\hspace{1cm}}$, and therefore $x = \underline{\hspace{1cm}}$. Now show that the two triangles are congruent and complete the proof.

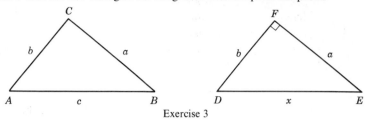

Exercise 3

Pythagorean Theorem. In any right triangle, the square of the length of the hypotenuse is equal to the sum of the squares of the lengths of the legs.

Proof. See Exercise 2 of 1.3.4.

Converse of **Pythagorean Theorem.** If the square of the length of one side of a triangle is equal to the sum of the squares of the lengths of the other two sides, then the triangle is a right triangle with the right angle opposite the first side.

Proof. See Exercise 3 of 1.3.4.

Exercises 1.3.5

1. Suppose x and y are any two positive numbers such that $x > y$. If the lengths of the sides of a triangle are $2xy$, $x^2 - y^2$, and $x^2 + y^2$, show that the triangle is a right triangle.

2. Find correct to three significant digits the length of the hypotenuse of a right triangle if the lengths of the legs are 751 and 684.

3. Prove that the length of the short leg of a 30–60 right triangle is half the length of the hypotenuse.

4. Prove that if ABC is a right triangle with $AC = BC$ and with right angle at C, then $(AC, BC, AB) \underset{p}{=} (1, 1, \sqrt{2})$.

5. The accompanying figure shows a right triangle with right angle at C and with $\angle ADC$ a right angle. Find the lengths x and y.

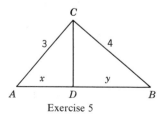

Exercise 5

6. Given a line m, a point P not on m, and two points R and Q on m. Prove that if $\angle RQP$ is a right angle, then $PQ < PR$.

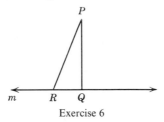

Exercise 6

7. Prove that each leg of a right triangle is shorter than the hypotenuse.

Definition. Let $\triangle ABC$ be given. If D is a point on $\overleftrightarrow{AB}$ such that B is between A and D, then $\angle DBC$ is an *exterior angle* of the triangle, $\angle ABC$ is its *adjacent interior* angle, and $\angle BAC$ and $\angle BCA$ are its *nonadjacent interior* angles.

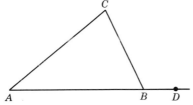

Exterior Angle Theorem. The measure of an exterior angle of a triangle is equal to the sum of the measures of the two nonadjacent interior angles.

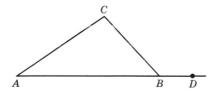

Proof. Let $\triangle ABC$ with exterior angle $\angle DBC$ be given. Then it follows from the triangle angle measure sum statement that $m\angle A + m\angle B + m\angle C = 180$. But $m\angle B + m\angle DBC = 180$ also. Therefore $m\angle A + m\angle B + m\angle C = m\angle B + m\angle DBC$ by substitution, and $m\angle A + m\angle C = m\angle DBC$ by subtraction.

Exterior Angle Theorem (Weak Form). The measure of an exterior angle of a triangle is greater than the measure of either nonadjacent interior angle.

Proof. This follows immediately from the preceding theorem.

1.4   *Parallelism and Polygons*

Two distinct coplanar lines either intersect (and their intersection is a set consisting of just one point) or do not intersect. Coplanar lines which do not intersect are called *parallel lines.* Parallel lines seem to abound in the world of man-made objects. We are reminded of parallel lines by the opposite edges of a table, by the marks on a piece of lined paper, and by some railroad tracks. Our physical experiences with parallelism fall short when it comes to experiencing lines which "never meet no matter how far they may be extended."

Do we know that parallel lines exist? We cannot answer yes or no on the basis of our physical experiences. In formal geometry we can answer the question. In Euclidean geometry and in the geometry of Bolyai and Lobachevsky there are parallel lines. It is a theorem in both of these geometries that if L is a line and P is a point not on L, then there is at least one line through P and parallel to L. In Euclidean geometry there is a postulate which states that there is only one line through P and parallel to L. In the geometry of Lobachevsky and Bolyai there is a postulate which states that there are at least two distinct lines through P and parallel to L. For our purpose we follow in the footsteps of Euclid. The following statement combines a theorem and a postulate of Euclid. We accept it as a true statement in our informal geometry.

Parallel Postulate. If a line and a point not on it are given, there is exactly one line through the point parallel to the given line.

A significant part of elementary geometry is concerned with the measures of the angles formed when two lines are "cut" by a transversal.

Definition. Let m and n be two distinct coplanar lines. A line t is called a *transversal* of m and n if it intersects their union in a set consisting of two distinct points.

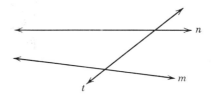

If m, n, t are the three lines which contain the sides of a triangle, then each of three lines is a transversal of the other two.

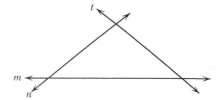

If *m* and *n* are parallel lines cut by a transversal *t*, then *m* is not a transversal of *t* and *n*, and *n* is not a transversal of *t* and *m*.

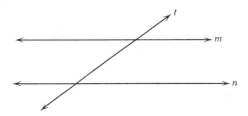

Let *m* and *n* be coplanar lines and *t* a transversal of them, cutting them in points *P* and *Q*. In the figure, *A, B, C, D, E, F, G, H* are eight angles formed

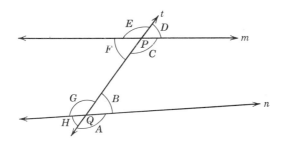

by the three lines. Each of these angles is the union of two rays, one lying on the transversal *t* and the other lying on one of the lines *m*, *n*. These eight angles form four pairs of vertical angles. Name them. They also form many pairs of supplementary angles. Name several of them.

Two angles, such as *B* and *F*, whose interiors lie on opposite sides of *t* and whose intersection is the segment $\overline{PQ}$ are called *alternate interior angles*. Name another pair of alternate interior angles.

Two angles, such as *B* and *C*, whose interiors lie on the same side of *t* and whose intersection contains the segment $\overline{PQ}$ but no other points of $\overleftrightarrow{PQ}$, are called *consecutive interior angles*.

Two angles, such as *B* and *D*, whose interiors lie on the same side of *t* and whose intersection contains a side of one of these angles, are called *corresponding angles*.

Theorem. Let m and n be coplanar lines cut by a transversal t. If the angles in one pair of alternate interior angles are congruent, then the angles in the other pair are also congruent. If the angles in one pair of corresponding angles are congruent, then the angles in every pair of corresponding angles are congruent. If the angles in one pair of consecutive interior angles are supplementary, then the angles in the other pair of consecutive interior angles are also supplementary.

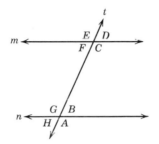

Proof. Suppose $\angle B \cong \angle F$. Then $m\angle B = m\angle F$, $m\angle B + m\angle G = 180$, $m\angle C + m\angle F = 180$, $m\angle B + m\angle G = m\angle C + m\angle F$, and $m\angle G = m\angle C$. The other parts of this theorem can be proved in a similar manner.

Theorem. If m and n are coplanar lines cut by a transversal t, and if the angles in one pair of alternate interior angles are congruent, then m and n are parallel.

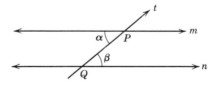

Proof. Let P and Q denote the points in which t intersects m and n, respectively, and let α and β denote the given pair of congruent alternate interior angles. If m and n intersect in point R, then either α or β is an exterior angle of $\triangle PQR$ and the other is a nonadjacent interior angle. In either case the measures of α and β are unequal, contradicting the given hypothesis. It follows that m and n do not intersect, hence that they are parallel.

It is now easy to prove the following theorem.

Theorem. If *m* and *n* are coplanar lines cut by a transversal *t*, and if one pair of consecutive interior angles are supplementary (or if one pair of corresponding angles are congruent), then the lines *m* and *n* are parallel.

The converse of this theorem and the converse of the preceding theorem are also true.

Theorem. If *m* and *n* are parallel lines cut by a transversal *t*, then the angles in each pair of alternate interior angles are congruent, the angles in each pair of corresponding angles are congruent, and each pair of consecutive interior angles are supplementary.

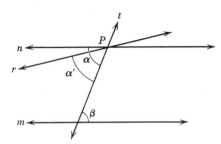

Proof. Let α and β denote one pair of alternate interior angles formed by the lines *m*, *n*, and *t*. Let *P* be the point in which *n* intersects *t*. If $m\angle\alpha \neq m\angle\beta$, let *r* be a line through *P* coplanar with *m* and *n* and forming with *m* and *t* a pair α' and β of alternate interior angles which are congruent. It follows from the second preceding theorem that *r* is parallel to *m*. Since *r* and *n* both pass through *P* and both are parallel to *m*, we have a situation which contradicts the Euclidean parallel postulate. It follows that $\alpha \cong \beta$. The remainder of the proof, which follows by an easy argument, is omitted.

Exercises 1.4.1

1. Given parallel lines *m* and *n* cut by parallel transversals *s* and *t* with intersections as labeled in the figure. Prove that $\overline{AB} \cong \overline{CD}$ by proving that they are corresponding sides of congruent triangles.

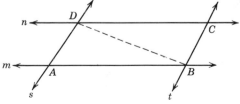

Exercise 1

2. Given two parallel lines m and n with intersecting transversals as in the figure. Prove that $(AD, DE, AE) \underset{p}{=} (BC, CE, BE)$.

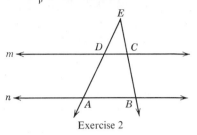

Exercise 2

3. Given several parallel lines cut by two transversals as in the figure. Prove that the lengths of the segments formed by p, n, m cutting t are proportional to the segments formed by p, n, m cutting s.

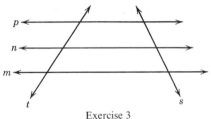

Exercise 3

An important concept in modern geometry is the concept of a convex set. A set of points is *convex* if for every pair of distinct points in the set, the segment joining these two points lies entirely in the set. A triangle, then, is not really a convex set since by definition a triangle is the union

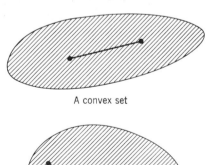

A convex set

Not a convex set

of three segments. Hence a segment joining two points on different sides of a triangle will contain points not in the triangle, as shown below. In

fact, the only points of the segment $\overline{AB}$ that are on the triangle are A and B. Nevertheless, it is customary to consider both the curve and its interior in deciding on convexity. Thus, for example, it is customary (although technically incorrect) to say that a triangle is a convex figure and we shall do so here. If a distinction is ever needed, we can say that a triangle, for example, is not a convex set but encloses a convex set and is called a *convex curve*. Similarly, in three dimensions, the bounding surface of a three-dimensional body may be called a *convex surface* although ordinarily we consider the union of the surface and the interior. Thus we may call a sphere a convex set even though, technically, it is the union of the sphere and the interior of the sphere that is a convex set, and a sphere itself is a convex surface but not a convex set.

With these agreements on language in mind let us now generalize from the idea of a triangle to that of a convex polygon.

A *convex polygon* is a plane figure $P_1P_2\ldots P_n$ which is the union of n, $n \geqslant 3$, segments, $\overline{P_nP_1}$, $\overline{P_1P_2}$, $\overline{P_2P_3},\ldots,\overline{P_{n-1}P_n}$, called the *sides* of the polygon, and having the following properties. Each side is *adjacent* to two other sides. Thus $\overline{P_nP_1}$ is adjacent to $\overline{P_1P_2}$ and to $\overline{P_{n-1}P_n}$. Each pair of adjacent sides intersect in a point which is a common endpoint of those two sides. Otherwise no side intersects any other side. If $\overline{P_iP_j}$ is any side of a polygon, then all of the polygon except that side lies on one side of $\overleftrightarrow{P_iP_j}$. The endpoints of the sides of a polygon are called its *vertices*. If $\overline{AB}$ and $\overline{BC}$ are two adjacent sides of a polygon, then $\angle ABC$ is an *angle* of the polygon. Two convex polygons are *congruent* if there is a one-to-one correspondence between their vertices such that the corresponding sides are congruent and the corresponding angles are congruent.

A polygon with three sides is a *triangle*, with four sides a *quadrilateral*, with five sides a *pentagon*, and so on. A polygon with 13 sides is a 13-gon. In general, a polygon with n sides is an n-gon.

A quadrilateral has two pairs of opposite sides and two pairs of opposite angles. If one pair of opposite sides are parallel (lie on parallel lines), it is a *trapezoid*. If a quadrilateral has two pairs of parallel sides, it is a *parallelogram*. A segment which joins two nonadjacent vertices of a polygon is called a *diagonal* of the polygon. A *rectangle* is a parallelogram with four right angles. A *square* is a rectangle with four congruent sides.

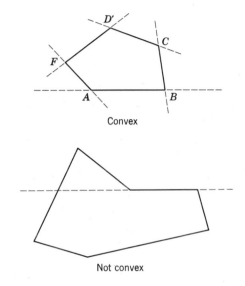

Convex

Not convex

Exercises 1.4.2

1. Prove: Opposite sides of a parallelogram are congruent.

2. Prove: If both pairs of opposite sides of a quadrilateral are congruent, then it is a parallelogram.

3. Prove: The diagonals of a parallelogram bisect each other.

4. Prove: If the diagonals of a quadrilateral bisect each other, it is a parallelogram.

5. Prove: If two opposite sides of a quadrilateral are congruent and parallel, then it is a parallelogram.

6. Prove: If a parallelogram has one right angle, it is a rectangle.

7. Prove: If two adjacent sides of a rectangle are congruent, then it is a square.

8. Prove: If the diagonals of a rectangle are perpendicular, it is a square.

1.5   *Areas of Rectangles*

The length of a segment, such as 6 feet, is a combination of a number and a unit which expresses the relationship between the length of this segment and the length of a standard or unit segment. It expresses the idea that the segment is six times as long as the segment which serves as the unit of length. The area of a rectangle, such as 10 square feet, expresses the relationship between the measure of the set of points lying on or within the rectangle and the measure of the set of points on or within a rectangle which is accepted as the unit. It might be better to talk about the area enclosed by a rectangle, or the area of a rectangular region, but we shall follow custom and call it the area of the rectangle.

We take as our unit rectangle a given square whose sides each have a length of 1. If the square is 1 foot on a side, its area is 1 square foot; if 1 yard on a side, then 1 square yard; etc. We shall not specify the unit in our development. The side of the unit square has a measure of 1 length unit; the area of this square has a measure of 1 area unit.

Our development of area is limited to convex polygonal regions and is based on several fundamental properties which we accept without proof. We call them our area postulates.

Area Existence Postulate. Every convex polygonal region has an area, and that area is a positive number.

Area Congruence Postulate. Congruent convex polygons have equal areas.

Area Additivity Postulate. If a convex polygonal region is divided or partitioned into a finite number of convex polygonal subregions by a

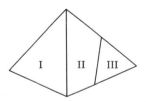

finite number of segments, two subregions having no points in common except perhaps along a boundary segment, then the area of the region is the sum of the areas of the subregions.

In this section we shall develop through a sequence of theorems the fact that the area of any rectangle is the product of its width and its length. *In each of the next five theorems we use a and b to denote the lengths of two adjacent sides of a given rectangle and A to denote its area.* Each of the numbers a and b is a positive real number. To prove that $A = ab$ in general, we consider a sequence of special cases which arise when we assume that a and b have special properties. Before proceeding with these proofs we review briefly the kinds of real numbers and their properties.

The simplest positive real numbers are the *natural numbers*: $1, 2, 3, \ldots$. These are the numbers used in counting. Some people call them the whole numbers; others call them the positive integers. Another type of real number is the *rational number*. A *rational number* is a real number which can be expressed as the quotient of two integers, for example, $\frac{1}{2}, \frac{2}{3}, \frac{134}{16}$. For our purposes here we consider every natural number to be a rational number, for example, $3 = \frac{3}{1} = \frac{27}{9}$. Also, every number which can be expressed as a finite decimal is a rational number, for example, $3.142 = \frac{3142}{1000}$. Real numbers which cannot be expressed as quotients of integers are called *irrational numbers*. For example, $\sqrt{2}$ is an irrational number and so are $\sqrt{3}, \sqrt[3]{5}, \pi$, and many other numbers.

An important property of an irrational number is that there are rational numbers very close to it, as close as you please as long as you do not insist on actual equality. For example, $\sqrt{2}$ lies between each x and y in the following lists.

x	y
1.4	1.5
1.41	1.42
1.414	1.415
1.4142	1.4143
1.41421	1.41422
$\vdots$	$\vdots$

Note that $1.41 < \sqrt{2} < 1.42$ and $1.42 - 1.41 = 0.01$; that $1.414 < \sqrt{2} < 1.415$ and $1.415 - 1.414 = 0.001$; etc.

In general, if i is any irrational number, there are two rational numbers, one of them less than i and one of them greater than i, whose difference is as small as you please, except that we cannot make the difference zero.

We proceed now to prove our five theorems which establish the area formula for a rectangle. Remember that a rectangular region is given and that a and b are the lengths of its sides.

Theorem. If a and b are natural numbers, then $A = ab$.

Proof. Using $a - 1$ parallel segments and $b - 1$ segments perpendicular to them, we can subdivide the given rectangular region into $a \cdot b$ congruent unit squares. Each unit square is congruent to the fundamental unit square which serves as unit area. Therefore the area of each of the ab unit squares is 1 and it follows from the additivity postulate that $A = 1 + 1 + 1 + \cdots + 1$, in which there are ab 1's in the indicated sum. Therefore $A = ab$.

Does this proof apply if our given rectangle is 1 by 4? 1 by 1? What do $a - 1$ and $b - 1$ become in these cases?

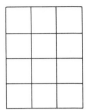

Theorem. If n is a natural number and if $a = 1/n$, $b = 1/n$, then $A = ab$.

Proof. If $n = 1$, the assertion is a trivial special case of the preceding theorem. Suppose, then, that $n \geqslant 2$. Subdivide a unit square into n^2 congruent squares using $n - 1$ parallel segments in one direction and $n - 1$ parallel segments perpendicular to them. Now A denotes the area

$$\frac{1}{n} \quad \frac{1}{n} \quad \frac{1}{n}$$

of the given rectangle (a square $1/n$ by $1/n$). By the area congruence postulate the area of each of the n^2 squares in our subdivided unit square is also A, and it follows from the area additivity postulate that $1 = n^2 A$, and hence that $A = 1/n^2$, $A = ab$.

Theorem. If a and b are rational numbers, then $A = ab$.

Proof. Let p, q, r be three natural numbers such that $a = p/r$ and $b = q/r$. For example, if $a = \frac{2}{3}$ and $b = \frac{5}{4}$, then we might have $p = 8$, $q = 15$, $r = 12$. Using $p - 1$ segments parallel to the side of length b and $q - 1$ segments parallel to the side of length a, the rectangle may be

$$\frac{5}{4}$$

$$\frac{2}{3}$$

subdivided into pq squares each $1/r$ by $1/r$. From the preceding theorem it follows that the area of each one of these little squares is $1/r^2$. From the additivity postulate it follows that $A = pq(1/r^2) = (p/r)(q/r) = a \cdot b$.

Theorem. If a is rational and b is irrational, then $A = ab$.

Proof. For $n = 1, 2, 3, \ldots$, let b_n be the n-decimal-place truncation of b, and let $c_n = b_n + 1/10^n$. (For example, if $b = \sqrt{2}$ and $n = 3$, then $b_n = 1.414$ and $c_n = 1.415$.) Let S_n, T_n, U_n, V_n denote the areas of the rectangles of side lengths a by b_n, a by $b - b_n$, a by $c_n - b$, and a by c_n,

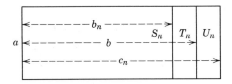

respectively. See if you can identify the area postulate, previous theorem, or other basis which justifies each of the following six steps.

1. $S_n = ab_n$, $V_n = ac_n$.
2. $A = S_n + T_n$, $V_n = S_n + T_n + U_n = A + U_n$.
3. $S_n > 0$, $T_n > 0$, $U_n > 0$.
4. $S_n < A < V_n$.
5. $ab_n < A < ac_n$.
6. $b_n < A/a < c_n$.

Statement 6 is true for every natural number n. (For example, if $a = 1$ and $b = \sqrt{2}$, then we have $1.4 < A/a < 1.5$ for $n = 1$, $1.41 < A/a < 1.42$ for $n = 2$, $1.414 < A/a < 1.415$ for $n = 3$, $1.4142 < A/a < 1.4143$ for $n = 4$, etc.) Note that A/a is a number, one and the same number, for every value of n. There is one and only one number which lies between b_n and c_n for every natural number n. It is the number b. Therefore $A/a = b$ and $A = ab$.

Theorem. If a and b are both irrational, then $A = ab$.

Proof. For $n = 1, 2, 3, \ldots$, let b_n be the n-decimal-place truncation of b, and let $c_n = b_n + 1/10^n$. Let S_n, T_n, U_n, V_n denote the areas of rectangles of side lengths a by b_n, a by $b - b_n$, a by $c_n - b$, and a by c_n, respectively. See if you can identify the area postulate, preceding theorem, or other basis which justifies each of the following six steps. (Note the similarity of these steps to the corresponding steps in the proof of the preceding theorem. Perhaps the bases are different.)

1. $S_n = ab_n$, $V_n = ac_n$.
2. $A = S_n + T_n$, $V_n = S_n + T_n + U_n = A + U_n$.
3. $S_n > 0$, $T_n > 0$, $U_n > 0$.
4. $S_n < A < V_n$.
5. $ab_n < A < ac_n$.
6. $b_n < A/a < c_n$.

As in the proof of the preceding theorem, we conclude that $A/a = b$, and hence that $A = ab$.

Exercises 1.5

1. Find the area of the rectangles whose dimensions are given. Give answers in compact form.

(a) 10^3 by 10^{-5}.

(d) $x^2 y$ by $y^2 z$.

(b) 754 by 85.3.

(e) 75 by 75.

(c) $\sqrt{2}$ by $\sqrt{8}$.

2. If the dimensions of a rectangle are $15\frac{1}{3}$ and $13\frac{1}{5}$, describe how to subdivide it into congruent squares.

3. Use a figure like the accompanying one to show that the area of a square $\sqrt{2}$ by $\sqrt{2}$ is 2. (Dissect a square 2 by 2 into four triangles and rearrange to make two congruent squares $\sqrt{2}$ by $\sqrt{2}$.)

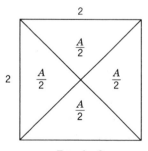

Exercise 3

1.6 *Areas of Polygons and Circles*

Theorem. Let a and b denote the lengths of two adjacent sides of a parallelogram; let h denote the perpendicular distance between the two sides of length b. Let K denote the area of the parallelogram. Then $K = bh$.

Proof. Consider first a parallelogram like the one in the next figure. Let F and E be points on $\overleftrightarrow{AB}$ such that $\overline{DF} \perp \overline{AB}$, $\overline{CE} \perp \overleftrightarrow{AB}$. Then $CDFE$

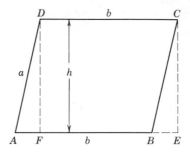

is a rectangle of area bh, $\triangle DFA \cong \triangle CEB$, and:

$$K = \text{Area of } \triangle DFA + \text{Area of trapezoid } DFBC$$
$$= \text{Area of } \triangle CEB + \text{Area of trapezoid } DFBC$$
$$= \text{Area of rectangle } DFEC$$
$$= bh.$$

Consider next a parallelogram like one in this figure. Then $CDFE$ is a rectangle of area bh, $\triangle DFA \cong \triangle CEB$, and

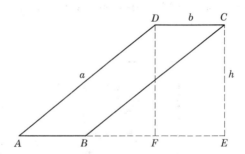

$$K = \text{Area of trapezoid } CDAE - \text{Area of } \triangle CBE$$
$$= \text{Area of trapezoid } CDAE - \text{Area of } \triangle DFA$$
$$= \text{Area of rectangle } CDFE$$
$$= bh.$$

Note that this last argument involving subtraction of area is applicable in the case of our first figure also.

Theorem. Given $\triangle ABC$. Let $b = AC$, let h denote the length of the altitude from B to $\overleftrightarrow{AC}$, and let K denote the area of the triangle. Then $K = \frac{1}{2}bh$.

Proof. Let D be a point coplanar with A, B, C, such that D and C are on opposite sides of $\overleftrightarrow{AB}$ and such that $\overleftrightarrow{DB}$ is parallel to $\overleftrightarrow{AC}$, and $DB = AC$.

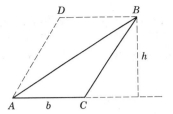

Then $ACBD$ is a parallelogram, $\triangle ABC \cong \triangle BAD$, and

$$\text{Area } \triangle ABC = K,$$
$$\text{Area } \triangle BAD = K,$$
$$\text{Area } ACBD = 2K,$$
$$\text{Area } ACBD = bh,$$
$$2K = bh,$$
$$K = \tfrac{1}{2}bh.$$

Theorem. Let $ABCD$ be a trapezoid with two parallel sides (called bases) of lengths a and b, and altitude (perpendicular distance between bases) h. Let K denote its area. Then $K = \tfrac{1}{2}(a + b)h$.

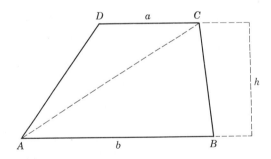

Proof.

$$K = \text{Area } \triangle ABC + \text{Area } \triangle ACD,$$
$$K = \tfrac{1}{2}bh + \tfrac{1}{2}ah,$$
$$K = \tfrac{1}{2}(a + b)h.$$

There are area formulas for other special polygons which we shall not discuss here. Of course a polygonal region can always be subdivided into

triangular regions. If a given polygonal region is subdivided into triangular regions, and if a base and corresponding altitude are measured
for each triangular region, then the area of the polygonal region can be
computed by finding the sum of the areas of the triangular regions.

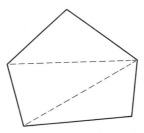

The perimeter of a figure is the "distance around it." For a polygon
this means the sum of the lengths of the sides (each a segment) of the
polygon. In physical geometry we can extend this notion to plane figures
which have curved boundaries. In elementary school or junior high school
geometry the perimeter, or *circumference*, of a circle is "discovered" by
measurement. Thus a circular disk of diameter 10 inches is rolled along a
chalk tray making one complete revolution. The distance along the chalk
tray between the initial point of contact and the terminal point of contact
is measured and found to be about $31\frac{3}{8}$ inches. In another experiment a
flexible steel measuring tape is used to measure the circumference. The
pupils discover that the circumference is about 31.4 inches. They divide

the circumference c by the diameter d to discover that $c/d = 3.14$, approximately. They do this for several circles with different diameters and conclude that the evidence supports the conclusion that the quotient of the
circumference and the diameter of a circle is the same number for all
circles. This number is called π; its decimal value to twenty-one significant
figures is 3.14159 26535 89793 23845.

We are now ready to write several important formulas. If c, d, r denote
the circumference, diameter, and radius of a circle, then:

$$\frac{c}{d} = \pi \qquad c = \pi d \qquad d = 2r \qquad c = 2\pi r.$$

Obtaining good decimal approximations for π requires more sophisticated mathematics than is usually presented in precollege level mathematics. The usual procedure is to approximate the circumference of a circle with the perimeter p_n of a regular inscribed polygon of n sides. (A regular

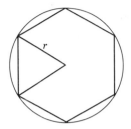

polygon has congruent sides and congruent angles. A polygon is inscribed in a circle if its vertices lie on the circle.) The circumference is defined as that number which p_n approaches as n gets larger and larger. The fact that this number is $2\pi r$ can be established using some elementary trigonometry and calculus.

A *central angle* of a circle is an angle in the plane of the circle and with its vertex at the center of the circle. A central angle of a circle intersects the circle in two points. These two points separate the points of the circle into parts called arcs. The degree measure of the smaller arc, or minor arc, is by definition the same as the degree measure of its central angle. If the

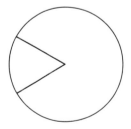

degree measure of the smaller arc is m, then the degree measure of the larger arc is $360 - m$. Every diameter of a circle separates the circle into two semicircles. Every semicircle has a degree measure of 180.

Linear measures of arcs are proportional to their degree measures. Thus the length of an 80° arc on a circle of radius 10 is $(80/360) \cdot 2\pi \cdot 10 = 1600\pi/360 = 40\pi/9$, or about 14.

The formula for computing the area of a circle from the length of its radius may be derived starting with the formula for the area of a triangle and using a limiting process. Let $\overline{A_1A_2}$ be one side of a regular n-gon inscribed in a given circle of radius r, and let θ be the central angle subtended by $\overleftrightarrow{A_1A_2}$ at the center O. If n is large, then θ is small, the perpendicular distance from O to $\overleftrightarrow{A_1A_2}$ is approximately r, the area of $\triangle A_1OA_2$ is approximately $\frac{1}{2}r \cdot A_1A_2$, and the area of the inscribed n-gon is approximately $\frac{1}{2}rp_n$, where p_n is the perimeter of the regular n-gon. We define the

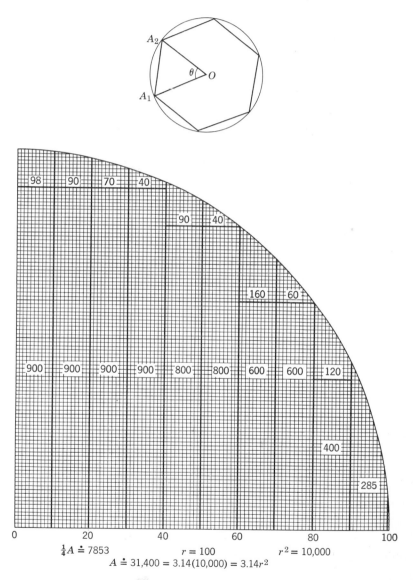

$$\frac{1}{4}A \doteq 7853 \qquad r = 100 \qquad r^2 = 10{,}000$$
$$A \doteq 31{,}400 = 3.14(10{,}000) = 3.14r^2$$

area of the circle to be that number which $\frac{1}{2}rp_n$ approaches as n gets larger and larger. Since p_n approaches $2\pi r$, it follows that $\frac{1}{2}rp_n$ approaches $\frac{1}{2}r(2\pi r)$, or πr^2.

One of the easiest ways to verify this formula experimentally is to draw a circle of radius r units using coordinate graph paper and to count the units of area. The picture shows one-fourth of the area of a circle of radius 100.

A sector of a circle is the portion of the circular region bounded by two radii and an arc of the circle. The area of a sector in a given circle varies directly as the measure of its arc. If the degree measure of arc is m and the radius is r, the area of the sector is $(m/360) \cdot \pi r^2$.

Exercises 1.6

1. Find the area of a parallelogram whose sides have lengths 5, 7, 5, 7 if the perpendicular distance between the two long sides is 4.

2. Find the area of triangle ABC if $AB = 5$ and the distance from C to $\overleftrightarrow{AB}$ is 10.

3. Find the area of a parallelogram which has two sides of length 10 and 15 if the measure of the angle formed by those two sides is 60.

4. Find the area of the trapezoid $ABCD$ in the figure.

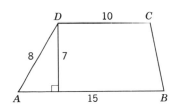

5. Find the area of the polygon $ABCD$ in the figure if $AC = 15$, $BD = 15$, and the perpendicular distance between the parallel lines through B and D is 10.

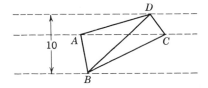

6. Find the circumference of a circle whose radius is 10. (Answer to 10 significant figures.)

7. Find the circumference of a circle whose area is 289π.

8. Find the area of a circle if its diameter is 5 inches.

9. Find the area of a triangle if two of its sides have length 5 and 6 and the measure of the angle included by those sides is 40. (Use trigonometrical tables.)

10. Find the area of a regular decagon inscribed in a circle of radius 10.

11. A circle of radius 12 is given. Find the area of a sector of that circle if the measure of the central angle of that sector is 20.

12. A circle of radius 12 is given. Find the area of a sector of that circle if the degree measure of its arc is 240.

Incidence

2.1 *Introduction*

To a large extent the approach to geometry in Chapter 1 has been informal. Beginning with Chapter 2 the approach to geometry is formal. Our development contains postulates which provide a formal basis for the most basic concepts in geometry. Our objective is to help students gain an appreciation for the foundations of elementary Euclidean geometry developed in a formal manner. Some of the definitions and theorems of Chapter 1 appear again in the formal development. This repetition seems desirable in view of our objective.

In Chapter 1 no attempt was made to provide a postulational basis for some of the most basic ideas in geometry. How do we know that two points determine a line, or that three noncollinear points determine a plane, or that a line in a plane separates that plane, or that a right angle has an interior, or that between every two distinct points there is another point, or that a plane contains an infinite number of points, or that a plane exists, for that matter?

We could agree that all unproved statements are postulates. But we wish to be more formal. In formal geometry our objective is to separate carefully the proved from the unproved, to state carefully the postulates, and to build a structure with a small number of postulates.

In informal geometry we make statements based on our experiences with physical space and objects. If an idea seems basic and intuitively obvious, we assume that our readers will accept it. In formal geometry we recognize formally as *undefined terms* all words denoting geometrical objects or relationships which we choose not to define, and we recognize as *postulates* all statements about geometrical objects or relationships which we choose not to prove and which collectively serve as the basis for proving theorems.

Some two thousand years ago Euclid organized geometrical knowledge into a formal system of definitions, postulates, and theorems. In modern times the structure which Euclid created has been examined critically and a variety of modern versions of the Euclidean structure have appeared. The postulates and definitions of this book are similar to those found in other modern versions of elementary Euclidean geometry, particularly those in which coordinates play a dominant role.

Incidence geometry is concerned with incidence relations among points, lines, and planes. Incidence geometry includes such ideas as: point P is on line L; line L passes through point P; line L intersects plane P; point P lies in plane p; point Q does not lie in plane q. The rest of Chapter 2 is concerned with incidence relations.

2.2   Incidence

In modern Euclidean geometry space is a set of points, every line is a set of points, every plane is a set of points, every line is a subset of space, and every plane is a subset of space. In our formal geometry we make no attempt to define *point*, *line*, and *plane*. We officially declare them undefined terms. We identify those properties of points, lines, and planes which we wish to accept officially without proof. We express these properties in statements called postulates. These properties and additional ones which we get by proving theorems are the properties we use in proving theorems.

Definition. *Space* is the set of all points.

Postulate 1. Space contains at least two distinct points.

Postulate 2. Every line is a set of points and contains at least two distinct points.

Postulate 3. If P and Q are any two distinct points, there is one and only one line which contains them.

The definition of space and these three postulates tell us something about space, although, of course, not very much. At this stage of the development we know that space is not the empty set (Why?), that every element of space is a point (Why?), that every element of a line is a point

(Why?), that the null set is not a line (Why?), and that there is at least one line in space (Why?).

We know from Postulate 1 that space contains at least two distinct points, say A and B. We know from Postulate 3 that there is one and only one line, say m, which contains A and B. We know from Postulate 2 that m is a set of points. Since space is the set of all points, we know that the line m is contained in space. Therefore there is at least one line in space.

If our objective is to build a structure of points, lines, and planes which is a mathematical description of physical space, then Postulates 1, 2, 3 are clearly not enough. They tell us nothing about planes and very little about lines. We cannot prove that there is at least one line with more than two points on it. We proved above that space contains at least one line. It is possible, on the basis of Postulates 1, 2, 3, that space contains only one line and that that line contains only two points. In other words, if A and B are two distinct points, if space is the set $\{A, B\}$, if this set is also a line, and if there are no other lines, then this is a space of two points satisfying the three postulates. A finite space is a space which has a finite number of points in it. A finite geometry is a finite space together with its structure of lines and planes. Thus $[S, L]$ is a finite geometry satisfying Postulates 1, 2, 3 if we specify the space S and the set of lines L as follows: $S = \{A, B\}$, $L = \{m\}$, where $m = \{A, B\}$. It is understood here that the listed elements of S are distinct points and that the only element of L is the line m. $[S, L]$ satisfies Postulate 1 since S contains at least two distinct points. It satisfies Postulate 2 since the only line m is a set of points consisting of at least two points. It satisfies Postulate 3 since for every pair of distinct points (there is only one pair) there is one and only one line (it is the line m) containing them.

Since all points of space might lie on one line in a geometry based on Postulates 1, 2, 3, it is clear that we need more postulates. It is convenient to introduce several definitions before we state more postulates.

Definition. The points of a set are *collinear* if and only if there is a line which contains all of them.

Definition. The points of a set are *coplanar* if and only if there is a plane which contains all of them.

Definition. Two sets *intersect* if their intersection is not the null set.

Postulate 4. No line contains all points of space.

Postulate 5. Every plane is a set of points and contains at least three noncollinear points.

Postulate 6. If P, Q, R are three noncollinear points, there is one and only one plane which contains them.

Postulate 7. No plane contains all points of space.

Postulate 8. If two distinct points of a line belong to a plane, then every point of the line belongs to the plane.

Postulate 9. If two distinct planes intersect, their intersection is a line.

Theorem 2.1. Space contains at least one line.

Proof. We proved that a space satisfying Postulates 1, 2, 3 contains at least one line. It follows that any space which satisfies Postulates 1, 2, 3 and other postulates, such as all the postulates from 1 to 9 inclusive, also contains at least one line.

Theorem 2.2. Space contains at least three distinct noncollinear points.

Proof. We know by Theorem 2.1 that there is at least one line in space. Let m be any line. We know by Postulate 2 that m is a set of points and contains at least two distinct points. Let A and B be two such distinct points. We know by Postulate 4 that no line contains all points of space. Therefore there is some point C not on m. Now A and B are on m whereas C is not. Therefore A, B, C are three distinct points. We know by Postulate 3 that m is the only line containing A and B. Since m does not contain C, it follows that no line contains A, B, and C. Therefore A, B, C are noncollinear and the proof is complete.

Theorem 2.3. Space contains at least three distinct lines.

Proof. Let A, B, C be three distinct noncollinear points (Theorem 2.2). Let $\overleftrightarrow{AB}$ denote the unique (meaning one and only one) line containing A and B (Postulate 3). Similarly, $\overleftrightarrow{BC}$ and $\overleftrightarrow{AC}$ are the unique lines containing B and C, and A and C, respectively. Since A, B, C are noncollinear, $\overleftrightarrow{AB}$ does not contain C, $\overleftrightarrow{BC}$ does not contain A, and $\overleftrightarrow{AC}$ does not contain B. (If one of these lines contained the third point, then the three points would be collinear, and we would have a contradiction.) $\overleftrightarrow{AB} \neq \overleftrightarrow{AC}$ since $\overleftrightarrow{AC}$ contains C whereas $\overleftrightarrow{AB}$ does not. $\overleftrightarrow{AB} \neq \overleftrightarrow{BC}$ since $\overleftrightarrow{BC}$ contains C whereas $\overleftrightarrow{AB}$ does not. $\overleftrightarrow{AC} \neq \overleftrightarrow{BC}$ since $\overleftrightarrow{AC}$ contains A and $\overleftrightarrow{BC}$ does not. It follows that $\overleftrightarrow{AB}$, $\overleftrightarrow{AC}$, $\overleftrightarrow{BC}$ are three distinct lines and the proof is complete.

Theorem 2.4. If two distinct lines intersect, they intersect in exactly one point.

Proof. Consider any two distinct lines that intersect. Then there is at least one point in their intersection. Let P be a point in their intersection. If there is a point Q distinct from P in their intersection, then these two distinct lines both contain P and Q, contradicting Postulate 3.

Therefore there is one and only one point in the intersection of two distinct lines that intersect.

Theorem 2.5. If P is a point, there is a plane that contains it.

Proof. Let P be a point. Let A, B, C be three distinct noncollinear points. If P is one of these three points, then it follows from Postulate 6 that there is a plane containing these three points, including, in particular, the point P. If P is not one of these three points, then P and two of these points are noncollinear. (If P were collinear with A and B, and also collinear with A and C, then since there is only one line containing P and A, it would follow that that line contained P, A, B, and C, contradicting the fact that A, B, C are noncollinear.) We may suppose the points named so that P, A, B are noncollinear. Then it follows from Postulate 6 that there is a unique plane containing P, A, B. Therefore there is a plane containing P.

Theorem 2.6. Space contains at least two distinct planes.

Proof. Let A, B, C be three distinct noncollinear points (Theorem 2.2) and p the unique plane which contains them (Postulate 6). Let D be a point not in p (Postulate 7). Then D, A, B are noncollinear. If this were not so, then the unique line containing A and B would also contain D, and D would be an element of p (Postulate 8), yielding a contradiction. There is a unique plane q containing D, A, B. Then $p \neq q$ since p contains C and q does not contain C. It follows that there are at least two distinct planes.

Theorem 2.7. Space contains at least four noncoplanar points.

Proof. In proving Theorem 2.6 we proved the existence of four noncoplanar points A, B, C, and D.

Theorem 2.8. If a line intersects a plane not containing it, the intersection is a set which contains only one point.

Proof. This follows immediately from Postulate 8.

Theorem 2.9. A line and a point not on it are contained in exactly one plane.

Proof. Let m be a line and P a point not on it. Let A and B be two distinct points on m (Postulate 2). Then m is the only line containing A and B (Postulate 3) and therefore A, B, P are noncollinear. There is exactly one plane p containing A, B, P (Postulate 6). This plane contains P and m (Postulate 8). Any other plane containing P and m would also contain A, B, and P. However, there is only one plane containing A, B, P. Therefore there is only one and only one plane containing m and P.

Theorem 2.10. If two distinct lines have a point in common, there is exactly one plane which contains them.

Proof. Let m and n be distinct lines which intersect in a point P. Then P is the only point in their intersection (Theorem 2.4). Let A, $A \neq P$, be another point on m; let B, $B \neq P$, be another point on n (Postulate 2). Since there is one and only one line, m, containing A and P (Postulate 3), and since it does not contain B, it follows that A, B, P are noncollinear. There is exactly one plane containing A, B, P; call it p (Postulate 6). Since p contains A and P, it contains m. Since p contains B and P, it contains n (Postulate 8). Therefore there is a plane, namely p, which contains m and n. If any plane q distinct from p contained m and n, then it would also contain the three noncollinear points A, B, P, contradicting Postulate 6. Therefore there is exactly one plane which contains m and n.

Exercises 2.2

1. Given the structure $[S, L]$ with

$$S = \{A, B, C\},$$
$$L = \{\{A, B\}, \ \{A, C\}, \ \{B, C\}\}.$$

In this finite geometry space S is a set of three distinct points and there are three distinct lines. Does this finite geometry satisfy Postulate 1? 2? 3? 4?

2. Given $[S, L]$ with

$$S = \{A, B, C\},$$
$$L = \{\{A\}, \ \{A, B\}, \ \{A, B, C\}\}.$$

In this finite geometry there are three distinct points and three distinct lines. Does this finite geometry satisfy Postulate 1? 2? 3? 4?

3. Given $[S, L, P]$ with

$$S = \{A, B, C, D\},$$
$$L = \{\{A, B\}, \ \{A, C\}, \ \{A, D\}, \ \{B, C\}, \ \{B, D\}, \ \{C, D\}\},$$
$$P = \{\{A, B, C\}, \ \{A, B, D\}, \ \{A, C, D\}, \ \{B, C, D\}\}.$$

In this finite geometry there are four distinct points, six distinct lines, and four distinct planes. Which of the nine postulates are satisfied by this finite geometry?

4. Given $[S, L, P]$ with S and L as in Exercise 3 but with P as follows:

$$P = \{\{A, B, C, D\}\}.$$

In this finite geometry there are four distinct points, six distinct lines, and one plane. Which of the nine postulates are satisfied by this geometry?

5. An "if-then" statement is true if the "if" part is false. Which of the nine postulates is true for the finite geometry of Exercise 4 because the "if" part is false in every instance?

6. Given Postulates I, II, III, IV, V as follows:

    I. Space S is a set of n distinct points where n is a positive integer and $n \geqslant 2$.

    II. Every line is a set of points and contains at least two distinct points.

    III. If P and Q are any two distinct points, there is exactly one line containing them.

    IV. If m and n are any two distinct lines, there is exactly one point which lies on both of them.

    V. If P is any point, there are exactly two distinct lines which contain it.

  (a) Given $[S, L]$ with $S = \{A, B\}$, $L = \{m\}$, where $m = \{A, B\}$, where A, B are distinct points, and there are no other points, and where m is the only line. Which of the Postulates I, II, III, IV, V are satisfied by the structure?

  (b) In Exercise (a) one of the postulates is satisfied because the "if" part of the statement is false in every instance. Which one?

  (c) Same as (a) except

$$S = \{A, B, C\}, \quad L = \{m_1, m_2, m_3\},$$

$$m_1 = \{A, B\}, \quad m_2 = \{A, C\}, \quad m_3 = \{B, C\}.$$

  (d) Same as (a) except

$$S = \{A, B, C, D\}, \quad L = \{m_1, m_2, m_3, m_4\},$$

$$m_1 = \{A, B, C\}, \quad m_2 = \{A, B, D\}, \quad m_3 = \{A, C, D\}, \quad m_4 = \{B, C, D\}.$$

7. Construct all geometries satisfying the following four postulates.

P1. Space S is a set of n points, n a positive integer, $n \leqslant 10$.

P2. A line is a non-null subset of S.

P3. Any two distinct lines have exactly one point in common.

P4. Every point lies on exactly two distinct lines.

Hints: 1. It is impossible to have only one point in S. Why?

      2. If there are exactly m distinct lines in space, then n is equal to the number of different combinations of m distinct things taken 2 at a time. Why?

      3. It is impossible to have $m = 2$. Why?

      4. If $m = 3$, then $n = 3$. If the lines are p, q, r, let $A = p \cap q$, $B = p \cap r$, $C = q \cap r$. Then $S = \{A, B, C\}$, $p = \{A, B\}$, $q = \{A, C\}$, $r = \{B, C\}$.

      5. If $m = 4$, what is n? Now name the points and the lines and establish the structure.

      6. If $m = 5$, what is n? Now name the points and the lines and establish the structure by naming the elements of each line.

8. Let (XYZ) be a statement about objects X, Y, Z and suppose given the following postulates T1 to T5:

T1. If (ABC), then A, B, C are distinct objects.

T2. If A, B, C are three distinct objects, then exactly one of the three statements, (ABC), (BAC), (ACB) is true (the other two are false).

T3. If (ABC), then (CBA).

T4. If (ABC), then there is an object D such that (DAB).

T5. If (ABC), then there is an object D such that (ADB).

(a) Prove : If (ABC), then there is an object D such that (BCD).

(b) Prove : If (ABC), then there is an object D such that (BDC).

CHAPTER 3

Distance and Coordinates on a Line

3.1 *Introduction*

In Chapter 2 we built a structure of points, lines, and planes on a foundation of nine postulates. These incidence postulates and the theorems deduced from them are statements about lines and planes considered as sets of points. No questions regarding size or shape, that is, no questions of measurement, are involved.

Our objective in this chapter is to introduce the concept of distance together with related topics. First, we introduce several postulates based on our experiences with measured distances. We relate them to the number line of elementary geometry by defining a coordinate system on a line and adopting a ruler postulate. The ruler postulate provides us with many coordinate systems on a line. This chapter is concerned with the various coordinate systems on a line and the use of these coordinate systems in defining and studying the subsets of a line.

3.2 *Distance*

A number line is a convenient device for showing certain relationships among real numbers. What relationships? One is the order relation. If the number y appears to the right of the number x in the number line

as it is usually drawn, this means that $y > x$. The number line shows betweenness for numbers. If y is between x and z in the picture, it means that the number y is between the real numbers x and z, so that $x < y < z$ or $x > y > z$. The number line may be used to compare "distances" between numbers. For example, 5 is farther from -1 than 4 is from -1. For another example, since $4 - 1 = 5 - 2$, the portion of the number line from 1 to 4 should have the same length as the portion from 2 to 5.

In the theory of real numbers, we agree that $|x - y|$ is a good answer to the question, "How far apart are the real numbers x and y?" Thus -3 and 5 are 8 units apart since $|(-3) - 5| = 8$. But what does "how far apart" for points mean? In the world of physical objects, we find an answer by using a physical ruler. In order to make a physical ruler graduated in inches, say, we need to know what 1 inch is. We can get into the business of measuring distances if we have two points that are 1 inch apart. By law, the inch is defined in terms of a meter. For many years the legal meter was described by a pair of marks on a platinum-iridium bar kept under prescribed conditions in France. The idea that two distinct points may be used as a unit for measuring distances furnishes the basis for the development of the distance concept in our formal geometry. In recent years the marks on the bar have given way to a more reliable standard. The legal meter is now based on the wave length of certain spectral lines.

Suppose any two distinct points in space are chosen. We could agree that the distance between them is 1, and that the distance between every other pair of points is determined by this agreement. If we say that the distance between two points A and B is k, we mean that they are k times as far apart as the two points which furnish us the unit.

Sometimes in geometry it is convenient to consider directed distances. For example, the distance from A to B may be 5 whereas the distance from B to A is -5. Directed distances are *not* part of our formal geometry. We agree that the distance between any two distinct points is a positive number.

We are now ready to formulate our distance postulate.

Postulate 10. If A and A' are any two distinct points, there exists a correspondence which associates with every pair of distinct points a unique positive number, the number assigned to the given pair $\{A, A'\}$ being one.

Definition. The pair of points, A and A', mentioned in Postulate 10 is called the *unit-pair*.

Definition. The number which corresponds with a pair of distinct points P, Q, as in Postulate 10, is called the *distance* between P and Q relative to the unit-pair $\{A, A'\}$.

Notation. The distance between P and Q relative to $\{A, A'\}$ is denoted by PQ (relative to $\{A, A'\}$), or by QP (relative to $\{A, A'\}$), since the pairs $\{P, Q\}$ and $\{Q, P\}$ are the same, or simply by PQ if we prefer not to specify the unit-pair.

Definition. The distance between any point P and itself, relative to any unit-pair $\{A, A'\}$, is zero.

3.3 *More Distance Postulates*

The use of a physical ruler for measuring distances suggests several basic properties of distance which are not mentioned in Postulate 10. If the distance between B and B' is 1 yard and between A and A' is 1 foot, then the distance between B and B' (relative to $\{A, A'\}$) is 3. Also, for every pair of points P and Q we have

$$\frac{PQ \text{ (relative to } \{A, A'\})}{PQ \text{ (relative to } \{B, B'\})} = 3.$$

In this last equation A, A', B, B' are fixed points and P and Q are variables. If the distance between two points using one unit-pair is three times the distance between these two points using another unit-pair, then the distance between any two points using the first unit-pair is three times the distance between these points using the second unit-pair.

Another property which we take for granted is as follows. Suppose P, Q, R are three distinct points and that the distance from P to R is ten times the distance from P to Q, when distances are relative to $\{A, A'\}$. How do the distances PQ and PR compare if distances are relative to some other unit-pair $\{B, B'\}$? The properties we want cannot be deduced from Postulate 10. We adopt two additional distance postulates to assure us that distances behave as distances should. Before we write these postulates, it is convenient to define a coordinate system on a line.

In a coordinate system on a line, points are matched with numbers (called their coordinates) in such a way that the distance between two points can be found by subtracting coordinates. Here is the complete definition.

Definition. Let $\{A, A'\}$ be any unit-pair and l any line. A *coordinate system* on l relative to $\{A, A'\}$ is a one-to-one correspondence between the set of all points in l and the set of all real numbers with the following property. If R and S are points on l matched with r and s, respectively, then RS (relative to $\{A, A'\}) = |r - s|$.

Definition. The *origin* of a coordinate system on a line is the point which is matched with 0. The *unit-point* of a coordinate system on a line is the point which is matched with 1. The number which is matched with a point in a coordinate system on a line is called the *coordinate* of that point.

These definitions tell us what a coordinate system on a line is, but they do not tell us that there are such things. Our next postulate will assure us of the existence of coordinate systems on a line. How many? How many do we want? When measuring distances along a line with a physical ruler, we may start at any point we choose, we may use any unit we want, and we measure distance to any other point in the line. We are now ready for the postulates.

Postulate 11. (*Ruler Postulate*). If $\{A, A'\}$ is any unit-pair, if l is any line, and if P and Q are any two distinct points on l, then there is exactly one coordinate system on l relative to $\{A, A'\}$ such that the origin of the coordinate system is P and the coordinate of Q is a positive number.

Postulate 12 (*Distance Ratio Postulate*). If $\{A, A'\}$ and $\{B, B'\}$ are any unit-pairs, then for every pair of distinct points P and Q and for every pair of distinct points R and S, it is true that

$$\frac{PQ \text{ (relative to } \{A, A'\})}{PQ \text{ (relative to } \{B, B'\})} = \frac{RS \text{ (relative to } \{A, A'\})}{RS \text{ (relative to } \{B, B'\})}.$$

Or equivalently

$$\frac{PQ \text{ (relative to } \{A, A'\})}{RS \text{ (relative to } \{A, A'\})} = \frac{PQ \text{ (relative to } \{B, B'\})}{RS \text{ (relative to } \{B, B'\})}.$$

There are many foot rulers. A distance measured using one foot ruler should be the same as when it is measured with another foot ruler. How does this idea appear in formal geometry? Suppose that $\{A, A'\}$ and $\{B, B'\}$ are two unit-pairs such that BB' (relative to $\{A, A'\}) = 1$. Since the distance between B and B' relative to $\{A, A'\}$ is 1, it seems that the distance between any two points, say P and Q, should be the same if taken relative to $\{B, B'\}$ as if taken relative to $\{A, A'\}$. This follows immediately from Postulate 12 if one takes $R = B$ and $S = B'$. Then RS (relative to $\{A, A'\}) = 1$ by hypothesis, and RS (relative to $\{B, B'\}) = 1$ by Postulate 10. Hence we have the following theorem.

Theorem 3.1 (*Unit Substitution Theorem*). If $\{A, A'\}$ and $\{B, B'\}$ are any unit-pairs such that BB' (relative to $\{A, A'\}) = 1$, and if P and Q are any points, then

$$PQ \text{ (relative to } \{B, B'\}) = PQ \text{ (relative to } \{A, A'\}).$$

An important special case of the ruler postulate is obtained by taking $\{P, Q\}$ as the unit-pair. It is the following theorem.

Theorem 3.2 (*The Origin Unit-Point Theorem*). If P and Q are any two distinct points on a line, then there is a unique coordinate system on that line with P as origin and with Q as unit-point.

The concept of betweenness is basic in geometry. In our development of formal geometry betweenness for points is defined in terms of betweenness for numbers. The following theorem is important for this development.

Theorem 3.3. Let P, Q, R, with $P \neq R$, be points on a line l. If the coordinate of Q is between the coordinates of P and R in some coordinate system on l, then the coordinate of Q is between the coordinates of P and R in every coordinate system on l.

Proof. Let $\{A, A'\}$ and $\{B, B'\}$ be any unit-pairs. Let C be a coordinate system relative to $\{A, A'\}$ on l and C' a coordinate system relative to $\{B, B'\}$ on l. Let p, q, r be the coordinates of P, Q, R, respectively, in C. Let p', q', r' be the coordinates of P, Q, R, respectively, in C'. Suppose q is between p and r. Then

$$p - r = (p - q) + (q - r), \quad |p - r| > |p - q|, \quad |p - r| > |q - r|,$$

$$\frac{PQ \text{ (relative to } \{A, A'\})}{PR \text{ (relative to } \{A, A'\})} = \frac{|p - q|}{|p - r|} < 1,$$

and

$$\frac{QR \text{ (relative to } \{A, A'\})}{PR \text{ (relative to } \{A, A'\})} = \frac{|q - r|}{|p - r|} < 1.$$

It follows from Postulate 12 that

$$\frac{|p' - q'|}{|p' - r'|} = \frac{|p - q|}{|p - r|} < 1, \quad \text{and} \quad \frac{|q' - r'|}{|p' - r'|} = \frac{|q - r|}{|p - r|} < 1.$$

It follows that q' is between p' and r'. For if q' were less than or equal to both p' and r', then $|q' - p'| \geq |p' - r'|$ or $|q' - r'| \geq |p' - r'|$, and

$$\frac{|q' - p'|}{|p' - r'|} \geq 1 \quad \text{or} \quad \frac{|q' - r'|}{|p' - r'|} \geq 1,$$

which is impossible.

Similarly, if q' were greater than or equal to both p' and r', then $|q' - p'| \geqslant |p' - r'|$ or $|q' - r'| \geqslant |p' - r'|$, and

$$\frac{|q' - p'|}{|p' - r'|} \geqslant 1 \quad \text{or} \quad \frac{|q' - r'|}{|p' - r'|} \geqslant 1,$$

which is impossible. Therefore q' is between p' and r'. Since C and C' are arbitrary coordinate systems on l, the proof is complete.

Exercises 3.3

1. Let P, Q, R be points on l with coordinates 10, 12, 15, respectively, in a coordinate system C. Does there exist a coordinate system C' on l in which the coordinates of P, Q, R are $-15, -10, -12$, respectively? Justify your answer.

2. Let P, Q, R be points on l with coordinates 10, 12, 15, respectively, in a coordinate system C. Does there exist a coordinate system C' on l in which the coordinates of P, Q, R are 5, 8, 10, respectively? Justify your answer.

3. Let P, Q, R be points on l with coordinates $-7, 8, 20$, respectively, in a coordinate system C. If the coordinates of P and Q in a coordinate system C' are 0 and 5, respectively, find the coordinate of R in the coordinate system C'.

4. If P, Q, R are points with $Q \neq R$, if $\{A, A'\}$, $\{B, B'\}$ are unit-pairs, and if

$$\frac{PQ \text{ (relative to } \{A, A'\})}{QR \text{ (relative to } \{A, A'\})} = 37,$$

   find

$$\frac{QR \text{ (relative to } \{B, B'\})}{PQ \text{ (relative to } \{B, B'\})}.$$

5. If P, Q, R are points with $P \neq R$ and $P \neq Q$, if $\{A, A'\}$ and $\{B, B'\}$ are unit-pairs, and if

$$\frac{PR \text{ (relative to } \{A, A'\})}{PQ \text{ (relative to } \{A, A'\})} = 10,$$

   find

$$\frac{PR \text{ (relative to } \{B, B'\})}{PQ \text{ (relative to } \{B, B'\})}.$$

6. If A, B, C, D, E are points on a line l with coordinates 0, 1, 2, 3, 4, respectively, in a system S, and if A and B have coordinates 100 and 80, respectively, in a coordinate system S', find the coordinates of C, D, E in S'.

7. Prove: If l is a line, if P is a point on l, if $\{A, A'\}$ is a unit-pair, there are two and only two distinct coordinate systems on l relative to $\{A, A'\}$ with P as origin.

8. Prove: If l is a line, if P and Q are two distinct points on l, there is exactly one coordinate system on l in which the coordinate of P is 0 and the coordinate of Q is 2.

9. Prove: If l is a line and if P and Q are any two distinct points on l, then there is exactly one coordinate system on l in which the coordinate of P is 17 and the coordinate of Q is 21.

3.4 Segments and Rays

In view of Theorem 3.3 it seems natural to base the concept of betweenness for points upon the concept of betweenness for coordinates.

Definition. If P, Q, R are points, then Q is *between* P and R if and only if P, Q, R are distinct collinear points and there is a coordinate system on the line which contains them in which the coordinate of Q is between the coordinates of P and R. Sometimes we write (PQR) to mean that "Q is between P and R."

Definition. A *segment* is a set consisting of two points, called its *endpoints*, and all the points between them. The segment with endpoints P and Q is denoted by $\overline{PQ}$. A point of a segment other than an endpoint is an *interior point* of the segment. The set of all interior points of a segment is the *interior of the segment*.

Definition. A *ray* is a set consisting of two distinct points P and Q and all points R such that (PRQ) or (PQR). The point P in this definition is the *endpoint* of the ray. The ray with endpoint P and containing the point Q, where $P \neq Q$, is denoted by $\overrightarrow{PQ}$. A point of a ray other than its endpoint is an *interior point* of the ray. The set of all interior points of a ray is the *interior of the ray*.

Definition. If P and Q are any two distinct points, then the set consisting of P and all points R such that (RPQ) is the *ray opposite* to $\overrightarrow{PQ}$. Sometimes we write "Opp $\overrightarrow{PQ}$" to mean "the ray opposite to $\overrightarrow{PQ}$."

Definition. The rays in a set of rays are called *concurrent* rays if they all have the same endpoint.

Definition. The rays in a set of rays are called *collinear* rays if there is a line which contains all of them.

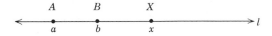

Let A and B be two distinct points of a line l and let their coordinates be a and b in some coordinate system. Suppose that $a < b$. Let X be a variable point on *l* and let its coordinate be *x*. Then, using set-builder notation, we have:

$$\overleftrightarrow{AB} = \{X : x \text{ is any real number}\},$$

$$\overrightarrow{AB} = \{X : x \geqslant a\},$$

$$\overline{AB} = \{X : a \leqslant x \leqslant b\},$$

$$\overline{BA} = \{X : x \leqslant b\},$$

$$\text{Opp } \overrightarrow{AB} = \{X : x \leqslant a\},$$

$$\text{Opp } \overrightarrow{BA} = \{X : x \geqslant b\}.$$

3.5   *Uniform Scale*

A comment on the notion of a uniform scale as it relates to a coordinate system may be in order here. It is true that the picture in Section 3.2 suggests a uniform scale, but it could be drawn otherwise if we wished. Conceivably it might look like this.

Our postulational basis does no violence to our ideas of uniform scale. The postulates seem to fit well with a picture like the one in Section 3.2. But our postulates do not tell us what the picture is "really like." Our postulates provide us with all that we need to develop the properties of distance in Euclidean geometry.

Someone might object and say that the last picture is impossible since $\overline{AB}$ is longer than $\overline{BC}$, although $AB = 1$ and $BC = 1$. The proper response to this objection is that $\overline{AB}$ may look longer than $\overline{BC}$ but that it is not. The picture suggests a coordinate system on a line, and indicates that in this coordinate system the coordinates of *A*, *B*, *C* are 0, 1, 2, respectively. Using coordinates in this coordinate system we compute distances to get $AB = 1$ and $BC = 1$. Therefore $\overline{AB}$ and $\overline{BC}$ have the same length. The Ruler Postulate does not say anything about using a physical ruler, and we should not infer anything from the properties of a physical ruler. Our inferences should be based on the postulates.

Someone might ask whether or not a coordinate system on a line might not look like this.

Our formal development does not tell us what to do or what not to do when we draw pictures. Betweenness for points is defined in terms of betweenness for numbers. If the coordinates of points A, B, C, in a co-ordinate system on a line are 0, 2, 1, respectively, then according to our development C is between A and B, and $\overline{AC}$ and $\overline{BC}$ have the same length. Of course, it would be natural to draw a picture like the following one for this situation (but you don't have to if you don't want to).

It should also be stated that once we understand these matters clearly, then we may agree for the purpose of the exercises, in order to save words, that hypotheses regarding betweenness relations among points may be communicated by pictures. But it should be understood that this is done for convenience. For some purposes a picture is worth a thousand words. But our purpose here is to build a foundation in which pictures are not an essential ingredient.

Exercises 3.5

1. Suppose P, Q, R are points on a line L and that a coordinate system is fixed. Prove: If Q is between P and R, then $PR = PQ + QR$.

2. Explain: It is possible for points P, Q, R on a line L to be such that $PR = PQ + QR$ and such that Q is not between P and R.

3.6 *Two Coordinate Systems on a Line*

Let a line l and two coordinate systems on it, called C and C', be given. Let A and B be two distinct points on l. Suppose that the coordinates of

	A	B	P	
	a	b	x	(C)
	a'	b'	x'	(C')

A and B are a and b, respectively, in C, and that they are a' and b', respectively, in C'. Let P be a variable point with coordinate x in C and coordinate x' in C'. We want to express x' in terms of x, a, b, a', and b'.

It follows from the distance ratio postulate that

$$\frac{|x - a|}{|b - a|} = \frac{|x' - a'|}{|b' - a'|} \quad \text{and} \quad \frac{|x - b|}{|b - a|} = \frac{|x' - b'|}{|b' - a'|}.$$

Then

$$(1) \quad \frac{x - a}{b - a} = \frac{x' - a'}{b' - a'} \qquad \text{or} \quad (2) \quad \frac{x - a}{b - a} = -\frac{x' - a'}{b' - a'}.$$

and

$$(3) \quad \frac{x - b}{b - a} = \frac{x' - b'}{b' - a'} \qquad \text{or} \quad (4) \quad \frac{x - b}{b - a} = -\frac{x' - b'}{b' - a'}.$$

But (1) implies (3), and (3) implies (1). Subtract 1 from both members of (1) to get (3). How can you get (1) from (3)? If (1) is not true for some point P, it follows that (2) and (4) are both true for that point. But (2) and (4) cannot both be true. For the difference of their left members [left of (2) minus left of (4)] is 1, whereas the difference in the same order of the right members is -1. Therefore equations (1) and (3) hold for every point P on l. This proves the following theorem.

Theorem 3.4 (*The Two-Coordinate-Systems Theorem*). Let a line l and two coordinate systems, C and C', on l be given. Let A and B be any two distinct points on l with coordinates a and b, respectively, in C, and with coordinates a' and b', respectively, in C'. If X is any point on l, and if its coordinates in C and C' are x and x', respectively, then $(x' - a')/(b' - a') = (x - a)/(b - a)$.

A second form of this theorem is as follows.

Theorem 3.5 (*The Linear Transformation Theorem*). If l is any line, and if C and C' are any coordinate systems on l, then there exist two numbers a, b, with $a \neq 0$, such that for any point P on l, its coordinate x in C is related to its coordinate x' in C' by the equation $x' = ax + b$.

Proof. Let D and E be any two distinct points on l. Let d and e be the coordinates of D and E, respectively, in C. Let d' and e' be the coordinates of D and E, respectively, in C'. Let P be any point on l and suppose its coordinates in C and C' are x and x', respectively. Then it follows from Theorem 3.4 that $(x' - d')/(e' - d') = (x - d)/(e - d)$. Then $x' = [(e' - d')/(e - d)] \cdot x + (d'e - de')/(e - d)$. Take $a = (e' - d')/(e - d)$ and $b = (d'e - de')/(e - d)$. Then $a \neq 0$ and $x' = ax + b$ for every point P on l.

A third form of this theorem is as follows.

Theorem 3.6 (*The Two-Point Theorem*). Let X_1 and X_2 be any two distinct points on a line l. Let x_1 and x_2 be the coordinates of X_1 and X_2 in some coordinate system C on l. Let X be any point on l. Suppose that its coordinate in the system C is x, and let its coordinate in the system with origin X_1 and unit-point X_2 be k. Then $x = x_1 + k(x_2 - x_1)$.

Proof. It follows from Theorem 3.4 that $(x - x_1)/(x_2 - x_1) = (k - 0)/(1 - 0)$, and hence that $x = x_1 + k(x_2 - x_1)$.

Exercises 3.6

Suppose P, Q, X are points on l, that $P \neq Q$, that the coordinates of P, Q, X in a coordinate system C are x_1, x_2, x, respectively, and that the coordinates of P, Q, X, are $0, 1, k$, respectively, in a coordinate system C'.

P	Q	X	
x_1	x_2	x	(C)
0	1	k	(C')

1. Complete the following statements:

$X \in \overline{PQ}$ if and only if _____ $\leqslant x \leqslant$ _____, or _____ $\leqslant x \leqslant$ _____.
$X \in \overline{PQ}$ if and only if _____ $\leqslant k \leqslant$ _____.
If $x_1 < x_2$, then $X \in \overline{PQ}$ if and only if _____ $\leqslant x \leqslant$ _____.
If $x_2 < x_1$, then $X \in \overline{PQ}$ if and only if _____ $\leqslant x \leqslant$ _____.
If $x_1 < x_2$, then $X \in \overrightarrow{PQ}$ if and only if x_____.
If $x_1 > x_2$, then $X \in \overrightarrow{PQ}$ if and only if x_____.
$X \in \overrightarrow{PQ}$ if and only if k_____.
$X \in \overrightarrow{QP}$ if and only if k_____.
$X \in \text{Opp } \overrightarrow{QP}$ if and only if k_____.

2. Suppose X is a point on $\overrightarrow{PQ}$ such that $PX = 2 \cdot PQ$. Complete the following proof that $k = 2$ and that $x = x_1 + 2(x_2 - x_1)$.
Proof: Using the coordinate system with P as origin and Q as unit-point (the k-coordinate system) we have $PX = k - 0 = k$, $2 \cdot PQ = 2(1 - 0) = 2$.

3. Suppose X is a point on the ray opposite to $\overrightarrow{PQ}$ such that $PX = 2 \cdot PQ$. Prove that $k = -2$ and that $x = x_1 - 2(x_2 - x_1)$.

4. Complete the proof that $k = \frac{1}{2}$ if and only if X is the midpoint of $\overline{PQ}$.
Proof: Suppose $k = \frac{1}{2}$. Then using the k-coordinate system we see that X is between P and Q since $\frac{1}{2}$ is between 0 and 1. Also $PX =$ _____ $-$ _____ $=$ _____ and $XQ =$ _____ $-$ _____ $=$ _____. Therefore $PX = XQ$ and X is the midpoint of $\overline{PQ}$.

Suppose next that X is the midpoint of $\overline{PQ}$, and that its coordinate is k. Since X is between P and Q, it follows that k is between _____ and _____. The $PX =$ _____ and $XQ =$ _____, and since $PX = XQ$, it follows that $k = \frac{1}{2}$.

5. If $x_1 = 7$, $x_2 = 12$, and if $PX/PQ = 5$, find k. (There are two possibilities.)

6. If $x_1 = 7$, $x_2 = 12$, and if $PX/PQ = 5$, find x.

In Exercises 7 and 8 fill the blank space with the proper restriction on k. If the domain of k is the entire real number system, write "k is real." Otherwise write equations or inequalities to restrict k properly.

7. If $x_1 = 7$, $x_2 = -5$, then $\overrightarrow{PQ} = \{X : x = x_1 + k(x_2 - x_1), \underline{\hspace{1cm}}\}$.

8. If $x_1 = 7$, $x_2 = -5$, then $\overline{PQ} = \{X : x = x_1 + k(x_2 - x_1), \underline{\hspace{1cm}}\}$.

9. If $x_1 = 7$, $x_2 = -5$ and if $PX = 11 \cdot XQ$, solve for x.

10. If $X_0, X_1, X_2, X_3, X_4, X_5, X_6, X_7, X_8, X_9, X_{10}$ are equally spaced points on l arranged in the order named, and if the k coordinates of X_0 and X_1 are 0 and 1, respectively, what are the k coordinates of the other nine points?

11. Given eleven equally spaced points on a line l as in Exercise 10. If the coordinates of X_0 and X_1 are 5 and -1, respectively, find the coordinates of the other nine points.

12. Suppose A and B are points on a line l with coordinates 4 and -8, respectively, in a coodinate system C, and with coordinates 0 and 1, respectively, in a coordinate system C'. Let x and k be the coordinates of a point P on l in the coordinate systems C and C', respectively. Then x and k are related as follows: $x = 4 + k(-8 - 4)$ for every point P on l. Use this information to complete the following table.

	k	x	Point on l or subset of l
(a)	0	4	A
(b)			B
(c)	$\frac{1}{2}$		Midpoint of $\overline{AB}$
(d)	$\frac{1}{3}$		P in $\overline{AB}$ and $AP = \underline{\hspace{1cm}} AB$
(e)		$-8 \leqslant x \leqslant 4$	
(f)	$k \geqslant 0$		
(g)	$k > 0$		Interior of $\overrightarrow{AB}$
(h)	3 or -3		
(i)		64	

13. Suppose that P, Q, R, S, T, U, V are points on a line. Data from four coordinate systems on this line are given in the chart below. Under "Relationship" (except for the first system) is the equation which relates the coordinate in that system to the coordinate in the first system. Complete the table.

			Coordinate of						
Coordinate system	Coordinate	Relationship	P	Q	R	S	T	U	V
First	x		0	3			−1		
Second	x'	$x' = 6x$				6			12
Third	x''	$x'' = x - 3$			7				
Fourth	x'''	$x''' =$	2	5				8	

3.7 *Length*

In our treatment of formal geometry we get distance by postulating it. To begin with, distance applies to a pair of points, that is, distance means a distance between two points. Later it is extended to apply to a point and a line, or pair of lines, or, indeed, to any pair of sets of points.

In our formal geometry we define length in terms of distance. To begin with, length applies to segments.

Definition. The *length* of a segment is the distance between its endpoints.

Thus if $\overline{PQ}$ is a given segment, then PQ is the distance between P and Q, and PQ is also the length of the segment $\overline{PQ}$. Note that length as well as distance is relative to some unit-pair. Thus PQ (relative to $\{A, A'\}$) denotes the distance between P and Q relative to the unit-pair $\{A, A'\}$; it also denotes the length of $\overline{PQ}$ relative to the unit-pair $\{A, A'\}$.

As stated in Chapter 1, we consider all segments to have the same shape, and they have the same size if and only if their lengths are equal. Our formal definition follows.

Definition. Two segments (whether distinct or not) are called *congruent* segments, and each is said to be *congruent to* the other, if they have the same length.

Notation. If $\overline{AB}$ and $\overline{CD}$ are segments, $\overline{AB} \cong \overline{CD}$ means that they are congruent segments (or that each is congruent to the other).

Theorem 3.7 (*Point Plotting Theorem*). Let $\{A, A'\}$ be any unit-pair, $\overrightarrow{RS}$ any ray, and p any positive number. Then there is exactly one point P on $\overrightarrow{RS}$ such that RP (relative to $\{A, A'\}$) $= p$.

Proof. Let C be the unique coordinate system in $\overleftrightarrow{RS}$ relative to $\{A, A'\}$ in which R is the origin and the coordinate of S is a positive number. Then there is exactly one point P on $\overleftrightarrow{RS}$ with coordinate p. Since $\overrightarrow{RS}$

is the set of all points on $\overleftrightarrow{RS}$ whose coordinates are non-negative, it follows that P is on $\overrightarrow{RS}$.

An alternate form of Theorem 3.7 follows.

Theorem 3.8 (*Unique Congruent Segment Theorem*). If $\overline{AB}$ is any segment and if $\overrightarrow{RS}$ is any ray, there is exactly one point P on $\overrightarrow{RS}$ such that $\overline{RP} \cong \overline{AB}$.

Proof. This follows immediately from the Point Plotting Theorem if one takes $p = AB$.

Exercises 3.7

1. Let A and B be two distinct points on a line l. Prove that there are two distinct points C and D on l such that $BC = 2 \cdot BA$ and $\overline{BC} \cong \overline{BD}$.

2. Simplify the following, given that A, B, C, D are distinct points on line l.
   (a) $AB + BC$, if B is between A and C.
   (b) $AB - BC$, if C is between A and B.
   (c) $\overline{AB} \cap \overline{BC}$, if B is between A and C.
   (d) $\overline{AB} \cap \overline{BC}$, if C is between A and B.
   (e) $\overline{AB} \cap \overrightarrow{AB}$.
   (f) $\overline{AB} \cup \overrightarrow{AB}$.
   (g) $\overleftrightarrow{AB} \cup \overrightarrow{BA}$.
   (h) AA.
   (i) $\overline{AB} \cap \overline{CD}$, if B is between A and C, and C is between B and D.

3. If $A, B, C, D, E, F, G, H, I, J$ are points on a line l with coordinates 1, 2, 3, 4, 5, 6, 7, 8, 9, 10, respectively, compute the following,

   (a) AB (relative to $\{A, B\}$).
   (b) AC (relative to $\{A, B\}$).
   (c) AH (relative to $\{A, B\}$).
   (d) CJ (relative to $\{A, C\}$).
   (e) HJ (relative to $\{A, G\}$).

4. Given two distinct points A and B on a line l. If the coordinates of A and B are -3 and 8, respectively, find the possible values of x, if x is the coordinate of a point X on l as restricted by the given statement.
   (a) $AX = XB$.
   (b) $\overline{AX} \cong \overline{AB}$.
   (c) $X \in \overline{AB}$ and $AX = 2 \cdot XB$.
   (d) $X \in \overrightarrow{AB}$, $X \notin \overline{AB}$, and $AX = 2 \cdot XB$.
   (e) $3 \cdot AX = 4 \cdot XB$.

5. Given two distinct points A and B of a coordinate system C on a line l. If the coordinates of A and B are -13 and 3, respectively, compute the coordinates of the following:

(a) The trisection points of $\overline{AB}$.

(b) The point C if B is the midpoint of $\overline{AC}$.

(c) The points P and Q if $\overline{BP} \cong \overline{BQ}$ and $\overline{BP} \cong \overline{BA}$.

(d) The points C and D, if C and D are on $\overrightarrow{AB}$, and if $AC = 2 \cdot AB$ and $AD = 5 \cdot AB$.

(e) The points X and Y, if $\overline{AX} \cong \overline{AY}$ and $3 \cdot AX = AB$.

CHAPTER 4

Convexity and Separation

4.1 *Convex Sets*

An important concept in modern mathematics is the concept of a convex body. In the development of a formal geometry, convex sets are introduced after segments since the concept of a convex set involves the concept of a segment. The concept of a convex set is useful in describing the relationship of a line to a plane that contains it or the relationship of a plane to space.

Definition. A set S is a *convex set* if and only if for every pair of distinct points, P and Q, in S, the segment $\overline{PQ}$ is a subset of S.

Theorem 4.1. The null set and all sets which contain only one point are convex sets.

Proof. Let S be a set which is either the null set or a set consisting of a single point. If *A and B are any two distinct points in S*, then $\overline{AB}$ is a subset of S. The preceding statement is true since the if-part (the italicized portion) of this if-then statement is false in every instance. For if A and B are any objects whatsoever, distinct or not, it is false that A and B are two distinct points in S. Also, an implication is true if the hypothesis part of the implication is false.

Theorem 4.2. If a convex set of points contains at least two distinct points, then it is an infinite set.

Proof. Assigned as an exercise.

Theorem 4.3. Every line is a convex set. Every ray is a convex set. Every segment is a convex set. Every plane is a convex set. Space is a convex set.

Proof. Assigned as an exercise.

Theorem 4.4. The intersection I of any family F of convex sets is a convex set.

Proof. If I is either the null set or a set which contains only one point, then it is a convex set. Suppose, then, that I contains at least two distinct points. Let A and B be any two distinct points in I. Then A and B are elements of every set in F. Since every set in F is a convex set, it follows that $\overline{AB}$ is a subset of every set in F, and therefore a subset of I. Since this holds for every pair of distinct points in I, it follows that I is a convex set.

4.2   *Separation*

In the world of physical objects the concept of separation is a basic one. One of the weaknesses of Euclid's geometry is that it does not adequately treat this concept. In our formal geometry we base the concept of separation on two postulates.

Postulate 13 (*The Plane Separation Postulate*). If P is any plane, and if L is any line in P, then all the points of P not on L form two nonintersecting convex sets H_1 and H_2, neither one empty, such that every segment joining a point of H_1 to a point of H_2 intersects L. In other words, H_1 and H_2 are convex sets satisfying the following properties:

1. $H_1 \neq \varnothing. \ H_2 \neq \varnothing$.
2. $H_1 \cap H_2 = \varnothing, H_1 \cap L = \varnothing, H_2 \cap L = \varnothing$.
3. $H_1 \cup L \cup H_2 = P$.
4. $A \in H_1$ and $B \in H_2 \Rightarrow \overline{AB} \cap L \neq \varnothing$.

Postulate 14 (*The Space Separation Postulate*). If P is any plane, then all the points of space not in P form two nonintersecting convex sets S and T, neither one empty, such that every segment which joins a point of S to a point of T intersects the plane P. In other words, S and T are convex sets satisfying the following properties:

1. $S \neq \varnothing, T \neq \varnothing$.
2. $S \cap T = \varnothing, S \cap P = \varnothing, T \cap P = \varnothing$.
3. $S \cup P \cup T$ is space.
4. $A \in S$ and $B \in T \Rightarrow \overline{AB} \cap P \neq \varnothing$.

Definitions. The convex sets H_1 and H_2 in Postulate 13 are called *halfplanes*. Each of them is called a *side* of the line L mentioned in the postulate. Each side of L is said to be *opposite* to the other side. The line L in Postulate 13 is called the *edge* of each of the halfplanes H_1 and H_2.

Definitions. The convex sets S and T in Postulate 14 are called *half-spaces*. Each of them is called a *side* of the plane P mentioned in the postulate. Each side is said to be *opposite* to the other. The plane P is the *edge* of each of the halfspaces.

Theorem 4.5. Let P be a plane, L a line in P, and H_1 and H_2 the opposite sides of L in this plane. Let A be a point in H_1 and B a point in H_2. Then the intersection of $\overline{AB}$ and L is a set containing one and only one point.

Proof. The intersection of $\overline{AB}$ and L contains at least one point since it cannot be empty according to the plane separation postulate. If the intersection contained two distinct points, then $\overline{AB}$ and L would have two distinct points in common and $\overleftrightarrow{AB} = L$. Then $A \in H_1$ and $A \in L$. But this is a contradiction since $H_1 \cap L = \varnothing$. Therefore the intersection contains one and only one point.

Theorem 4.6. Let P be a plane and S and T the two halfspaces which are the opposite sides of P. Let A be an element of S and B an element of T. Then the intersection of $\overline{AB}$ and P is a set containing one and only one point.

Proof. Assigned as an exercise.

Theorem 4.7. Let P be a plane, L a line in P, A a point on one side H of L in P, and B a point of L. Then every point of $\overrightarrow{BA}$ except B is a point of H.

Proof. Assigned as an exercise.

Theorem 4.8. Let P be a plane, H a side of P, A a point of H, and B a point of P. Then every point of $\overrightarrow{BA}$ except B is a point of H.

Proof. Assigned as an exercise.

Theorem 4.9. Every halfplane contains infinitely many points.

Proof. Assigned as an exercise.

Theorem 4.10. Every halfplane contains at least three noncollinear points.

Proof. Let P be a plane. L a line in P, and H one side of L in P. Let A and B be two distinct points of L, and C a point in H. Let A' be a point between A and C, and B' a point between B and C. It follows from Theorem 4.7 that A' and B' are elements of H. Then A', B', and C are noncollinear points in H. For if they were collinear, then C would be a point of L. But this is impossible since C is a point in H.

Theorem 4.11. Every halfspace contains at least four noncoplanar points.

Proof. Assigned as an exercise.

Theorem 4.12. Every halfplane has one and only one edge.

Proof. Let H be a halfplane. Now H is a halfplane because there is a plane P, a line L, and a halfplane H_1, which with H satisfy the plane separation postulate. Since L is "an" edge of H, it follows that H has at least one edge.

Suppose now that there is a plane P', a line L', and a halfplane H_1', such that $L \neq L'$ and such that P', L', H, and H_1', satisfy the plane separation postulate. Since H contains three noncollinear points (Theorem 4.10), and since $H \subset P$ and $H \subset P'$, it follows that $P = P'$. Why? Then $H_1 \cup L = H_1' \cup L'$, $H_1 \cap L = \varnothing$, $H_1' \cap L' = \varnothing$. Suppose $L \neq L'$. Then there is a point Q such that $Q \in L$ and $Q \notin L'$. Why?

Let R be any point in H. Then the interior of $\overrightarrow{QR}$ is a subset of H and the interior of the ray opposite to $\overrightarrow{QR}$ is a subset of H_1. But $Q \notin L'$. Also $Q \notin H$. Why? Therefore $Q \in H_1'$. Why? Then $\overrightarrow{QR}$ intersects L' in some point T. Since T is an interior point of $\overrightarrow{QR}$, it is an element of H. Thus T is an element of the intersection of H and L'. But H, L', H_1' is a decomposition of P as in the plane separation postulate. Therefore $H \cap L' = \varnothing$. (Contradiction.)

Therefore H has only one edge. It follows that every halfplane has one and only one edge.

Theorem 4.13. Every halfspace has one and only one edge.

Proof. Assigned as an exercise.

Theorem 4.14. If H_1 and H_2 are opposite sides of a line L in a plane P, and if H_1 and H_2' are opposite sides of L in P, then $H_2 = H_2'$. If S_1 and S_2 are opposite sides of a plane P, and if S_1 and S_2' are opposite sides of P, then $S_2 = S_2'$.

Proof. Assigned as an exercise.

Theorem 4.15. The union of a halfplane and its edge is a convex set. The union of a halfspace and its edge is a convex set.

Proof. Let H and L be a halfplane and its edge, respectively. Let A and B be two distinct points in $H \cup L$. If A and B are elements of H, then $\overline{AB} \subset H$ (since H is a convex set) and $\overline{AB} \subset (H \cup L)$. If A and B are elements of L, then $\overline{AB} \subset L$ (since L is a convex set) and $\overline{AB} \subset H \cup L$. If $A \in H$ and $B \in L$, then the interior of $\overrightarrow{BA}$ is contained in H. Then $\overrightarrow{BA} \subset (H \cup L)$, and $\overline{BA} \subset (H \cup L)$. Similarly, if $A \in L$ and $B \in H$, then $\overline{AB} \subset (H \cup L)$. Since every segment joining two distinct points of $H \cup L$ is a subset of $H \cup L$, it follows that $H \cup L$ is a convex set.

Let S be a halfspace and P its edge. Let $T = S \cup P$. Let A and B be two distinct points of T. If A and B are both in S or both in P, then $\overline{AB}$ is a subset of S, or of P, since they are both convex sets. If one of the points, say A, is in P, and B is in S, then the interior of $\overrightarrow{AB}$ lies in S. Then $\overrightarrow{AB} \subset (S \cup P)$ and $\overline{AB} \subset (S \cup P)$. Thus in every case $\overline{AB} \subset (S \cup P)$. It follows that $S \cup P$ is a convex set.

Exercises 4.2

1. Prove Theorem 4.2.
2. Prove Theorem 4.3.
3. Prove Theorem 4.6.
4. Prove Theorem 4.7.
5. Prove Theorem 4.8.
6. Prove Theorem 4.9.
7. Prove Theorem 4.11.
8. Prove Theorem 4.13.
9. Prove Theorem 4.14.
10. Is the intersection of two planes which do not intersect a convex set? Explain.
11. Prove: If L is a line and P is a plane, then $L \cap P$ is a convex set.
12. Prove: The union of two distinct intersecting lines is not a convex set.
13. Let A be any set of points. Let C be the intersection of all convex sets each of which contains A. (C is called the convex hull of A.) Does there exist a set A for which the set C is not convex? Explain.

CHAPTER 5

Angles

5.1 *The Angle Concept*

The concept of an angle is basic in the study of geometry. The word "angle" may be defined in several different ways. An angle may be considered as a particular set of points, actually as the union of two concurrent rays. It may be considered as a set of two concurrent rays, or as an ordered pair of concurrent rays, or as a rotation of one ray about its endpoint. It may be considered, too, as the union of two rays and all the rays between those two rays. In trigonometry we might think of an angle as an ordered pair of concurrent rays (the initial side and the terminal side of the angle), together with a sign (+ or −) to indicate whether the

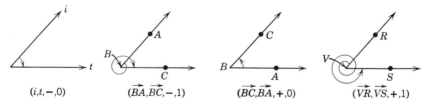

$(i,t,-,0)$ $(\overrightarrow{BA},\overrightarrow{BC},-,1)$ $(\overrightarrow{BC},\overrightarrow{BA},+,0)$ $(\overrightarrow{VR},\overrightarrow{VS},+,1)$

rotation is counterclockwise or clockwise, and a natural number to indicate the number of extra complete revolutions. "Straight angles" and "zero angles" are included in the concept of angle as we use it in trigonometry. The admission of such angles into our formal geometry would complicate matters, particularly in the treatment of the interior and the exterior of an angle. We can get what we want in elementary geometry by adopting the following definition of angle.

Definition. An *angle* is the union of two rays which have the same endpoint but which do not lie in the same line. Each of the two rays is called a *side of the angle*. The common endpoint of the two rays is called the *vertex of the angle*.

Note that the definition of an angle might be rephrased as follows: An angle is the union of two concurrent, noncollinear rays. Since an angle is the union of two sets of points, it is a set of points. Each side of an angle is a set of points. Every angle contains both of its sides and its vertex. Each side of an angle contains the vertex of the angle. The intersection of the two sides is the vertex; the union of the two sides is the angle. The angle which is the union of two rays, $\overrightarrow{BA}$ and $\overrightarrow{BC}$, is sometimes denoted by the symbol $\angle ABC$. In such a symbol the middle letter denotes the vertex of the angle.

Sometimes we speak of an angle determined by two noncollinear segments with a common endpoint. If $\overline{BA}$ and $\overline{BC}$ are two such segments, then the angle which is determined by them is $\angle ABC = \overrightarrow{BA} \cup \overrightarrow{BC}$. The angle determined by two given noncollinear segments with a common endpoint is the one and only angle which contains the union of the given segments.

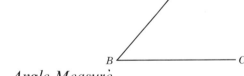

5.2   *Angle Measure*

In elementary geometry we use protractors, semicircular or circular, to find the measure of an angle in degrees. Units other than degrees are

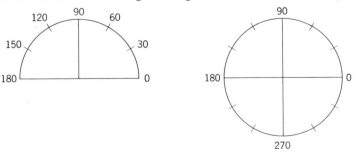

frequently used to express angle measure, for example, radians, mils, right angles, and revolutions. There is no logical reason for using one unit in preference to another. However, it will make things simpler if we use one measuring system, so we shall use degree measure exclusively from this point on. We are now ready to make it official.

Postulate 15 (*Angle Measure Postulate*). There exists a correspondence which associates with each angle in space a unique number between 0 and 180.

Definition. The number which is associated with an angle, by Postulate 15, is called the *measure of the angle.*

Notation. The measure of $\angle ABC$ is denoted by the symbol $m\angle ABC$.

Definition. Two angles (distinct or not) are *congruent* if and only if they have the same measure. In symbols, $\angle ABC \cong \angle DEF$ if and only if $m\angle ABC = m\angle DEF$.

As far as Postulate 15 is concerned, the measure of every angle might be 5. It is clear, then, that we need more postulates. In Chapter 3 we gave distance its properties by defining a coordinate system of a line and then adopting a ruler postulate. We get the distance between two points by subtracting the coordinate of one of the points from the coordinate of the other. In this chapter we give angle measure its properties by defining a ray-coordinate system and then adopting a protractor postulate. In this treatment we get the measure of an angle by subtracting the ray-coordinate of one side of an angle from the ray-coordinate of the other side, and making an adjustment if the result exceeds 180.

Definition. Let V be a point in a plane P. A *ray-coordinate system* in P relative to V is a one-to-one correspondence between the set of all rays in P with endpoint V and the set of all numbers x such that $0 \leqslant x < 360$ with the following property: if r and s correspond to distinct rays $\overrightarrow{VR}$ and $\overrightarrow{VS}$, respectively, then

$$\left\{ \begin{array}{ll} m\angle RVS = |r - s| & \text{if} \quad |r - s| < 180, \\ m\angle RVS = 360 - |r - s| & \text{if} \quad |r - s| > 180, \\ \overrightarrow{VR} \text{ and } \overrightarrow{VS} \text{ are opposite rays} & \text{if and only if} \quad |r - s| = 180. \end{array} \right.$$

The last three lines in the above definition may be reworded as follows:

$$\left\{ \begin{array}{ll} m\angle RVS = \min(|r - s|, \quad 360 - |r - s|) & \text{if} \quad |r - s| \neq 180, \\ \overrightarrow{VR} \text{ and } \overrightarrow{VS} \text{ are opposite rays} & \text{if and only if} \quad |r - s| = 180. \end{array} \right.$$

Definitions. The number which is associated with a ray in a ray-coordinate system is called the *ray-coordinate* of the ray. The ray whose ray-coordinate is zero is called the *zero-ray* of the ray-coordinate system.

Postulate 16 (*The Protractor Postulate*). If $\angle AVB$ is any angle in a plane P, then there is a unique ray-coordinate system in P relative to V such that $\overrightarrow{VA}$ is the zero-ray and such that every ray $\overrightarrow{VX}$ with X and B on the same side of $\overleftrightarrow{VA}$ corresponds to a number less than 180.

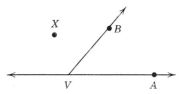

An implication of the protractor postulate is the following theorem.

Theorem 5.1 (*Angle Construction Theorem*). If H is a halfplane with edge $\overleftrightarrow{VA}$ and if r is any number such that $0 < r < 180$, then there is one and only one angle, $\angle AVX$, with X in H and such that $m\angle AVX = r$.

Proof. Let B be any point in H. Then there is a unique ray-coordinate system in which the ray-coordinate of $\overrightarrow{VA}$ is zero and the ray coordinate of $\overrightarrow{VB}$ is a positive number less than 180. In this ray-coordinate system there is exactly one ray $\overrightarrow{VX}$ with ray-coordinate r. It follows from the definition of a ray-coordinate system that $m\angle AVX = r - 0 = r$.

Suppose there were two such angles, $\angle AVX$ and $\angle AVY$. Then there is a ray-coordinate system in which the ray-coordinates of $\overrightarrow{VA}, \overrightarrow{VX}, \overrightarrow{VY}$ are 0, x, y, respectively, and $0 < x < 180, 0 < y < 180$. Then $m\angle AVX = x - 0 = x = r$, and $m\angle AVY = y - 0 = y = r$. Therefore $x = y$, $\overrightarrow{VX} = \overrightarrow{VY}$, and $\angle AVX = \angle AVY$. It follows that there is one and only one angle satisfying the requirements of the theorem.

Our next theorem relates angle measures and ray-coordinates.

Theorem 5.2. Given $\angle AVB$ in a plane p and a ray-coordinate system S relative to V in p. If $m\angle AVB = m$ and the ray-coordinates of $\overrightarrow{VA}$ and $\overrightarrow{VB}$ in S are a and b, respectively, then

1. $b - a = m$ if $a < b < 180 + a.$
2. $a - b = m$ if $b < a < 180 + b.$
3. $b - a = 360 - m$ if $a + 180 < b.$
4. $a - b = 360 - m$ if $b + 180 < a.$

Proof. If $a < b < 180 + a$, then $|b - a| = b - a < 180$ and it follows from the definition of a ray-coordinate system that $m = b - a$. Similarly, if $b < a < 180 + b$, then $m = a - b$. If $180 + a < b$, then $|b - a| =$

$b - a > 180$, $m = 360 - (b - a)$, and $b - a = 360 - m$. If $180 + b < a$, then $|b - a| = a - b > 180$, $m = 360 - (a - b)$, and $a - b = 360 - m$.

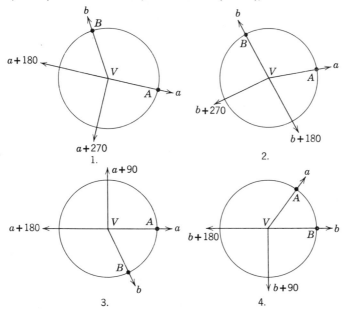

1.

2.

3.

4.

In the next two sections we develop equations which express the relationship between two ray-coordinate systems in a plane relative to the same point.

Exercises 5.2

Let S be a ray-coordinate system in a plane p relative to a point V. Let $\overleftrightarrow{AA'}$, $\overleftrightarrow{BB'}$ be distinct lines in p which intersect at V and which are such that $\overrightarrow{VA'}$, $\overrightarrow{VB'}$ are the rays which are opposite to $\overrightarrow{VA}$, $\overrightarrow{VB}$, respectively. Let a, a', b, b' denote the ray-coordinates in S of $\overrightarrow{VA}$, $\overrightarrow{VA'}$, $\overrightarrow{VB}$, $\overrightarrow{VB'}$, respectively. Let $m = m\angle AVB$.

1. If $a = 50$, $b = 150$, find m.

2. If $a = 50$, $b = 200$, find m.

3. If $a = 100$, $b = 75$, find a', b'.

4. If $a = 300$, $b = 125$, find m.

5. If $a = 300$, $b = 115$, find m.

6. If $a = 300$, $b = 200$, find a', b'.

7. If $a = 10$, $m = 150$, $b < 190$, find b.

8. If $a = 10$, $m = 150$, $b > 190$, find b.

9. If $a = 300$, $m = 100$, $b < 120$, find b.

10. If $a = 300$, $m = 100$, $b > 120$, find b.

11. If $a = 140$, $m = 100$, find two possible values for b.

12. If $a = 340$, $m = 100$, find two possible values for b.

13. If $a = 340$, $m = 10$, find two possible values for b.

14. If $a = 140$, $m = 150$, find two possible values for b.

15. If $a = 100$, $b = 150$, find $m\angle BVA'$.

16. If $a = 100$, $b = 150$, find $m\angle B'VA$.

17. If $a = 100$, $b = 150$, find $m\angle A'VB'$.

18. If $a = 100$, $m = 110$, $b > a$, what are the possible values of b?

19. If $a = 100$, $m = 90$, $b > a$, what are the possible values of b?

20. If $a = 300$, $m = 170$, $b < a$, what are the possible values of b?

5.3 *Congruent Numbers*

It is convenient to use the concept of numbers that are congruent relative to a certain modulus. This is a basic concept in classical number theory.

Definition. a is congruent to b modulo m if $a - b$ is an integral multiple of m. In symbols, $a \equiv b \pmod{m}$ if $a - b = km$ for some integer k.

Thus $400 \equiv 40 \pmod{360}$ since $400 - 40 = 1 \cdot 360$, and $360 \equiv 0 \pmod{360}$ since $360 - 0 = 1 \cdot 360$. Note that if $a \equiv b \pmod{m}$, then $b \equiv a \pmod{m}$. For if $a - b = km$ where k is an integer, then $b - a = -km$ where $-k$ is an integer.

Consider a variable x with domain given by $0 \leqslant x < 360$. Suppose x' is defined in terms of x by the statement $x' \equiv x + 50 \pmod{360}$, where it is understood that $0 \leqslant x' < 360$. Here x' is defined as a function of x. This function establishes a one-to-one correspondence between the set R of all real numbers from 0 to 360, 0 included, 360 excluded, and the set R. The following table lists some of the corresponding pairs.

x	0	100	200	300	309.99	310	350	359.99
x'	50	150	250	350	359.99	0	40	49.99

Think of the x numbers as the ray-coordinates in one system relative to a point V. If x and y are the ray-coordinates of the sides of the $\angle XVY$, then $m\angle XVY = \min(|x - y|, 360 - |x - y|)$. The following table A lists the values of $m\angle XVY$ for various values of x and y. Table B is similar to table A. The x' and y' values in B are related to the corresponding values in A where the numbers that correspond are matched as x and x' are matched in the function just described. Note for every entry that

$$\min (|x - y|, \quad 360 - |x - y|) = \min (|x' - y'|, \quad 360 - |x' - y'|).$$

It seems plausible that if $x' \equiv x + 50 \,(\text{mod } 360)$, then the x' numbers work just as well as the x numbers in computing angle measures from ray-coordinates.

Table A					
x \ y	15	115	215	315	345
0	15	115	145	45	15
100	85	15	115	145	115
200	175	85	15	115	145
300	75	175	85	15	45
350	25	125	135	35	5

Table B					
x' \ y'	65	165	265	5	35
50	15	115	145	45	15
150	85	15	115	145	115
250	175	85	15	115	145
350	75	175	85	15	45
40	25	125	135	35	5

Exercises 5.3

1. If $x' \equiv x + 200 \,(\text{mod } 360)$, construct the table C which corresponds with table A above as B corresponds to A when $x' \equiv x + 50 \,(\text{mod } 360)$.

2. If $x' \equiv -x + 50 \,(\text{mod } 360)$, construct the table D which corresponds to Table A above.

3. If $x' \equiv -x + 200 \,(\text{mod } 360)$, construct the table E which corresponds to Table A above.

5.4 *The Two-Coordinate-Systems Theorem*

Let $\overleftrightarrow{AA'}$ and $\overleftrightarrow{BB'}$ be distinct lines in a plane P and intersecting at V. Let $\overrightarrow{VA}, \overrightarrow{VB}$ be opposite to $\overrightarrow{VA'}, \overrightarrow{VB'}$, respectively. There is a unique ray-coordinate system S in P relative to V with zero-ray $\overrightarrow{VA}$ and in which the coordinate of $\overrightarrow{VB}$, briefly cd. $\overrightarrow{VB}$ (in S), is a number between 0 and 180. There is a unique ray-coordinate system S' in P relative to V with zero-ray $\overrightarrow{VA}$ and such that cd .$\overrightarrow{VB}$ (in S') is a number between 180 and 360. Why? It follows that there are exactly two ray-coordinate systems in P relative to V in which the coordinate of $\overrightarrow{VA}$ is 0.

Let $\overrightarrow{VX}$ be any ray in P with endpoint V. Let x and x' be its coordinates in S and S' respectively. If $\overrightarrow{VX} = \overrightarrow{VA}$, then $x = x' = 0$. If $\overrightarrow{VX} = \overrightarrow{VA'}$, then $x = x' = 180$. If X and B lie on the same side of $\overleftrightarrow{AA'}$, then $0 < x < 180$, $m\angle AVX = x$, $180 < x' < 360$, $m\angle AVX = 360 - x'$, and therefore $x = 360 - x'$. If X and B lie on opposite sides of $\overleftrightarrow{AA'}$, then $180 < x < 360$, $m\angle AVX = 360 - x$, $0 < x' < 180$, $m\angle AVX = x'$, and hence $360 - x = x'$. Notice that in all cases $x' \equiv -x + 360 \,(\mathrm{mod}\ 360)$. Hence we have the following theorem.

Theorem 5.3. If S and S' are two different ray-coordinate systems with zero-ray $\overrightarrow{VA}$, then for all x it is true that $x' \equiv -x + 360 \,(\mathrm{mod}\ 360)$, or what amounts to the same thing, $x' \equiv -x \,(\mathrm{mod}\ 360)$.

Again, let $\overleftrightarrow{AA'}$ and $\overleftrightarrow{BB'}$ be distinct lines in a plane P and intersecting at V. Let $\overrightarrow{VA}$, $\overrightarrow{VB}$ be opposite to $\overrightarrow{VA'}$, $\overrightarrow{VB'}$, respectively. Let S be the unique ray-coordinate system in P relative to V with zero-ray $\overrightarrow{VA}$ and in which cd. $\overrightarrow{VB}$ is a number between 0 and 180. There is a unique ray-coordinate system S'' in P relative to V in which cd. $\overrightarrow{VA'}$ is 0 and cd. $\overrightarrow{VB}$ is a number between 0 and 180. There is a unique ray-coordinate system S''' in P relative to V in which cd. $\overrightarrow{VA'}$ is 0 and cd. $\overrightarrow{VB}$ is a number between 180 and 360. S'' and S''' are the only ray-coordinate systems in P relative to V in which cd. $\overrightarrow{VA'}$ is 0.

Let $\overrightarrow{VX}$ be a ray in P with endpoint V. Let x, x'', x''' be its coordinates in S, S'', S''', respectively. If $\overrightarrow{VX} = \overrightarrow{VA'}$, then $x = 180$, $x'' = x''' = 0$. If $\overrightarrow{VX} = \overrightarrow{VA}$, then $x = 0$, $x'' = x''' = 180$. If X and B are on the same side of $\overleftrightarrow{AA'}$, then $0 < x < 180$, $0 < x'' < 180$, $180 < x''' < 360$, $180 - x = m\angle AVX = x'' = 360 - x'''$. If X and B lie on opposite sides of $\overleftrightarrow{AA'}$, then $x - 180 = m\angle A'VX = 360 - x'' = x'''$. Notice that in all cases $x'' \equiv -x + 180 \,(\mathrm{mod}\ 360)$ and $x''' \equiv x + 180 \,(\mathrm{mod}\ 360)$. Thus we have the following theorem.

Theorem 5.4. If S and S' are ray-coordinate systems in P relative to V such that cd. $\overrightarrow{VA}$ (in S) $= 0$ and cd. $\overrightarrow{VA'}$ (in S') $= 0$, and if x and x' are the coordinates of $\overrightarrow{VX}$ in S and S', respectively, then either $x' \equiv x + 180 \,(\mathrm{mod}\ 360)$ for all x, or $x' \equiv -x + 180 \,(\mathrm{mod}\ 360)$ for all x.

Again, let $\overleftrightarrow{AA'}$ and $\overleftrightarrow{BB'}$ be distinct lines in a plane P and intersecting at V. Let $\overrightarrow{VA}$, $\overrightarrow{VB}$ be opposite to $\overrightarrow{VA'}$, $\overrightarrow{VB'}$, respectively. Let S be the unique ray-coordinate system in P relative to V with zero-ray $\overrightarrow{VA}$ and in which cd. $\overrightarrow{VB}$ is a number between 0 and 180. Consider $\overleftrightarrow{AA'}$ as fixed and suppose $\overleftrightarrow{BB'}$ may be chosen in any way so long as cd. $\overrightarrow{VB}$ (in S) is a number b between 0 and 180. We wish to consider the relationship between the coordinates in S and the ray-coordinates in any system in which the zero-ray is neither $\overrightarrow{VA}$ nor $\overrightarrow{VA'}$, in other words, between S and any system S^* except those which we compared with S in Theorems 5.3 and 5.4.

Since b may be any number between 0 and 180, it follows that we may take b so that $\overrightarrow{VB}$ or $\overrightarrow{VB'}$ is the zero-ray of S^*. Note that $m\angle BVA = b$,

$m\angle BVA' = 180 - b$, $m\angle A'VB' = (180 + b) - 180 = b$, $m\angle B'VA = 360$
$-(180 + b) = 180 - b$. If the zero-ray of S^* is $\overrightarrow{VB}$, then the coordinate
of $\overrightarrow{VA}$ in S^* is b or $360 - b$. If the zero-ray of S^* is $\overrightarrow{VB'}$, then the coordinate
of $\overrightarrow{VA}$ in S^* is $180 - b$ or $360 - (180 - b) = 180 + b$.

Let S_1, S_2, S_3, S_4 be the ray-coordinate systems whose zero-rays are
$\overrightarrow{VB}, \overrightarrow{VB}, \overrightarrow{VB'}, \overrightarrow{VB'}$, respectively, and in which the ray-coordinates of $\overrightarrow{VA}$
are b, $360 - b$, $180 - b$, $180 + b$, respectively. Let $\overleftrightarrow{CC'}$ and $\overleftrightarrow{DD'}$ be two
lines in P intersecting at V such that $\overrightarrow{VC}$ and $\overrightarrow{VD}$ are opposite to $\overrightarrow{VC'}$ and
$\overrightarrow{VD'}$, respectively. Let cd. $\overrightarrow{VC}$ (in S) $= c$, cd. $\overrightarrow{VD}$ (in S) $= d$, and suppose
$0 < c < b < d < 180$.

	$\overrightarrow{VA}$	$\overrightarrow{VC}$	$\overrightarrow{VB}$	$\overrightarrow{VD}$	$\overrightarrow{VA'}$	$\overrightarrow{VC'}$	$\overrightarrow{VB'}$	$\overrightarrow{VD'}$
S	0	c	b	d	180	$180 + c$	$180 + b$	$180 + d$
S_1	b	$b - c$	0	$360 - (d - b)$	$180 + b$	$180 + (b - c)$	180	$180 - (d - b)$
S_2	$360 - b$	$360 - (b - c)$	0	$d - b$	$180 - b$	$180 - (b - c)$	180	$180 + (d - b)$
S_3	$180 - b$	$180 - (b - c)$	180	$180 + (d - b)$	$360 - b$	$360 - (b - c)$	0	$d - b$
S_4	$180 + b$	$180 + (b - c)$	180	$180 - (d - b)$	b	$b - c$	0	$360 - (d - b)$

The table shows the ray-coordinates of the rays listed across the top
in the systems listed along the left side. The entries in the S-row and the
$\overrightarrow{VA}, \overrightarrow{VB}, \overrightarrow{VA'}, \overrightarrow{VB'}$ columns follow easily from the sentences immediately
preceding the table and from the fact that two rays are opposite if and
only if their coordinates in a ray-coordinate system differ by 180.

Since $m\angle BVC = b - c$, it follows

that cd. $\overrightarrow{VC}$(in S_1) $= b - c$ or $360 - (b - c)$,

that cd. $\overrightarrow{VC}$(in S_2) $= b - c$ or $360 - (b - c)$,

that cd. $\overrightarrow{VC}$(in S_3) $= 180 - (b - c)$ or $180 + (b - c)$, and

that cd. $\overrightarrow{VC}$(in S_4) $= 180 - (b - c)$ or $180 + (b - c)$.

Suppose cd. $\overrightarrow{VC}$(in S_1) $= 360 - (b - c)$. Then

$c = m\angle AVC = 360 - (b - c) - b$ or $c = 360 - [360 - (b - c) - b]$,

$c = 360 - 2b + c$ or $c = 2b - c$, and

$b = 180$ or $b = c$.

Suppose cd. $\overrightarrow{VC}$(in S_2) $= b - c$. Then

$c = m\angle AVC = 360 - b - (b - c)$ or

$c = 360 - [360 - b - (b - c)]$,

$c = 360 - 2b + c$ or $c = 2b - c$,   and

$b = 180$ or $b = c$.

Suppose cd. $\overrightarrow{VC}$(in S_3) $= 180 + (b - c)$.   Then

$c = m\angle AVC = 180 + (b - c) - (180 - b)$ or

$c = 360 - [180 + (b - c) - (180 - b)]$,

$c = 2b - c$ or $c = 360 - 2b + c$,   and

$b = c$ or $b = 180$.

Suppose cd. $\overrightarrow{VC}$(in S_4) $= 180 - (b - c)$.   Then

$c = m\angle AVC = 180 + b - 180 - (b - c)$ or

$c = 360 - [(180 + b) + 180 - (b - c)]$,

$c = 2b - c$ or $c = 360 - 2b + c$,   and

$b = c$ or $b = 180$.

Since $c < b < 180$ it follows that these four suppositions are untenable and hence that

$$\text{cd. } \overrightarrow{VC} \text{ (in } S_1) = b - c,$$
$$\text{cd. } \overrightarrow{VC} \text{ (in } S_2) = 360 - (b - c),$$
$$\text{cd. } \overrightarrow{VC} \text{ (in } S_3) = 180 - (b - c),$$
$$\text{cd. } \overrightarrow{VC} \text{ (in } S_4) = 180 + (b - c).$$

The ray-coordinates of $\overrightarrow{VC}$ as entered in the table are easily computed.

Since $m\angle BVD = d - b$ it follows

that   cd. $\overrightarrow{VD}$ (in S_1) $= d - b$ or $360 - (d - b)$,

that   cd. $\overrightarrow{VD}$ (in S_2) $= d - b$ or $360 - (b - b)$,

that   cd. $\overrightarrow{VD}$ (in S_3) $= 180 + (d - b)$ or $180 - (d - b)$,   and

that   cd. $\overrightarrow{VD}$ (in S_4) $= 180 + (d - b)$ or $180 - (d - b)$.

Suppose cd. $\overrightarrow{VD}$ (in S_1) $= d - b$. Then

$d = m\angle AVD = d - b - b$ or $b - (d - b)$ or $360 - d + 2b$

or $360 + d - 2b$,   and

$b = 0$ or $b = d$ or $b = d + 180$ or $b = 180$.

Suppose cd. $\overrightarrow{VD}$ (in S_2) $= 360 - (d - b)$. Then

$d = m\angle AVD = 360 - (d - b) - (360 - b)$ or

$360 - b - [360 - (d - b)]$ or

360 less one of these two numbers,

$d = -d + 2b$ or $d = d - 2b$ or $d = 360 + d - 2b$ or

$d = 360 - d + 2b$,   and

$d = b$ or $b = 0$ or $b = 180$ or $d = 180 + b$.

Suppose cd. $\overrightarrow{VD}$ (in S_3) $= 180 - (d - b)$. Then

$d = m\angle AVD = [180 - (d - b)] - [180 - b]$ or

$[180 - b] - [180 - (d - b)]$,   or

360 less one of these two numbers;

$d = -d + 2b$,   or $d = d - 2b$,   or

$d = 360 + d - 2b$,   or $d = 360 - d + 2b$;   and

$d = b$,   or $b = 0$,   or $b = 180$,   or $d = 180 + b$.

Suppose cd. $\overrightarrow{VD}$ (in S_4) $= 180 + (d - b)$. Then

$d = m\angle AVD = 180 + (d - b) - (180 + b)$ or

$(180 + b) - [180 + (d - b)]$

or 360 less one of these two numbers;

$d = d - 2b$,   or $d = 2b - d$,   or $d = 360 - (d - 2b)$,   or

$d = 360 - (2b - d)$;   and

$b = 0$,   or $b = d$,   or $d = b + 180$,   or $b = 180$.

Since $0 < b < d < 180$, it follows that these four suppositions are untenable and hence that

$$\text{cd. } \overrightarrow{VD} \text{ (in } S_1) = 360 - (d - b),$$
$$\text{cd. } \overrightarrow{VD} \text{ (in } S_2) = d - b,$$
$$\text{cd. } \overrightarrow{VD} \text{ (in } S_3) = 180 + (d - b),$$
$$\text{cd. } \overrightarrow{VD} \text{ (in } S_4) = 180 - (d - b).$$

The coordinates for $\overrightarrow{VD'}$ as entered in the table are easily computed.

Let $\overrightarrow{VX}$ be any ray in P with endpoint V and let x, x_1, x_2, x_3, x_4 denote its ray-coordinates in S, S_1, S_2, S_3, S_4, respectively.

If $\overrightarrow{VX} = \overrightarrow{VA}$, then $x = 0$, $x_1 = b$, $x_2 = 360 - b$, $x_3 = 180 - b$, and $x_4 = 180 + b$. If $\overrightarrow{VX} = \overrightarrow{VC}$, then $x = 0, x_1 = b - c, x_2 = 360 - (b - c)$, $x_3 = 180 - (b - c)$, and $x_4 = 180 + (b - c)$. Note that for both of these sets of values as well as all the other values obtained by taking $\overrightarrow{VX}$ in turn as $\overrightarrow{VB}$, $\overrightarrow{VD}$, $\overrightarrow{VA'}$, $\overrightarrow{VC'}$, $\overrightarrow{VD'}$, that $x_1 \equiv -x + b \,(\text{mod } 360)$, $x_2 \equiv x - b \,(\text{mod } 360)$, $x_3 \equiv x + 180 - b \,(\text{mod } 360)$, $x_4 \equiv -x + 180 + b$ (mod 360).

Combining the results of this reasoning and Theorems 5.3 and 5.4 we have the following important theorem.

Theorem 5.5 (*Two-Coordinate-Systems Theorem*). If S and S' are any two ray-coordinate systems in P relative to V, and if x and x' are the ray-coordinates of $\overrightarrow{VX}$ in S and S', respectively, then there is a number b, $0 \leqslant b < 360$, such that $x' \equiv x + b \,(\text{mod } 360)$ for all x, or there is a number b, $0 \leqslant b < 360$, such that $x' \equiv -x + b \,(\text{mod } 360)$ for all x.

Example 1. If cd. $\overrightarrow{VA}$ (in S) $= 10$, cd. $\overrightarrow{VA}$ (in S') $= 30$, cd. $\overrightarrow{VB}$ (in S) $= 305$, cd. $\overrightarrow{VB}$ (in S') $= 325$, find the relationship between x' and x.

Solution. If there is a number b such that $0 \leqslant b < 360$ and such that $x' \equiv -x + b \,(\text{mod } 360)$ for all x, then $30 \equiv -10 + b \,(\text{mod } 360)$ and $b = 40$. Also $325 \equiv -305 + b \,(\text{mod } 360)$ and $b = 270$. (Contradiction.)

It follows that there is a number b such that $0 \leqslant b < 360$ and such that $x' \equiv x + b \,(\text{mod } 360)$ for all x. Then $30 \equiv 10 + b \,(\text{mod } 360)$ and $325 \equiv 305 + b \,(\text{mod } 360)$. Therefore $b = 20$, and therefore $x' \equiv x + 20 \,(\text{mod } 360)$ for all x.

Example 2. If cd. $\overrightarrow{VA}$ (in S) $= 10$, cd. $\overrightarrow{VA}$ (in S') $= 30$, cd. $\overrightarrow{VB}$ (in S) $= 325$, cd. $\overrightarrow{VB}$ (in S') $= 75$, find the relationship between x' and x.

Solution. If a relationship of the form $x' \equiv x + b \,(\text{mod } 360)$ exists, then $30 \equiv 10 + b \,(\text{mod } 360)$, $b = 20$, $75 \equiv 325 + b \,(\text{mod } 360)$, $b = 110$. (Contradiction.) Therefore there is a number b, $0 \leqslant b < 360$, such that $x' \equiv -x + b \,(\text{mod } 360)$ for all x. Then $30 \equiv -10 + b \,(\text{mod } 360)$ and $b = 40$. Therefore $x' \equiv -x + 40 \,(\text{mod } 360)$ for all x.

Exercises 5.4

1. Complete the following table and express x' in terms of x.

	$\overrightarrow{VA}$	$\overrightarrow{VB}$	$\overrightarrow{VA'}$	$\overrightarrow{VB'}$	$\overrightarrow{VX}$
S	0	90	180	270	x
S'	90	0			x'

2. Given the following table. Express x' in terms of x.

	$\overrightarrow{VA}$	$\overrightarrow{VB}$	$\overrightarrow{VX}$
S	175	0	x
S'	100	285	x'

3. Given the following table. Express x' in terms of x if it is also given that cd. $\overrightarrow{VB}$ (in S') is between 270 and 360.

	$\overrightarrow{VA}$	$\overrightarrow{VB}$	$\overrightarrow{VX}$
S	0	100	x
S'	200		x'

4. Given the following table. Express x' in terms of x.

	$\overrightarrow{VA}$	$\overrightarrow{VB}$	$\overrightarrow{VC}$	$\overrightarrow{VX}$
S	0	180	90	x
S'	180	0	90	x'

5. Given the following table. Express x' in terms of x.

	$\overrightarrow{VA}$	$\overrightarrow{VB}$	$\overrightarrow{VC}$	$\overrightarrow{VX}$
S	0	180	270	x
S'	180	0	90	x'

6. Given the following table. Express x' in terms of x.

	$\overrightarrow{VA}$	$\overrightarrow{VB}$	$\overrightarrow{VC}$	$\overrightarrow{VX}$
S	0	180	90	x
S'	0	180	270	x'

7. Given $x' \equiv x - 15 \pmod{360}$. Find a number b such that $0 \leqslant b < 360$ and such that $x' \equiv x + b \pmod{360}$.

8. Given $x' \equiv 300 - x \pmod{360}$. Complete the following table.

S	0	40	80	120	160	200	240	280	320	350
S'										

9. Given cd. $\overrightarrow{VA} = 300$, cd. $\overrightarrow{VB} = 100$. Find the ray-coordinate of $\overrightarrow{VC}$ if $m\angle AVC = m\angle CVB = 80$.

10. Given cd. $\overrightarrow{VA} = 300$, cd. $\overrightarrow{VB} = 100$. Find the ray-coordinate of $\overrightarrow{VD}$ if $m\angle AVD = m\angle DVB = 100$. How is $\overrightarrow{VD}$ related to $\overrightarrow{VC}$ of Exercise 9?

5.5   *Betweenness for Rays*

We defined betweenness for points on a line in terms of coordinates. We showed that if the coordinate of B is between the coordinates of A and C in one coordinate system, then the coordinate of B is between the coordinates of A and C in every coordinate system. We are now ready to consider betweenness for rays.

Definition. Let $\overrightarrow{VA}$, $\overrightarrow{VB}$, $\overrightarrow{VC}$ be three distinct concurrent rays in a plane P. The *ray* $\overrightarrow{VB}$ *is between the rays* $\overrightarrow{VA}$ *and* $\overrightarrow{VC}$ if and only if there is a ray-coordinate system in P relative to V in which the ray-coordinates of $\overrightarrow{VA}$, $\overrightarrow{VB}$, $\overrightarrow{VC}$ are 0, b, c, respectively, and $0 < b < c < 180$.

This definition is not symmetrical with respect to the roles played by the rays $\overrightarrow{VA}$ and $\overrightarrow{VC}$. It might seem possible for $\overrightarrow{VB}$ to be between $\overrightarrow{VA}$ and $\overrightarrow{VC}$, but not between $\overrightarrow{VC}$ and $\overrightarrow{VA}$. We settle the matter in the following theorem.

Note that it is possible to have three distinct coplanar concurrent rays such that no one of them is between the other two.

Theorem 5.6. Let $\overrightarrow{VA}$, $\overrightarrow{VB}$, $\overrightarrow{VC}$ be three distinct concurrent rays in a plane P. If $\overrightarrow{VB}$ is between $\overrightarrow{VA}$ and $\overrightarrow{VC}$, then $\overrightarrow{VB}$ is between $\overrightarrow{VC}$ and $\overrightarrow{VA}$.

Proof. From the definition of betweenness for rays, we know that there is a ray-coordinate system S in which the ray-coordinates of $\overrightarrow{VA}$, $\overrightarrow{VB}$, $\overrightarrow{VC}$ are 0, b, c, respectively, and $0 < b < c < 180$. Also, no pair of these rays consists of opposite rays. From the protractor postulate it follows that there is a ray-coordinate system S' in which the ray-coordinates of $\overrightarrow{VC}$, $\overrightarrow{VB}$, $\overrightarrow{VA}$ are 0, b', c', respectively, and $0 < b' < 180$, $0 < c' < 360$, $c' \neq 180$. From the definitional properties of a coordinate system we get, using both S and S', that

$$* \begin{cases} m\angle AVB = b = \min(|c' - b'|, 360 - |c' - b'|), \\ m\angle AVC = c = \min(c', 360 - c'), \\ m\angle BVC = c - b = b'. \end{cases}$$

Suppose (1) that $c' > 180 + b'$. Then $c' > 180, |c' - b'| = c' - b' > 180$. From the relations (*) it follows that

$$b = 360 - (c' - b'),$$

$$c = 360 - c',$$

$$c - b = b'.$$

Then $(360 - c') - (360 - c' + b') = b'$ and $b' = 0$, which is a contradiction.

Suppose (2) that $180 < c' < 180 + b'$. Then $|c' - b'| = c' - b' < 180$. From (*) it follows that

$$b = c' - b',$$

$$c = 360 - c',$$

$$c - b = b'.$$

Then $360 - c' - (c' - b') = b'$ and $c' = 180$, which is a contradiction.

Suppose (3) that $0 < c' < b'$. Then $|c' - b'| = b' - c' < 180$. From (*) it follows that

$$b = b' - c',$$

$$c = c',$$

$$c - b = b'.$$

Then $c' - (b' - c') = b'$ and $b' = c'$, which is a contradiction.

Since suppositions (1), (2), and (3) all lead to contradictions, since b' and c' are distinct numbers between 0 and 360, and since neither one is 180, it follows that $0 < b' < c' < 180$, and hence that $\overrightarrow{VB}$ is between $\overrightarrow{VC}$ and $\overrightarrow{VA}$.

Definition. A ray is called a *midray* of an angle if it is between the sides of the angle and if it makes with them two congruent angles.

Theorem 5.7. Every angle has a unique midray.

Proof. Let $\angle AVC$ be given and suppose that $m\angle AVR = r$. It follows from the protractor postulate that there is a ray-coordinate system in the plane of $\angle AVC$ in which the ray coordinates of $\overrightarrow{VA}$ and $\overrightarrow{VC}$ are 0 and r, respectively. In order for $\overrightarrow{VB}$ to be a midray of $\angle AVC$ it is necessary and sufficient that its ray-coordinate be a number x between 0 and r and that $r - x = x - 0$. Why? Since there is one and only one such number x, actually $x = r/2$, it follows that there is one and only one ray which is the midray of $\angle AVC$. Since $\angle AVC$ is an arbitrary angle, the proof is complete.

Theorem 5.8 (*Betweenness Angles Theorem*). If $\overrightarrow{VB}$ is between $\overrightarrow{VA}$ and $\overrightarrow{VC}$, then $m\angle AVC = m\angle AVB + m\angle BVC$.

Proof. Assigned as an exercise.

Theorem 5.9 (*Converse of Betweenness Angles Theorem*). If $\overrightarrow{VA}$, $\overrightarrow{VB}$, $\overrightarrow{VC}$ are distinct coplanar rays in a plane F, and if $m\angle AVC = m\angle AVB + m\angle BVC$, then $\overrightarrow{VB}$ is between $\overrightarrow{VA}$ and $\overrightarrow{VC}$.

Proof. Assigned as an exercise.

Theorem 5.10. If A, B, C, D, V are distinct points in a plane F, if B, C, D all lie on the same side $\overleftrightarrow{AV}$, if $\overrightarrow{VB}$ is between $\overrightarrow{VA}$ and $\overrightarrow{VC}$, and if $\overrightarrow{VC}$ is between $\overrightarrow{VB}$ and $\overrightarrow{VD}$, then $\overrightarrow{VB}$ is between $\overrightarrow{VA}$ and $\overrightarrow{VD}$, and $\overrightarrow{VC}$ is between $\overrightarrow{VA}$ and $\overrightarrow{VD}$.

Proof. There is a ray-coordinate system S in F relative to V with zero-ray $\overrightarrow{VA}$ and with ray-coordinates b, c, d for $\overrightarrow{VB}, \overrightarrow{VC}, \overrightarrow{VD}$, respectively, such that $0 < b < c < 180$ and $0 < d < 180$.

There is a ray-coordinate system S' in F relative to V with zero-ray $\overrightarrow{VD}$ and with ray-coordinates c', b', a', for $\overrightarrow{VC}, \overrightarrow{VB}, \overrightarrow{VA}$, respectively, such that $0 < c' < b' < 180$ and $0 < a' < 180$.

Following is a tabulation of these coordinates and the measures of several angles computed from these coordinates.

	S	S'
$\overrightarrow{VA}$	0	a'
$\overrightarrow{VB}$	b	b'
$\overrightarrow{VC}$	c	c'
$\overrightarrow{VD}$	d	0
$m\angle AVB$	b	$|a' - b'|$
$m\angle BVC$	$c - b$	$b' - c'$
$m\angle DVC$	$|d - c|$	c'
$m\angle AVC$	c	$|a' - c'|$
$m\angle AVD$	d	a'
$m\angle BVD$	$|d - b|$	b'

Now $\overrightarrow{VB}$ is between $\overrightarrow{VA}$ and $\overrightarrow{VD}$ if and only if $0 < b < d < 180$, and in view of Theorem 5.6, this is true if and only if $0 < b' < a' < 180$. Suppose $\overrightarrow{VB}$ is not between $\overrightarrow{VA}$ and $\overrightarrow{VD}$. Then $0 < d < b < 180$ and $0 < a' < b' < 180$. Then

$$m\angle AVB = b = b' - a',$$

$$m\angle AVD = d = a',$$

$$m\angle BVD = b - d = b'.$$

Then $b' = b - d = (b' - a') - a'$, and $a' = 0$. (Contradiction.)

Therefore $\overrightarrow{VB}$ is between $\overrightarrow{VA}$ and $\overrightarrow{VD}$.

Also, $\overrightarrow{VC}$ is between $\overrightarrow{VA}$ and $\overrightarrow{VD}$ if and only if $0 < c < d < 180$, and if and only if $0 < c' < a' < 180$. Suppose $\overrightarrow{VC}$ is not between $\overrightarrow{VA}$ and $\overrightarrow{VD}$.

Then $0 < d < c < 180$ and $0 < a' < c' < 180$. Then

$$m\angle AVC = c = c' - a,$$

$$m\angle AVD = d = a',$$

$$m\angle CVD = c - d = c'.$$

Then $c' = c - d = (c' - a') - a'$ and $a' = 0$. (Contradiction.)
Therefore $\overrightarrow{VC}$ is between $\overrightarrow{VA}$ and $\overrightarrow{VD}$.

Exercises 5.5

In Exercises 1–7 let $\overrightarrow{VA}$, $\overrightarrow{VB}$, $\overrightarrow{VC}$ be distinct concurrent rays in a plane P, with coordinates a, b, c, respectively, in a ray-coordinate system S in P relative to V, and with coordinates a', b', c', respectively, in a ray-coordinate system S' in P relative to V.

1. If $a = 0$, $b = 60$, $c = 120$, $a' = 10$, $b' = 310$, find c'.

2. If $a' = 50$, $b' = 350$, $c' = 15$, prove that $\overrightarrow{VC}$ is between $\overrightarrow{VA}$ and $\overrightarrow{VB}$.

3. If $a = 50$, $b = 80$, $a' = 300$, prove that either $b' = 270$ or $b' = 330$.

4. If $a = 300$, $b = 100$, $c = 180$, prove that $\overrightarrow{VC}$ is not between $\overrightarrow{VA}$ and $\overrightarrow{VB}$.

5. If $a = 10$, $b = 5$, $c = 15$, prove that $\overrightarrow{VB}$ is not between $\overrightarrow{VA}$ and $\overrightarrow{VC}$.

6. If $0 < a < b < c < 180$, prove that $\overrightarrow{VB}$ is between $\overrightarrow{VA}$ and $\overrightarrow{VC}$.

7. If $a < b < c + 360 < a + 180$, prove that $\overrightarrow{VB}$ is between $\overrightarrow{VA}$ and $\overrightarrow{VC}$.

8. Prove Theorem 5.8.

9. Prove Theorem 5.9.

5.6   *Interior and Exterior of an Angle*

There are several ways to approach the concept of the interior of an angle. We may think of it as the union of the interiors of all rays between

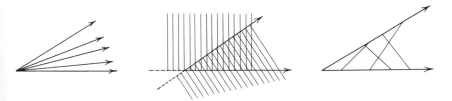

the sides of the angle. We may think of it as the intersection of two half-planes. The interior of $\angle ABC$ is the intersection of the A-side of $\overleftrightarrow{BC}$ and the C-side of $\overleftrightarrow{AB}$. We may also think of it as the union of the interiors of all segments which join an interior point of one side to an interior point of the other side. We base our formal development on a definition in terms of halfplanes.

Definition. The interior of an angle, say $\angle ABC$, is the intersection of two halfplanes, the A-side of $\overleftrightarrow{BC}$ and the C-side of $\overleftrightarrow{AB}$.

Theorem 5.11. The interior of an angle is a convex set.

Proof. Assigned as an exercise.

Theorem 5.12. Every point in the interior of an angle is an interior point of a ray between the sides of the angle.

Proof. Let D be a point in the interior of a given angle, $\angle ABC$. Then D is on the C-side of $\overleftrightarrow{AB}$ and on the A-side of $\overleftrightarrow{BC}$. Suppose $m\angle ABC = s$. Then there is a unique ray-coordinate system S in which the ray-coordinates of $\overrightarrow{BA}$ and $\overrightarrow{BC}$ are 0 and s, respectively. Let r be the ray-coordinate of $\overrightarrow{BD}$ in the system S. Since D and C are in the same halfplane with edge $\overleftrightarrow{AB}$ it follows that $0 < r < 180$.

Next, there is a unique ray-coordinate system S' in which the ray-coordinate of $\overrightarrow{BC}$ and $\overrightarrow{BA}$ are 0 and s, respectively. Let r' be the ray-coordinate of $\overrightarrow{BD}$ in the system S'. Since A and D are in the same halfplane with edge $\overleftrightarrow{BC}$, it follows that $0 < r' < 180$. It follows from the protractor postulate, using both coordinate systems, that

$$
\begin{array}{ccc}
 & S & S' \\
m\angle ABC = & s & = & s \\
m\angle ABD = & r & = |r' - s| \\
m\angle DBC = |s - r| = & r'
\end{array}
$$

Then ($r = r' - s$ or $r = s - r'$) and ($r' = s - r$ or $r' = r - s$). Then ($r = r' - s$ or $r = s - r'$) and ($r = s - r'$ or $r = r' + s$). It follows that $r = s - r'$, and since $r' > 0$, that $r < s$. It follows from the definition of betweenness for rays that $\overrightarrow{BD}$ is between $\overrightarrow{BA}$ and $\overrightarrow{BC}$. Therefore D is an interior point of a ray between the sides of $\angle ABC$. Since D is an arbitrary point in the interior of an arbitrary angle, the proof is complete.

Theorem 5.13. If a ray is between the sides of an angle, then its interior is contained in the interior of the angle.

Proof. Let D be any interior point of a ray $\overrightarrow{BD}$ between the sides of a given angle, $\angle ABC$. Then $\overrightarrow{BD}$ is between $\overrightarrow{BA}$ and $\overrightarrow{BC}$, also between $\overrightarrow{BC}$ and $\overrightarrow{BA}$. (See Theorem 5.6.) It follows from the definition of betweenness for rays that D and C are on the same side of $\overleftrightarrow{AB}$, and that D and A are on the same side of $\overleftrightarrow{BC}$. It follows that D is in each of the halfplanes, the

C-side of $\overleftrightarrow{AB}$ and the A-side of $\overleftrightarrow{BC}$. Therefore D is in the interior of $\angle ABC$. Since D is an arbitrary interior point of the ray $\overrightarrow{BD}$, it follows that the interior of the ray $\overrightarrow{BD}$ is contained in the interior of $\angle ABC$. Since the proof applies to any angle and any ray between the sides of the angles, the proof is complete.

Theorem 5.14. The union of the interiors of all rays between the sides of an angle is the interior of the angle.

Proof. This follows immediately from Theorems 5.12 and 5.13.

Theorem 5.15. If $\overline{AC}$ is any segment joining an interior point of one side of $\angle ABC$ to an interior point of the other side, then the interior of $\overline{AC}$ is contained in the interior of $\angle ABC$.

Proof. Let A, B, C be any three noncollinear points. Let P be the unique plane determined by A, B, and C. Then $\overleftrightarrow{BC}$ is the edge of a halfplane H_1 which contains A, and $\overleftrightarrow{AB}$ is the edge of a halfplane H_2 which contains C. The interior of $\overrightarrow{CA}$ is a subset of H_1 and the interior of $\overrightarrow{AC}$ is a subset of H_2. Why? Therefore the interior of $\overline{AC}$ is a subset of H_1 and of H_2. It follows that the interior of $\overline{AC}$ is contained in $H_1 \cap H_2$, which is the interior of $\angle ABC$. Since A, B, C are any three noncollinear points, the proof is complete.

It seems appropriate to comment here on the possibility of a converse to Theorem 5.15. Using only the postulates which we have adopted so far, it is impossible to prove this converse. The converse is a theorem in Euclidean geometry, but it is not a theorem in neutral geometry. Neutral geometry, or absolute geometry, is the formal geometry which is based on all of the Euclidean postulates except the parallel postulate, which we shall adopt somewhat later in our formal development. Neutral geometry allows for the possibility that there might be three distinct lines in a plane, call them m, n, and p, such that m and n intersect, and m and p do not, and n and p do not. As suggested in the figure, the line p is a subset of the interior of $\angle APB$, and no point of p lies on a segment which joins an interior point of $\overrightarrow{PA}$ to any interior point of $\overrightarrow{PB}$.

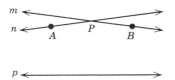

In SMSG Geometry With Coordinates there is an Interior of an Angle Postulate. It is essentially the same statement as the following theorem.

Theorem 5.16. If $\angle AVB$ is any angle,

1. Let R be the union of the interiors of all rays between the sides of the angle.
2. Let I be the intersection of the following pair of halfplanes, the B-side of $\overleftrightarrow{AV}$ and the A-side of $\overleftrightarrow{BV}$.
3. Let S be the union of the interiors of all segments joining an interior point of $\overrightarrow{VA}$ and an interior point of $\overrightarrow{VB}$.

Then $R = I$ and $I \supset S$.

Proof. This theorem is simply a combination of Theorems 5.14 and 5.15.

Definition. The *exterior of an angle* is the set of all points in the plane of the angle which do not lie on the angle and which do not lie in the interior of the angle.

If I is the interior of $\angle ABC$, if E is its exterior, and if $\angle ABC$ is contained in plane P, then $E = P - (\angle ABC \cup I)$. (The subtraction operation used here is the usual one for sets:

$$S - T = \{x : x \in S \text{ and } x \notin T\}.)$$

Theorem 5.17. Let $\overleftrightarrow{AC}$ and $\overleftrightarrow{BD}$ be two distinct lines which intersect at a point V such that (AVC) and (BVD). (Remember that (AVC) means that V is between A and C.) If P is any point in the interior of $\angle AVB$ and Q is any point in the interior of $\angle AVD$, then $\overline{PQ}$ intersects $\angle AVB$.

Proof. Let points P and Q as in the statement of the theorem be given. Since P is in the interior of $\angle AVB$, it lies on the A-side of $\overleftrightarrow{BD}$ and on the B-side of $\overleftrightarrow{AC}$. Since Q is in the interior of $\angle AVD$, it lies on the A-side of $\overleftrightarrow{BD}$ and on the D-side of $\overleftrightarrow{AC}$. Therefore P and Q lie on the same side of

$\overleftrightarrow{BD}$ and on opposite sides of $\overleftrightarrow{AC}$. It follows from the plane separation postulate that $\overline{PQ}$ intersects $\overleftrightarrow{AC}$ but does not intersect $\overleftrightarrow{BD}$.

Now suppose that $\overline{PQ}$ intersects $\overrightarrow{VC}$ in a point E. Then $E \neq V$ since $\overline{PQ}$ does not intersect $\overleftrightarrow{BD}$. Since the interior of the ray $\overrightarrow{VC}$ lies in the not-Q-side of $\overleftrightarrow{BD}$, it follows that $\overline{EQ}$ intersects $\overleftrightarrow{BD}$ and therefore $\overline{PQ}$ intersects

$\overleftrightarrow{BD}$. This is a contradiction. Therefore $\overleftrightarrow{PQ}$ does not intersect $\overrightarrow{VC}$. But $\overleftrightarrow{PQ}$ intersects $\overleftrightarrow{AC}$. Therefore $\overleftrightarrow{PQ}$ intersects $\overrightarrow{VA}$ and hence $\angle AVB$.

Theorem 5.18. If $\overleftrightarrow{AC}$ and $\overleftrightarrow{BD}$ are distinct lines which intersect at V, $[(AVC)$ and $(BVD)]$, if P is any point in the interior of $\angle AVB$, and if Q is any point of $\angle AVD$, then $\overline{PQ}$ intersects $\angle AVB$.

Proof. Assigned as an exercise.

Theorem 5.19. Let A, B, C, D, V, P as in Theorem 5.18 be given. If Q is any point in the interior of $\angle CVD$, then $\overline{PQ}$ intersects $\angle AVB$.

Proof. Since P lies on the A-side of $\overleftrightarrow{BD}$ and Q lies on the C-side of $\overleftrightarrow{BD}$, and since A and C lie on opposite sides of $\overleftrightarrow{BD}$ (why?), it follows that P and Q lie on opposite sides of $\overleftrightarrow{BD}$. Therefore $\overline{PQ}$ intersects $\overleftrightarrow{BD}$. If $\overline{PQ}$ intersects $\overrightarrow{VB}$, the proof is complete. If $\overline{PQ}$ does not intersect $\overrightarrow{VB}$, then it intersects $\overrightarrow{VD}$ in some point, call it R. Then it follows from Theorem 5.18 that $\overline{RP}$ intersects $\angle AVB$. But $\overline{RP}$ is a subset of $\overline{PQ}$. Therefore $\overline{PQ}$ intersects $\angle AVB$. Then in all cases $\overline{PQ}$ intersects $\angle AVB$ and the proof is complete.

Definition. If P is a plane, if A, B, C are pairwise disjoint nonempty subsets of P ($A \cap B = \varnothing, A \cap C = \varnothing, B \cap C = \varnothing$) such that $A \cup B \cup C = P$, and if every segment joining a point of A to a point of B intersects C, then we shall say that C *separates* the plane P.

Theorem 5.20. Every angle separates the plane which contains it.

Proof. Let $\angle ABC$ be any angle, I its interior, and E its exterior. Then $\angle ABC$, I, E are three pairwise disjoint nonempty sets whose union is the plane of $\angle ABC$, call it P. It follows from Theorems 5.17, 5.18, and 5.19 that every segment joining a point of I to a point of E intersects $\angle ABC$. Therefore $\angle ABC$ separates P.

Exercises 5.6

1. Prove Theorem 5.11.

2. Write a proof of the theorem which results when the statement of Theorem 5.17 is changed so that Q is a point in the interior of $\angle BVC$.

3. Prove Theorem 5.18.

4. Let I be the interior of an angle, $\angle ABC$. Prove that the interiors of the rays between $\overrightarrow{BA}$ and $\overrightarrow{BC}$ *simply cover* I, that is, that every point of I is an interior point of one and only one of the rays between $\overrightarrow{BA}$ and $\overrightarrow{BC}$.

5. In the figure, the set $S = \overrightarrow{BA} \cup \overrightarrow{BC} \cup \overrightarrow{CD}$ seems to separate a plane. Formulate this carefully as a complete statement whose meaning is clear without a picture. Then outline the main steps in its proof.

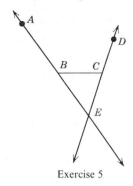

Exercise 5

6. In the figure, the interior of $\angle AVB$ seems to be separated by the interior of $\overline{AB}$. Write a careful definition of "separate" as it is used here. Then prove that the interior of $\overline{AB}$ separates the interior of $\angle AVB$. An alternate task here is to prove that $\overline{AB}$ separates the union of $\angle AVB$ and its interior.

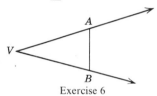

Exercise 6

5.7   *Angle Relationships*

Although we have chosen to exclude "straight angles" from our formal geometry, we often need to consider figures like the following one, which suggests the idea of a "straight angle."

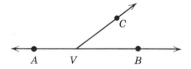

Definition. If the union of two angles is the union of three distinct concurrent rays, two of which are opposite rays, then the two angles are called a *linear pair* of angles.

In other words α and β are a linear pair of angles if and only if there are four distinct points A, B, C, V such that (AVB) and A, B, C are non-collinear, $\alpha = \angle AVC$, and $\beta = \angle BVC$. These two angles have a common vertex, V, and a common side $\overrightarrow{VC}$.

Theorem 5.21. The sum of the measures of the two angles in any linear pair of angles is 180.

Proof. Let $\angle AVC$ and $\angle CVB$ be any linear pair of angles. In the plane of A, B, C there is a ray-coordinate system relative to V in which the ray-coordinates of $\overrightarrow{VA}$ and $\overrightarrow{VB}$ are 0 and 180, respectively, and the ray-coordinate of $\overrightarrow{VC}$ is some number r between 0 and 180. It follows from the definition of a ray-coordinate system that $m\angle AVC = r$, $m\angle CVB = 180 - r$, and hence that $m\angle AVC + m\angle CVB = 180$.

Theorem 5.22. Let A, B, O, X, Y be distinct coplanar points such that A and B are on the same side of $\overleftrightarrow{XY}$, O is between X and Y, and $\overrightarrow{OA}$ is between $\overrightarrow{OX}$ and $\overrightarrow{OB}$. Then

$$m\angle XOA + m\angle AOB + m\angle BOY = 180.$$

Proof. Assigned as an exercise.

Definition. Two coplanar angles are called a pair of *adjacent angles* if and only if they have one side in common and the intersection of their interiors is empty.

Note that every linear pair of angles is also a pair of adjacent angles.

Theorem 5.23. Two adjacent angles, such that the sum of their measures is 180, are a linear pair of angles.

Proof. Assigned as an exercise.

Definitions. An angle whose measure is 90 is called a *right angle*. An angle whose measure is less than 90 is called an *acute angle*. An angle whose measure is greater than 90 is called an *obtuse angle*.

Definition. Two lines are called *perpendicular* lines, and each is said to be perpendicular to the other if their union contains a right angle.

Definition. Two sets, S and T, each of which is a segment, a ray, or a line, are called *perpendicular* sets, and each is said to be perpendicular to the other if there are two perpendicular lines, m and n, such that m contains S and n contains T.

Definition. Two angles (whether distinct or not) are called *congruent* angles, and each is said to be congruent to the other if they have the same measure.

Definition. Two angles (whether distinct or not) are called *supplementary* angles, and each is said to be a *supplement* of the other if the sum of their measures is 180.

Definition. Two angles (whether distinct or not) are called *complementary* angles, and each is said to be a *complement* of the other if the sum of their measures is 90.

Definition. Two angles, A and B, are called *vertical* angles if there are two lines, m and n, such that $A \cup B = m \cup n$.

Exercises 5.7

1. Prove Theorem 5.22.

2. Prove Theorem 5.23.

3. Prove: Any two right angles are congruent to each other.

4. Prove: If two angles are congruent and supplementary, then each of them is a right angle.

5. Prove: If two angles are complementary, then each of them is acute.

6. Prove: Supplements of congruent angles are congruent.

7. Prove: Complements of congruent angles are congruent.

8. Prove: If two angles are supplementary and neither one of them is a right angle, then one of them is acute and the other is obtuse.

9. If $\angle A$ and $\angle B$ are supplementary, and if $m\angle A = m\angle B + 30$, find $m\angle A$.

10. If $\angle A$ and $\angle B$ are complementary, and if $m\angle A = 3 \cdot m\angle B$, find $m\angle A$.

11. Prove: Any two vertical angles are congruent.

12. Prove: If l and m are perpendicular lines whose union contains a right angle, then that union is the union of four distinct right angles.

13. Prove: If F is a plane, if L is a line in F, and if P is a point on L, then there is one and only one line M through P and perpendicular to L.

14. Prove: If $\angle AVB$, $\angle BVC$, $\angle CVA$ are three coplanar angles such that the interiors of no two of them intersect, then the sum of the measures of the three angles is 360. *Hint:* There is a ray-coordinate system S in which the ray-coordinate of $\overrightarrow{VA}$ is 0 and the ray-coordinate of $\overrightarrow{VB}$ is a positive number less than 180. Then the ray-coordinate of $\overrightarrow{VC}$ must be a positive number between 180 and 360. Why?

CHAPTER 6

Polygons

6.1   Triangles and Quadrilaterals

Definitions. If A, B, and C are three noncollinear points, then the union of the three segments $\overline{AB}$, $\overline{BC}$, $\overline{CA}$ is a *triangle*. We denote it $\triangle ABC$. Each of the three points A, B, C, is a *vertex* of the triangle. Each of the segments, $\overline{AB}$, $\overline{BC}$, $\overline{CA}$, is a *side* of the triangle. Each of the angles, $\angle CAB$, $\angle ABC$, $\angle BCA$, is an *angle* of the triangle. A vertex and a side which does not contain it are said to be *opposite* each other. An angle and a side of a triangle are *opposite* each other if the vertex of that angle does not lie on that side. A vertex, or angle, and a side of a triangle which are not opposite are *adjacent* to each other. The *interior of a triangle* is the intersection of the interiors of its three angles. The *exterior of a triangle* is the set of all points in the plane of the triangle which are not elements of the triangle or of its interior.

Let a triangle, $\triangle ABC$, and the plane P which contains it be given. Let H_1, H_2, H_3, denote the C-side of $\overleftrightarrow{AB}$, the B-side of $\overleftrightarrow{AC}$, and the A-side of $\overleftrightarrow{BC}$, respectively. Then the interiors of $\angle CAB$, $\angle ABC$, $\angle BCA$ are $H_1 \cap H_2$, $H_3 \cap H_1$, $H_2 \cap H_3$, respectively. Then it follows from elementary set ideas that:

$$\text{Interior of } \triangle ABC = (H_1 \cap H_2) \cap (H_3 \cap H_1) \cap (H_2 \cap H_3)$$

$$= H_1 \cap H_2 \cap H_3.$$

97

Therefore the interior of a triangle is the intersection of three halfplanes, each containing a vertex of the triangle and having as edge the line which contains the side opposite that vertex. Note that H_1 contains all of $\triangle ABC$

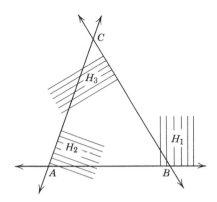

except $\overline{AB}$, H_2 contains all of $\triangle ABC$ except $\overline{CA}$, and H_3 contains all of $\triangle ABC$ except $\overline{BC}$. Therefore the interior of a triangle is the intersection of the three halfplanes, each of which has a side of the triangle in its edge and contains all of the rest of the triangle. Also, since

$$(H_1 \cap H_2) \cap (H_2 \cap H_3) = H_1 \cap H_2 \cap H_3,$$

for example, we see that the interior of a triangle is the intersection of the interiors of any two of its angles.

Theorem 6.1. The interior of any triangle is a convex set.

Proof. Assigned as an exercise.

Theorem 6.2 (*The Triangle Separation Theorem*). Every triangle separates the plane which contains it.

Proof. Let $\triangle ABC$ in a plane F be given. Let P be any point in its interior, and let Q be any point in its exterior. We shall show that $\overline{PQ}$ intersects $\triangle ABC$. Thus a triangle separates the plane which contains it.

Since Q is in the exterior and P is in the interior of $\triangle ABC$, Q and P lie on opposite sides of at least one of the lines which contain the sides of the triangle. Suppose, to be definite, that P and Q lie on opposite sides of $\overleftrightarrow{AB}$. Then $\overline{PQ}$ intersects $\overleftrightarrow{AB}$ in one and only one point, call it R. We shall consider three cases which exhaust all possibilities.

Case 1. $R \in \overline{AB}$. In this case $\overline{PQ}$ intersects $\overline{AB}$ and hence $\triangle ABC$.

Case 2. $R \notin \overline{AB}$, and $\overrightarrow{AR}$ and $\overrightarrow{AB}$ are opposite rays. In this case R and P are on opposite sides of $\overleftrightarrow{AC}$ and on the same side of $\overleftrightarrow{BC}$, actually the A-side of $\overleftrightarrow{BC}$. Then $\overline{RP}$ intersects $\overleftrightarrow{AC}$, but not Opp $\overrightarrow{CA}$. Now the interior of $\overline{RP}$ lies on the C-side of $\overleftrightarrow{AB}$. Therefore $\overline{RP}$ does not intersect Opp $\overrightarrow{AC}$. It follows that $\overline{RP}$ intersects $\overline{AC}$, and since $\overline{RP} \subset \overline{PQ}$ and $\overline{AC} \subset \triangle ABC$, it follows that $\overline{PQ}$ intersects $\triangle ABC$.

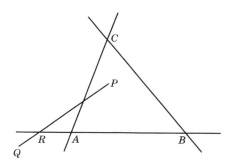

Case 3. $R \notin \overline{AB}$, and $\overrightarrow{BR}$ and $\overrightarrow{BA}$ are opposite rays. This case may be treated in a manner similar to that used for Case 2. In this case we may prove that $\overline{PQ}$ intersects $\overline{BC}$, and hence $\triangle ABC$.

This completes the proof of the triangle separation theorem.

Theorem 6.3. If P is a point in the interior of $\angle BAC$, then $\overrightarrow{AP}$ intersects $\overline{BC}$.

Proof. Since P is in the interior of $\angle BAC$, it follows that $\overrightarrow{AP}$ is between $\overrightarrow{AB}$ and $\overrightarrow{AC}$, and hence that $m\angle BAP + m\angle PAC = m\angle BAC$.

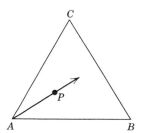

Let Q be any interior point of the ray opposite to $\overrightarrow{AP}$. Since the interior of $\overrightarrow{AQ}$ and B lie on opposite sides of $\overleftrightarrow{AC}$, it follows that the rays $\overrightarrow{AQ}$ and $\overrightarrow{CB}$ do not intersect, and hence that $\overrightarrow{AQ}$ does not intersect $\overline{BC}$.

Suppose, contrary to the assertion of the theorem, that $\overrightarrow{AP}$ does not intersect $\overline{BC}$. Then $\overleftrightarrow{AP}$ does not intersect $\overline{BC}$. It follows that B and C are in the same halfplane with edge $\overleftrightarrow{AP}$. Also $\overrightarrow{AB}, \overrightarrow{AP}, \overrightarrow{AC}$ are distinct rays. Therefore either $\overrightarrow{AB}$ is between $\overrightarrow{AP}$ and $\overrightarrow{AC}$, or $\overrightarrow{AC}$ is between $\overrightarrow{AP}$

and $\overrightarrow{AB}$. Therefore $m\angle PAB + m\angle BAC = m\angle PAC$ or $m\angle PAC + m\angle CAB = m\angle PAB$. This result together with the result in the first paragraph of this proof implies that $m\angle PAB = 0$ or that $m\angle PAC = 0$. Since this is impossible, it follows that $\overrightarrow{AP}$ intersects $\overline{BC}$.

Theorem 6.4. Given $\triangle ABC$ and a line L in the same plane. If L intersects all three sides of the triangle, then it contains at least one of the vertices of the triangle. In other words, if L contains none of the vertices, then it does not intersect all three sides.

Proof. Let $\triangle ABC$ and line L in the plane of $\triangle ABC$ be given. Suppose L contains no vertex of the triangle and, contrary to the assertion of the theorem, that it contains interior points of all three sides. Then A and B lie on opposite sides of L, B and C lie on opposite sides of L, and A and C lie on opposite sides of L. But there are only two sides of L, say H_1 and H_2. If $A \in H_1$, then $B \in H_2$, then $C \in H_1$, then $A \in H_2$. (Contradiction.) Therefore if L contains no vertex of the triangle, it does not intersect all three sides.

Theorem 6.5. Given $\triangle ABC$ and a line L in its plane. If L contains an interior point of $\overline{AB}$, then it intersects one or both of the other sides.

Proof. If L contains an interior point of $\overline{AB}$ and also the point C, or if L contains two distinct interior points of $\overline{AB}$, then it intersects both of the other sides, $\overline{AC}$ and $\overline{BC}$. If L contains exactly one interior point of $\overline{AB}$, and if L does not contain C, then C lies either on the A-side of L or on the B-side of L. Since A and B lie on opposite sides of L, it follows that either C and A, or else C and B, lie on opposite sides of L. Therefore either $\overline{AC}$ or $\overline{BC}$ intersects L.

Theorem 6.6. If a line in the plane of a triangle intersects the interior of the triangle, then it also intersects the triangle.

Proof. Let $\triangle ABC$ and a line L in its plane be given. Suppose P is a point on L and that it lies in the interior of $\triangle ABC$. Suppose, contrary to the assertion of the theorem, that L does not intersect $\triangle ABC$. Then A, B, C all lie on the same side of L, call it H. Also, $\overrightarrow{AP}$ intersects $\overline{BC}$ in some interior point of $\overline{BC}$, call it Q. Then Q lies in H (why?), and P lies in H. Why? This is impossible. Why? Therefore, if a line intersects the interior of a triangle and lies in the plane of the triangle, it intersects the triangle.

A natural extension of the idea of a triangle is the idea of a quadrilateral and more generally a polygon.

Definitions. If A, B, C, D are four distinct coplanar points, such that no three of them are collinear, and such that no one of the segments

$\overline{AB}, \overline{BC}, \overline{CD}, \overline{DA}$ intersects any other one of them at a point which is not one of its endpoints, then the union of the four segments is called a *quadrilateral*. In order to identify a quadrilateral we may call it quadrilateral *ABCD*, or briefly *ABCD*. Each of the segments $\overline{AB}, \overline{BC}, \overline{CD}, \overline{DA}$ is called a *side* of the quadrilateral. Each of the points *A, B, C, D* is called a *vertex* of the quadrilateral. The *angles* of quadrilateral *ABCD* are $\angle DAB$, $\angle ABC$, $\angle BCD$, and $\angle CDA$. The *diagonals* of quadrilateral *ABCD* are the segments $\overline{AC}$ and $\overline{BD}$. Two distinct sides which have a common vertex are called *adjacent* sides; two sides which do not have a common vertex are called *opposite* sides. A vertex (or an angle) and a side of a quadrilateral are said to be *adjacent* if the side contains the vertex (or the vertex of the angle). If a side and a vertex (angle) of a quadrilateral are not *adjacent*, then we say that they are *opposite* to each other.

A quadrilateral is a *convex quadrilateral* if each line which contains a side of the quadrilateral is the edge of a halfplane whose closure contains the quadrilateral. (The closure of a halfplane is the union of the halfplane and its edge.) It is easy to see that quadrilateral *ABCD* is a convex quadrilateral if and only if *A* and *B* are on the same side of $\overleftrightarrow{CD}$, *and B* and *C* are on the same side of $\overleftrightarrow{AD}$, *and C* and *D* are on the same side of $\overleftrightarrow{AB}$, *and D* and *A* are on the same side of $\overleftrightarrow{BC}$.

Let $P_1, P_2, \cdots, P_{n-1}, P_n, (n \geqslant 3)$ be *n* distinct coplanar points such that the *n* segments $\overline{P_1P_2}, \overline{P_2P_3}, \cdots, \overline{P_{n-1}P_n}, \overline{P_nP_1}$ have the following two properties:

1. No two segments intersect except possibly at their endpoints.

2. No two segments with a common endpoint are collinear.

Then the union of the *n* segments is a *polygon*. We may identify it as polygon $P_1P_2 \cdots P_n$. Each of the points P_i is called a *vertex* of the polygon. Each of the segments $\overline{P_iP_j}$ is called a *side* of the polygon. The meanings of opposite and adjacent, or consecutive, as applied to parts of a polygon are suggested by their meanings when they apply to parts of a quadrilateral. A segment joining two opposite vertices of a polygon is a *diagonal* of the polygon.

A polygon is a *convex polygon* if every side lies on the edge of a halfplane whose closure contains the polygon. The *interior* of a convex polygon is the intersection of all halfplanes *H* such that (1) the edge of *H* contains a side of the polygon and (2) the closure of *H* contains the polygon.

Polygons of 5, 6, 7, 8, 9, 10, and 12 sides are called *pentagons, hexagons, heptagons, octagons, nonagons, decagons,* and *dodecagons,* respectively. Sometimes a polygon of *n*-sides is called an *n-gon.* For example, a 23-gon is a polygon having exactly 23 sides.

Theorem 6.7. The interior of a convex polygon contains the interior of each of its diagonals.

Proof. Let P, S, D be a convex polygon, one of its sides, and one of its diagonals, respectively. Let H be the halfplane whose edge contains S and whose closure contains P. If an endpoint of D is also an endpoint of S, then the other endpoint of D lies in H, and the interior of D lies in H. If neither endpoint of D is an endpoint of S, then D joins two points of H. Therefore D is a subset of H. Thus in every case the interior of D lies in H.

Let $H_1, H_2, \cdots, H_n$ be the n halfplanes, each of which has an edge which contains a side of P and a closure which contains all of P. Then the interior of D is contained in each H_i, $i = 1, 2, \cdots, n$, and hence in their intersection, which is the interior of the polygon.

Theorem 6.8. The diagonals of a convex quadrilateral intersect at a point in its interior.

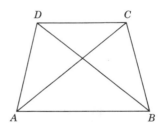

Proof. Let $ABCD$ be a convex quadrilateral. Since C lies on the D-side of $\overleftrightarrow{AB}$ and on the B-side of $\overleftrightarrow{AD}$, it follows that C is in the interior of $\angle BAD$ and hence that $\overrightarrow{AC}$ intersects $\overline{BD}$. See Theorem 6.3. Similarly, $\overrightarrow{CA}$ intersects $\overline{BD}$. It follows that $\overrightarrow{AC}$ and $\overline{BD}$ intersect in a point which belongs to both of the rays $\overrightarrow{CA}$ and $\overrightarrow{AC}$. Since no three vertices of a quadrilateral are collinear, it follows that $\overleftrightarrow{AC}$ and $\overline{BD}$ cannot intersect at A or B or C or D. It follows that $\overline{AC}$ and $\overline{BD}$ intersect at a point which is an interior point of both diagonals, and hence a point in the interior of the quadrilateral. This completes the proof.

Theorem 6.9. If $ABCD$ is a quadrilateral, then A and B lie on the same side of $\overleftrightarrow{CD}$, or C and D lie on the same side of $\overleftrightarrow{AB}$.

Proof. If the quadrilateral is convex, the assertion follows immediately from the definition of convex quadrilateral.

Suppose, contrary to the assertion of the theorem, that A and B lie on opposite sides of $\overleftrightarrow{CD}$ *and* that C and D lie on opposite sides of $\overleftrightarrow{AB}$. Then $\overline{AB}$ intersects $\overleftrightarrow{CD}$, and $\overline{CD}$ intersects $\overleftrightarrow{AB}$. It follows that $\overline{AB}$ and $\overline{CD}$ intersect. Since no three of the vertices of a quadrilateral are collinear, it follows that $\overline{AB}$ and $\overline{CD}$ intersect at an interior point of both segments. Since this is impossible according to the definition of a quadrilateral, it follows that A and B lie on the same side of $\overleftrightarrow{CD}$ or that C and D lie on the same side of $\overleftrightarrow{AB}$. This completes the proof.

Given a quadrilateral, it follows from Theorem 6.9 that it can be named $ABCD$ so that C and D lie on the same side of $\overleftrightarrow{AB}$. We suppose that this has been done. From Theorem 6.9 it also follows that B and C lie on the same side of $\overleftrightarrow{AD}$, or A and D lie on the same side of $\overleftrightarrow{BC}$. If B and C lie on opposite sides of $\overleftrightarrow{AD}$, we may rename the quadrilateral again by interchanging A and B and interchanging C and D. Then C and D will lie on the same side of $\overleftrightarrow{AB}$, and B and C will lie on the same side of $\overleftrightarrow{AD}$.

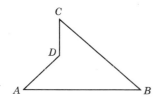 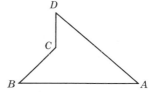

Definition. Given a quadrilateral $ABCD$ lying in a plane F and so named that C and D lie on the same side of $\overleftrightarrow{AB}$, and that B and C lie on the same side $\overleftrightarrow{AD}$, the *interior of ABCD* and the *exterior of ABCD* are defined as follows. ("Int" means "interior of" and "Ext" means "exterior of.")

Int $ABCD$ = Int $\triangle ABC \cup$ Int $\overline{AC} \cup$ Int $\triangle ACD$.

Ext $ABCD$ = F − (Int $ABCD \cup ABCD$).

Theorem 6.10. The interior of a convex polygon is a convex set.

Proof. Assigned as an exercise.

Theorem 6.11. The union of a convex polygon and its interior is a convex set.

Proof. Assigned as an exercise.

Theorem 6.12. Every quadrilateral separates the plane which contains it.

Proof. Assigned as an exercise.

Theorem 6.13. Every convex polygon separates the plane which contains it.

Proof. Assigned as an exercise.

Exercises 6.1

1. Prove Theorem 6.1.

2. Prove Theorem 6.10.

3. Prove Theorem 6.11.

4. Prove Theorem 6.12.

5. Prove Theorem 6.13.

6. Define tetrahedron, interior of tetrahedron, and exterior of tetrahedron.

7. Given tetrahedron $ABCD$, P a point in its interior, and Q a point in the intersection of the following halfspaces: the not-D-side of plane ABC, the C-side of plane ABD, the B-side of plane ACD, the A-side of plane BCD. Prove that $\overline{PQ}$ intersects the tetrahedron.

8. Outline a proof of the theorem that every tetrahedron separates its interior from its exterior.

6.2   Triangle Congruences

As discussed in Chapter 1, congruence is a concept which has its roots in the idea of "same size and shape." In physical geometry we experience congruence through observation and measurement. Sometimes we assist our observation by placing objects in positions relative to each other which will help us to see any difference in size or shape the objects may have.

In our formal geometry congruence is first introduced as a binary relation defined on the set of all segments. Suppose a unit-pair for distances is fixed. Let S, T, U, $\cdots$ denote segments. Then by definition, $S \cong T$ means that the length of S is the same as the length of T. For every ordered pair (S, T), where S and T are segments, not necessarily distinct, the statement $S \cong T$ is either true or it is false (not both). Thus congruence for segments is a binary relation on the set of all segments. This binary relation is an equivalence relation, that is, it is reflexive, symmetric, and transitive. The congruence relation partitions the set of all segments into pairwise disjoint subsets, in which each subset is a set of congruent segments and such that a segment in one subset is not congruent to a segment in any other subset.

In our formal geometry congruence appears next in connection with angles. Just as it seems natural to think of segments with the same length as having "same size and shape," so it seems natural to think of two angles with the same measure as having the "same size and shape." Congruence for angles is an equivalence relation defined on the set of all angles.

In Chapter 1 we described some physical experiments to suggest a definition and some statements regarding congruent triangles. In this section we define congruence for triangles, adopt one postulate, and prove several basic theorems.

Definition. A one-to-one correspondence, $ABC \leftrightarrow DEF$, between the set of vertices of one triangle and the set of vertices of a second triangle (or between the set of vertices of a triangle and itself) is called a *congruence* between the triangles if and only if the elements in each of the six pairs of corresponding parts $(\{\overline{AB}, \overline{DE}\}, \{\overline{AC}, \overline{DF}\}, \{\overline{BC}, \overline{EF}\}, \{\angle A, \angle D\}, \{\angle B, \angle E\}, \{\angle C, \angle F\})$ are congruent to each other.

Definition. $\triangle ABC$ is *congruent* to $\triangle DEF$ with $ABC \leftrightarrow DEF$ if and only if $ABC \leftrightarrow DEF$ is a congruence.

Notation. $\triangle ABC \cong \triangle DEF$ means that $\triangle ABC$ is congruent to $\triangle DEF$ with $ABC \leftrightarrow DEF$.

Postulate 17 (*The S.A.S. Postulate*). Given $\triangle ABC$ and $\triangle DEF$. If $\overline{AB} \cong \overline{DE}$, $\overline{AC} \cong \overline{DF}$, $\angle A \cong \angle D$, then $\triangle ABC \cong \triangle DEF$.

This may be stated in words as follows: Given triangle T_1 and triangle T_2 (not necessarily distinct). If there is a one-to-one correspondence between the set of vertices of T_1 and the set of vertices of T_2 and if two sides and their included angle of T_1 are congruent, respectively, to the corresponding parts of T_2, then the triangles T_1 and T_2 are congruent under that one-to-one correspondence between vertices, that is, the remaining three parts of T_1 are congruent, respectively, to the corresponding parts of T_2.

Theorem 6.14 (A.S.A.). Given $\triangle ABC$ and $\triangle DEF$. If $\overline{AB} \cong \overline{DE}$, $\angle A \cong \angle D$, $\angle B \cong \angle E$, then $\triangle ABC \cong \triangle DEF$.

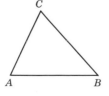 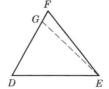

Proof. Let $\triangle ABC$ and $\triangle DEF$ be given with $\overline{AB} \cong \overline{DE}$, $\angle A \cong \angle D$, $\angle B \cong \angle E$. Either $AC = DF$, or $AC > DF$, or $AC < DF$. Suppose $AC < DF$. Then there is a point G between D and F such that $AC = DG$. Why? Then $\triangle ABC \cong \triangle DEG$. Why? Then $\angle GED \cong \angle CBA$. Why? Now G is in the interior of $\angle DEF$. Why? Then $\overrightarrow{EG}$ is between $\overrightarrow{ED}$ and $\overrightarrow{EF}$ (Why?) and $m\angle DEG + m\angle GEF = m\angle DEF$. Why? It follows that $m\angle DEF > m\angle DEG$. But $m\angle DEG = m\angle ABC$. Why? Therefore $m\angle DEF > m\angle ABC$ and $\angle E$ is not congruent to $\angle B$. Since this contradicts one of the hypotheses, it follows that AC is not less than DE. Similarly it may be shown that AC is not greater than DE. Therefore $AC = DE$ and $\overline{AC} \cong \overline{DE}$. It then follows from the S.A.S. postulate that $\triangle ABC \cong \triangle DEF$.

Theorem 6.15 (*Isosceles Triangle Theorem*). Given $\triangle ABC$. If $\overline{AB} \cong \overline{AC}$, then $\angle ABC \cong \angle ACB$.

Proof. Since $\overline{AB} \cong \overline{AC}$, $\angle BAC \cong \angle CAB$, $\overline{AC} \cong \overline{AB}$, it follows from the S.A.S. postulate that $\triangle ABC \cong \triangle ACB$, and hence that $\angle ABC \cong \angle ACB$.

Theorem 6.16 (*Converse of the Isosceles Triangle Theorem*). Given $\triangle ABC$. If $\angle ABC \cong \angle ACB$, then $\overline{AB} \cong \overline{AC}$.

Proof. Assigned as an exercise.

Theorem 6.17 (S.S.S.). Given $\triangle ABC$ and $\triangle DEF$. If $\overline{AB} \cong \overline{DE}$, $\overline{AC} \cong \overline{DF}$, $\overline{BC} \cong \overline{EF}$, then $\triangle ABC \cong \triangle DEF$.

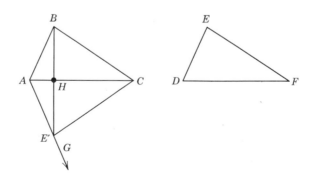

Proof. Let $\overrightarrow{AG}$ be a ray in the plane of $\triangle ABC$ such that $\angle CAG \cong \angle FDE$ and B and G are on opposite sides of $\overleftrightarrow{AC}$. (How do you know there is such a ray? Is it unique?) Let E' be a point on $\overrightarrow{AG}$ such that $AE' = DE$. (How do you know there is such a point? Is it unique?) Then $\triangle AE'C \cong \triangle DEF$. Why? We proceed now to prove that $\triangle ABC \cong \triangle DEF$.

Since B and E' are on opposite sides of $\overleftrightarrow{AC}$, it follows that $\overrightarrow{BE'}$ has an interior point H on $\overleftrightarrow{AC}$. Suppose, as suggested in the figure, that H is an interior point of $\overline{AC}$. Then $AB = DE$, $DE = AE'$, and $AB = AE'$. Also $BC = EF$, $EF = E'C$ (Why?), and $BC = E'C$. Now $\overrightarrow{BH}$ is between $\overrightarrow{BA}$ and $\overrightarrow{BC}$. Why? $\triangle ABE'$ and $\triangle CBE'$ are isosceles triangles. $\angle ABH \cong$ $\angle AE'H$. $\angle CBH \cong \angle CE'H$. Then $m\angle ABH + m\angle CBH = m\angle ABC$, $m\angle AE'H + m\angle CE'H = m\angle AE'C$. Why? Therefore $m\angle ABC = m\angle AE'C$. But $m\angle AE'C = m\angle DEF$. Why? Therefore $m\angle ABC = m\angle DEF$. Finally, then, $\triangle ABC \cong \triangle DEF$ by the S.A.S. postulate.

The remainder of the proof (the case or cases in which H is not between A and C) is assigned as an exercise.

Exercises 6.2

1. Prove Theorem 6.16.

2. Complete the proof of Theorem 6.17.

3. Prove: The median from the vertex of an isosceles triangle to the base bisects the vertex angle and is perpendicular to the base.

4. Prove: Any two medians of a triangle intersect at an interior point of the triangle.

5. Prove: If each diagonal of a quadrilateral is the perpendicular bisector of the other diagonal, then the quadrilateral is equilateral and each diagonal bisects two angles of the quadrilateral.

6. Given $\triangle ABC$ with $AB = AC$ and medians $\overline{BE}$, $\overline{CF}$, from B to $\overline{AC}$ and from C to $\overline{AB}$, respectively. If $\overline{BE}$ and $\overline{CF}$ intersect in point G, prove that $\triangle BGC$ is an isosceles triangle.

7. Prove: The measure of an exterior angle of a triangle is greater than the measure of either nonadjacent interior angle. *Hint:* Given $\triangle ABC$ with exterior angle $\angle CBF$. The accompanying figure may help you to see a proof that $m\angle CBF > m\angle ACB$.

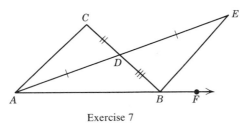

Exercise 7

8. Prove: The sum of the measures of two angles of any triangle is less than 180. *Hint:* Use Exercise 7.

9. If L is a line and P is a point not on L, there is at least one line through P and perpendicular to L. *Hint:* The figure.

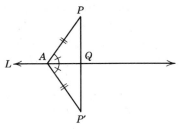

Exercise 9

CHAPTER 7

Parallelism and Similarity

7.1 Introduction

About 150 years ago, a revolution in mathematical thought began with the discovery of a geometrical theory which differed from the classical theory of space formulated by Euclid about 300 B.C. For 2000 years Euclid's *Elements* was considered an accurate description of physical space. It was believed to be the only way in which the human mind could conceive of space. It is understandable, then, that the development of non-Euclidean geometry had an impact on mathematical thought comparable to that of Darwin in biology, Copernicus in astronomy, and Einstein in physics.

How did this revolution come about? Perhaps its origin is in the *Elements* itself. Although Euclid lists his postulates at the beginning, he refrains from using one of them until he apparently can go no further without it. This is the famous fifth postulate which is commonly known today in the following form.

Postulate 18. (*Euclid's Parallel Postulate*). If *P* is a point not on a line *L*, there is exactly one line through *P* and parallel to *L*.

It is possible that Euclid refrained from using the parallel postulate in the first part of the *Elements* because he thought it more complicated than his other postulates, or perhaps he thought he might be able to prove it using his other postulates.

The parallel postulate is a "powerhouse." From it we get a lot of interesting and useful geometry, for example, the sum of the measures of the angles of a triangle is 180, parallel lines are everywhere equidistant, the existence of rectangles, the theory of area for polygons, the theory of similarity, and the Pythagorean theorem.

Before we exploit the parallel postulate in our development of formal Euclidean geometry, we shall investigate further the part of Euclid's geometry which does not depend upon the parallel postulate. We call this neutral geometry. In a sense, neutral geometry is the common part of Euclidean geometry and the non-Euclidean geometry of Bolyai and Lobachevsky. Their postulates are the same up to the point where the parallel postulate is introduced. The geometry of Bolyai and Lobachevsky includes a postulate to the effect that if P is a point not on a line L, then there are two distinct lines through P and parallel to L. In neutral geometry we have neither Euclid's parallel postulate nor the Bolyai–Lobachevsky parallel postulate.

We assume that parallel lines, transversals, alternate interior angles, etc., have been defined as in Chapter 1.

7.2   *Some Basic Theorems in Neutral Geometry*

Theorem 7.1 (*The Exterior Angle Theorem*). The measure of an exterior angle of a triangle is greater than the measure of either nonadjacent interior angle.

Proof. Exercise 7 of 6.2.

Theorem 7.2 (*Corollary of the Exterior Angle Theorem*). The sum of the measures of two angles of a triangle is less than 180.

Proof. Exercise 8 of 6.2.

Theorem 7.3 (*Perpendicular Existence Theorem*). Given any line L and any point P lying in a plane F, there is exactly one line in F containing P and perpendicular to L.

Proof. If P is on L, the result follows from the protractor postulate. For the case in which P is not on L, see Exercise 9 of 6.2.

Theorem 7.4 (*Parallel Existence Theorem*). Given any line L and any point P not on L, there exists at least one line M through P and parallel to L.

Proof. Let p be the unique line through P and perpendicular to L. Let M be the unique line through P, in the plane of P and L, which is perpendicular to p. Suppose that M is not parallel to L. Then M and L intersect to form a triangle with one interior angle a right angle and a nonadjacent exterior angle a right angle. Since this contradicts the exterior angle theorem, it follows that M is parallel to L.

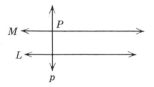

7.3 *Parallelism in Neutral Geometry*

In this section we have several theorems which give conditions for parallelism. The converses of these theorems are not part of neutral geometry.

Theorem 7.5. Let two distinct coplanar lines be given. If a transversal of the lines is perpendicular to each of them, then the lines are parallel.

Proof. Assigned as an exercise.

Theorem 7.6. Let two distinct coplanar lines be given. If two alternate interior angles determined by a transversal of the lines are congruent, then the lines are parallel.

Proof. Assigned as an exercise.

Theorem 7.7. Let two distinct coplanar lines be given. If two corresponding angles determined by a transversal of the lines are congruent, then the lines are parallel.

Proof. Assigned as an exercise.

Theorem 7.8. Let two distinct coplanar lines be given. If two consecutive interior angles determined by a transversal of the lines are supplementary then the lines are parallel.

Proof. Assigned as an exercise.

Exercises 7.3

1. Prove Theorem 7.5.
2. Prove Theorem 7.6.
3. Prove Theorem 7.7.
4. Prove Theorem 7.8.

7.4 *Angle Measure Sum in Neutral Geometry*

Definition. The *angle measure sum* of a polygon is the sum of the measures of its angles.

Theorem 7.9. Let L be a line and P a point not on L. If there are two distinct lines through P and parallel to L, then there exists at least one triangle whose angle measure sum is less than 180.

Proof. Let L be a line and P a point not on L. Let $\overleftrightarrow{PX}$ and $\overleftrightarrow{PY}$ be distinct lines through P parallel to L. Suppose, contrary to the assertion of the theorem, that the angle measure sum of every triangle is greater than or equal to 180. Let $\overleftrightarrow{PQ}$ be perpendicular to L at Q. Let X and X' be points of $\overleftrightarrow{PX}$ on opposite sides of P, and Y and Y' be points of $\overleftrightarrow{PY}$ on opposite sides of P. Then at least one of the angles $\angle XPQ$, $\angle X'PQ$, $\angle YPQ$, $\angle Y'PQ$ is an acute angle. Why? Suppose that names have been assigned so that $\angle XPQ$ is an acute angle. Let $\overleftrightarrow{PZ}$ be the line in the plane

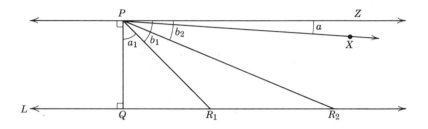

of P and L which is perpendicular to $\overline{PQ}$ at P. Suppose that Z and X lie on the same side of $\overleftrightarrow{PQ}$. Let $m\angle ZPX = a$. Then $a < 90$.

Let R_1 be the point of L which lies on the X-side of $\overleftrightarrow{PQ}$ and such that $QR_1 = PQ$. Let $m\angle QPR_1 = a_1$. Then $m\angle QR_1P = a_1$, $2a_1 + 90 \geq 180$, and $a_1 \geq 45$. Let $m\angle ZPR_1 = b_1$. Then $b_1 + a_1 = 90$ and $b_1 \leq 45$. Also $b_1 > a$.

Now we repeat the argument with a new triangle. Take point R_2 on $\overrightarrow{QR_1}$ such that $QR_2 = QR_1 + R_1P$. Then $PR_1 = R_1R_2$. Let $a_2 = m\angle R_1PR_2$. Then $m\angle R_1R_2P = a_2$ and $2a_2 + (180 - a_1) \geq 180$, $2a_2 \geq a_1$, $a_2 \geq \frac{45}{2}$. Let $b_2 = m\angle ZPR_2$. Then $b_2 = 90 - a_1 - a_2 \leq 90 - 45 - \frac{45}{2} = \frac{45}{2}$. Also $b_2 > a$.

Continuing in this manner we obtain a sequence of real numbers $b_1, b_2, b_3, \ldots$, such that $b_1 < 45$, $b_2 < \frac{45}{2}$, and in general $b_n < 45/2^{n-1}$, and such that $b_n > a$ for all n. This implies that $45/2^{n-1} > a$ for all n and hence that $2^{n-1} < 45/a$ for all n. This conclusion is false since $45/a$ is a fixed number and 2^{n-1} increases beyond any bound as n increases. Therefore our supposition is untenable and the theorem is proved.

Theorem 7.10. Given $\triangle ABC$. There is a triangle, $\triangle A'B'C'$, with the same angle measure sum as $\triangle ABC$ and such that $m\angle A' \leq \frac{1}{2}m\angle A$.

Proof. Let D be the midpoint of $\overline{BC}$. Let E be the point on $\overrightarrow{AD}$ such that $AE = 2 \cdot AD$. Then $\triangle ADC \cong \triangle EDB$. Why? Then labeling the angles as

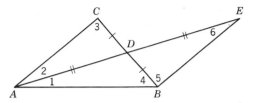

indicated in the figure, we have

$$m\angle A + m\angle B + m\angle C = m\angle 1 + m\angle 2 + m\angle 3 + m\angle 4,$$
$$= m\angle 1 + m\angle 6 + m\angle 5 + m\angle 4,$$
$$= m\angle EAB + m\angle ABE + m\angle BEA.$$

Also,

$$m\angle A = m\angle 1 + m\angle 6.$$

Therefore (1) $m\angle 1 \leqslant \frac{1}{2}m\angle A$ or (2) $m\angle 6 \leqslant \frac{1}{2}m\angle A$. Why? If (1), then $\triangle A'B'C'$, with $A' = A$, $B' = B$, $C' = E$, is the required triangle. If (2), then $\triangle A'B'C'$, with $A' = E$, $B' = B$, $C' = A$, is the required triangle.

Theorem 7.11. The angle measure sum of any triangle is less than or equal to 180.

Proof. Suppose the theorem is false. Then there is a triangle, $\triangle ABC$, whose angle measure sum is $180 + p$ for some number $p > 0$. Applying Theorem 7.10, there is a triangle, $\triangle A_1B_1C_1$, with angle measure sum $180 + p$ and with $m\angle A_1 \leqslant \frac{1}{2}m\angle A$. The theorem may be applied repeatedly to yield a sequence of triangles

$$\triangle A_1B_1C_1, \quad \triangle A_2B_2C_2, \quad \triangle A_3B_3C_3, \quad \dots,$$

each with angle measure sum $180 + p$, and such that

$$m\angle A \geqslant 2m\angle A_1 \geqslant 4m\angle A_2 \dots.$$

It follows for all positive integers n that $m\angle A_n \leqslant (m\angle A)/2^n$. Let n be a positive integer such that $(m\angle A)/2^n \leqslant p$. How do you know that there is such an integer n? Then $m\angle A_n \leqslant p$, $m\angle A_n + m\angle B_n + m\angle C_n = 180 + p$, and $m\angle B_n + m\angle C_n \geqslant 180$. Since this contradicts Theorem 7.2, the proof is complete.

Theorem 7.12. The angle measure sum of any quadrilateral is less than or equal to 360.

Proof. Let quadrilateral *ABCD* be given. If *ABCD* is not a convex quadrilateral, then the interior of one of its diagonals is a subset of the exterior of the quadrilateral, for example, diagonal $\overline{BD}$ for quadrilateral *ABCD* in the figure, and there is a convex quadrilateral *A′B′C′D′* whose

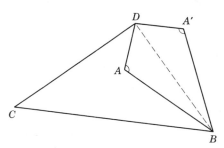

angle measure sum is greater than the angle measure sum of *ABCD*. For the example in the figure take *A′* on the opposite side of $\overleftrightarrow{BD}$ from *A*, so that $\angle ADB \cong \angle A'DB$ and $\overline{AD} \cong \overline{A'D}$. Then quadrilateral *A′BCD* is convex and has a greater angle measure sum than does *ABCD*.

We consider, then, a convex quadrilateral *ABCD*. Its angle measure sum is the sum of the angle measure sums of $\triangle ABC$ and $\triangle ACD$, and it is therefore less than or equal to $2 \cdot 180$, or 360. This completes the proof.

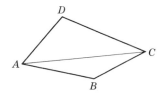

7.5   *Rectangles in Neutral Geometry*

The long history of Euclidean geometry includes attempts by many men to prove that the parallel postulate is a logical consequence of the other Euclidean postulates. Saccheri (1667–1733) made an extensive study of what now are called Saccheri quadrilaterals in his attempt to prove the postulate.

Definition. A *Saccheri quadrilateral* is a quadrilateral which has two congruent sides each perpendicular to a (the same) third side. In the figure *ABCD* is a Saccheri quadrilateral with $AD = BC$, $\overline{AD} \perp \overline{AB}$, $\overline{BC} \perp \overline{AB}$. Saccheri proved (using neutral geometry postulates) for the quadrilateral of our figure that $\angle C \cong \angle D$. He then considered three possibilities as follows:

1. $m\angle C = 90$ (the right-angle hypothesis).
2. $m\angle C < 90$ (the acute-angle hypothesis).
3. $m\angle C > 90$ (the obtuse-angle hypothesis).

Saccheri proved that the obtuse angle hypothesis is impossible in neutral geometry. (Note that we have proved what amounts to the same thing in Theorem 7.12.) He tried to prove that the acute-angle hypothesis is impossible in neutral geometry. He thought that he had proved it; but he had not. He did prove some interesting theorems of the following forms: "If the right-angle hypothesis holds, then ...''; and "If the acute-angle hypothesis holds, then...." Several such theorems are included here.

For the purpose of this section we consider a rectangle as a Saccheri quadrilateral satisfying the right-angle hypothesis, as in the following definition.

Definition. A *rectangle* is a convex quadrilateral $ABCD$ with four right angles and with at least one pair of opposite sides congruent.

Theorem 7.13. If $ABCD$ is a rectangle with $AB = CD$, then $BC = DA$.

Proof. Let rectangle $ABCD$ with $AB = CD$ be given.

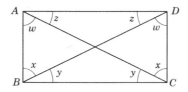

Using the S.A.S. postulate we can prove that $\triangle DAB \cong \triangle ADC$ and $\triangle ABC \cong \triangle DCB$. It follows that four pairs of congruent angles are formed by the diagonals $\overline{AC}$ and $\overline{BD}$, as indicated in the figure in which lower case letters denote angle measures. From Theorem 7.11 it follows that $x + z \leqslant 90$, $y + w \leqslant 90$. But $x + z + y + w = 180$. Therefore $x + z = y + w = 90$. But $x + y = z + w = 90$. Therefore $x = w$ and $y = z$. Then it follows from the A.S.A. theorem that $\triangle DAB \cong \triangle CBA$, and hence that $BC = DA$.

Theorem 7.14. The opposite sides of a rectangle are parallel.

Proof. Use Theorem 7.5.

Theorem 7.15. If there is a rectangle $ABCD$ and if p is any positive number, then there is a rectangle $ABEF$ with $AF > p$.

Proof. Let a rectangle $ABCD$ be given. Let n be a positive integer such that $n \cdot AD > p$. We use $ABCD$ as a "building block" to construct quadrilaterals DCC_2D_2, $D_2C_2C_3D_3$, ..., each congruent to $ABCD$. To do this, take $D_2, D_3, \ldots$, on $\overrightarrow{AD}$ so that $AD_2 = 2 \cdot AD$, $AD_3 = 3 \cdot AD$, ..., and $C_2, C_3, \ldots$, on $\overrightarrow{BC}$ so that $BC_2 = 2 \cdot BC$, $BC_3 = 3 \cdot BC$, ...

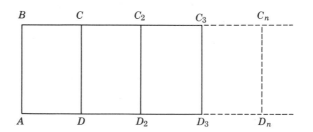

It follows from the S.A.S. postulate that $\triangle BCD \cong \triangle C_2CD$. Then $BD = DC_2$, $m\angle BDC = m\angle C_2DC$, $m\angle ADB = m\angle D_2DC_2$, $\triangle ADB \cong \triangle D_2DC_2$ (Why?), and $m\angle DD_2C_2 = 90$ (Why?). Similarly, $m\angle D_2C_2C = 90$. Therefor ABC_2D_2 is a rectangle. It is easy to extend this argument to prove that ABC_nD_n is a rectangle. But $AD_n = n \cdot AD > p$. Therefore ABC_nD_n is a rectangle with one side of length more than p, and the proof is complete.

Theorem 7.16. If one rectangle exists and if p is any positive number, then there is a rectangle all four of whose sides have length more than p.

Proof. Assigned as an exercise.

Theorem 7.17. If one rectangle exists and if p and q are any positive numbers, then there exists a rectangle with two adjacent sides of length p and q.

Proof. It follows from Theorem 7.16 that there is a rectangle $ABCD$ with $AB > p$ and $AD > q$. Let B' be the point on $\overrightarrow{AB}$ such that $AB' = p$.

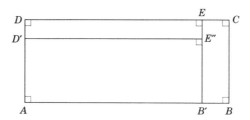

Let E be the foot of the perpendicular from B' to $\overleftrightarrow{DC}$. We shall show that $AB'ED$ is a rectangle. It has right angles at A, E, and D. We will show that it has a right angle at B'. Suppose $m\angle AB'E > 90$. Then the angle measure sum of quadrilateral $AB'ED$ exceeds 360 and this contradicts Theorem 7.12. Suppose $m\angle AB'E < 90$. Then $m\angle BB'E > 90$ and the angle measure sum of quadrilateral $BB'EC$ exceeds 360, again contradicting Theorem 7.12. It follows that $m\angle AB'E = 90$ and that $AB'ED$ is a rectangle. Similarly there is a point D' on $\overrightarrow{AD}$ such that $AD' = q$. There is a perpendicular from D' to $\overleftrightarrow{B'E}$ with foot E''. We can prove as above that $AB'E''D'$ is a rectangle, and since it has two adjacent sides of lengths p and q, the proof is complete.

Theorem 7.18. If one rectangle exists, then the angle measure sum of every right triangle is 180.

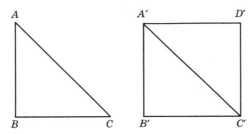

Proof. Let $\triangle ABC$ be a given right triangle with B the vertex of the right angle. Let $A'B'C'D'$ be a rectangle with $A'B' = AB$, $B'C' = BC$ (Theorem 7.17). Then $\triangle ABC \cong \triangle A'B'C'$ (Why?) and these two triangles have the same angle measure sum; call it p. Now the angle measure sum of $A'B'C'D'$ is $4 \cdot 90 = 360$. Let q be the angle measure sum of $\triangle A'C'D'$. Then $p + q = 360$ and, since $p \leqslant 180$, $q \leqslant 180$ (Theorem 7.11), it follows that $p = 180$. Since $\triangle ABC$ is an arbitrary right triangle, the proof is complete.

Theorem 7.19. If one rectangle exists, then the angle measure sum of every triangle is 180.

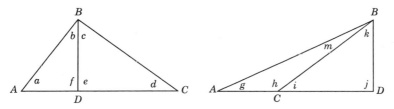

Proof. If△*ABC* is a right triangle, the result follows from Theorem 7.18. If △*ABC* is not a right triangle, a "proof by addition or subtraction" using right triangles is suggested by the figures. Use lower case letters to denote the measures of the angles as suggested in the figures. Then

$$a + b + c + d = (a + b + f) + (c + d + e) - (e + f)$$

$$= 180 + 180 - 180$$

$$= 180.$$

$$g + m + h = (g + m + k + j) + (i + h) - (i + j + k)$$

$$= 180 + 180 - 180$$

$$= 180.$$

Theorem 7.20. If one rectangle exists, then Euclid's parallel postulate holds.

Proof. Suppose, contrary to the assertion of the theorem, that one rectangle exists and that the parallel postulate is not true. Then there is a point *P* and a line *L*, with *P* not on *L*, and with two distinct lines L_1 and L_2 through *P* and parallel to *L*. (According to Theorem 7.4 there is at least one line through *P* and parallel to *L*. If the parallel postulate fails, there must be at least one instance in which there is more than one line through a given point and parallel to a given line.) It follows from Theorem 7.9 that there is a triangle whose angle measure sum is less than 180. It follows from Theorem 7.19 that the angle measure sum of every triangle is 180. Since this is a contradiction, the proof is complete.

Theorem 7.21. If Euclid's parallel postulate holds, then there is a rectangle.

Proof. Suppose *F* is a plane, *L* is a line in *F*, and *P* is a point not on *L* but in *F*. Let *L'* be the unique line through *P* and parallel to *L*. Let *Q* be the foot of the perpendicular from *P* to *L*. Let $M = \overleftrightarrow{PQ}$. Let *R* be any point other than *Q* on *L*. Let *M'* be the unique line through *R* and parallel

to *M*. Then *M'* is not parallel to *L'*. (If *M'* were parallel to *L'*, then *M'* and *L* would be two distinct lines each parallel to *L'* and passing through the point R, contradicting the parallel postulate.) Let S be the point in which M' intersects L'.

The line in F which is perpendicular to L at R is also parallel to M (Theorem 7.5). Since there is only one line through R parallel to M, it follows that $\overline{SR} \perp \overline{QR}$. Similarly, $\overline{SP} \perp \overline{PQ}$ and $\overline{SP} \perp \overline{SR}$. Therefore $PQRS$ is a quadrilateral with four right angles.

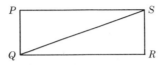

Let P' be a point such that it and R are on opposite sides of $\overleftrightarrow{QS}$ and such that $\angle P'SQ \cong \angle RQS$. Then $\overleftrightarrow{P'S} \parallel \overleftrightarrow{QR}$ (Theorem 7.6), and since Euclid's parallel postulate holds, it follows that $\overleftrightarrow{PS} = \overleftrightarrow{P'S}$ and $\angle PSQ \cong \angle RQS$. It follows from the A.S.A. theorem that $\triangle PQS \cong \triangle RSQ$. Therefore $PQ = RS$ and $PQRS$ is a rectangle.

7.6   *Parallel Postulate Equivalents*

In view of Theorems 7.20 and 7.21 we have arrived at a remarkable result, namely the following theorem.

Theorem 7.22. Euclid's parallel postulate is logically equivalent to the existence of a rectangle.

Another remarkable theorem is the following one.

Theorem 7.23. Euclid's parallel postulate is logically equivalent to the existence of a triangle with angle measure sum of 180.

Proof. Assume, first, the parallel postulate. Then there exists a rectangle, call it $ABCD$. Then $AB = CD$, $BC = AD$ (Theorem 7.13), and the four angles of the rectangle are right angles. It follows from the S.S.S. theorem

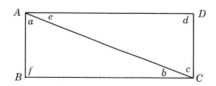

that $\triangle ABC \cong \triangle DCA$. Then, in terms of the notation of the figure, we have

$$a + b \leqslant 90, \quad c + e \leqslant 90, \quad a + b + c + e = 2 \cdot 90,$$

$$a + b = 90, \quad c + e = 90, \quad a + b + f = 180.$$

It follows that $\triangle ABC$ is a triangle with angle measure sum of 180.

Assume, next, that there is a triangle, say $\triangle ABC$, with angle measure sum 180. Suppose first that $\triangle ABC$ is not a right triangle, and the vertices

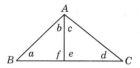

have been renamed if necessary so that $m\angle A \geqslant m\angle B$, $m\angle A \geqslant m\angle C$. Then $m\angle B < 90$, $m\angle C < 90$. Let D be the foot of the perpendicular from A to $\overleftrightarrow{BC}$. Then in terms of notation of the figure we have

$$a + b + c + d + e + f = 180 + 2 \cdot 90 = 360.$$

But $a + b + f \leqslant 180$ and $c + d + e \leqslant 180$. It follows that $a + b + f = 180$, and hence that there is a right triangle with angle measure sum 180.

Suppose given then $\triangle ABC$, a right triangle with angle measure sum 180 and with right angle at B. Let D be the unique point on the A-side of $\overleftrightarrow{BC}$ such that $\overline{CD} \perp \overline{BC}$ and $DC = AB$. In terms of the notation of the figure we have $a + b = 90$, $b + c = 90$, and $a = c$. Also $AB = CD$ and $AC = CA$.

Therefore $\triangle BAC \cong \triangle DCA$. Then $f = d = 90$, $b + c = b + a = 90$, $a + e = a + b = 90$, and $ABCD$ is a rectangle. It then follows from Theorem 7.22 that Euclid's parallel postulate holds. Since the parallel postulate implies the existence of a triangle with angle measure sum 180, and conversely, since the existence of a triangle with angle measure sum 180 implies the parallel postulate, it follows that they are logically equivalent.

Theorem 7.24. If the angle measure sum of one triangle is 180, then the angle measure sum of every triangle is 180.

Proof. Assigned as an exercise.

Theorem 7.25. If the angle measure sum of one triangle is less than 180, then the angle measure sum of every triangle is less than 180.

Proof. Assigned as an exercise.

Theorem 7.26. Given a line L and a point P not on L. If there is only one line through P parallel to L, then Euclid's parallel postulate holds.

Proof. Let a line L and a point P not on L be given. Suppose, contrary to the assertion of the theorem, that there is only one line through P and parallel to L, and that Euclid's parallel postulate does not hold. Then no rectangle exists. Let A and B be points on L and let Q be a point in the plane of P and L so that $ABQP$ is a Saccheri quadrilateral with right angles at A and B. Since $ABPQ$ is not a rectangle, it follows that its angles at P and Q are congruent acute angles. Since the line in the plane of P and L that is perpendicular to $\overrightarrow{PA}$ at P is parallel to $\overleftrightarrow{AB}$, and since there is only one line through P and parallel to $\overleftrightarrow{AB}$, it follows that $\overleftrightarrow{PQ}$ is not parallel to $\overleftrightarrow{AB}$. Then $\overleftrightarrow{PQ}$ intersects $\overleftrightarrow{AB}$ forming a right triangle with an acute exterior angle. Since this contradicts the weak form of the exterior angle theorem, our proof is complete.

Theorem 7.27. Given a line L and a point P not on L. Given a line M and a point Q not on M. If there are two distinct lines through P and parallel to L, then there are two distinct lines through Q and parallel to M.

Proof. Assigned as an exercise.

Exercises 7.6

1. Prove Theorem 7.16.

2. Prove Theorem 7.24.

3. Prove Theorem 7.25.

4. Prove Theorem 7.27.

7.7 Parallel Line Theorems

In this section we accept Euclid's parallel postulate and develop several theorems regarding properties of parallelism in Euclidean geometry. Several of these theorems are converses of theorems in the section on parallelism in neutral geometry.

Theorem 7.28. If two lines are parallel, then any two alternate interior angles determined by a transversal of the lines are congruent.

Proof. Let $\overleftrightarrow{AB}$ and $\overleftrightarrow{CD}$ be two parallel lines and $\overleftrightarrow{BC}$ a transversal of them. Suppose A and D are on opposite sides of $\overleftrightarrow{BC}$. Suppose, contrary

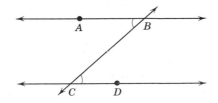

to the assertion of the theorem, that $\angle ABC$ and $\angle BCD$ are not congruent. Then it follows from the protractor postulate that there is a ray $\overrightarrow{BE}$ with E and D on opposite sides of $\overleftrightarrow{BC}$, such that $m\angle EBC = m\angle BCD$. It follows from Theorem 7.6 that $\overleftrightarrow{EB} \parallel \overleftrightarrow{CD}$. Then $\overleftrightarrow{EB}$ and $\overleftrightarrow{AB}$ are distinct lines through B and parallel to $\overleftrightarrow{CD}$. Since this contradicts the parallel postulate, it follows that our supposition that $\angle ABC$ and $\angle BCD$ are not congruent is untenable, and hence that the angles in any pair of alternate interior angles are congruent. This completes the proof.

Theorems 7.29, 7.30, 7.31 follow easily from Theorem 7.28.

Theorem 7.29. If two lines are parallel, then any two corresponding angles determined by a transversal of the lines are congruent.

Theorem 7.30. If two lines are parallel, then any two consecutive interior angles determined by a transversal of them are supplementary.

Theorem 7.31. If a transversal is perpendicular to one of two parallel lines, it is perpendicular to the other also.

7.8 *Parallelograms*

Definition. Two segments are *parallel* if the lines which contain them are parallel.

Definition. A *parallelogram* is a quadrilateral each of whose sides is parallel to the side opposite it.

Theorem 7.32. In any parallelogram, each side is congruent to the side opposite it.

Proof. Assigned as an exercise.

Theorem 7.33. If two sides of a quadrilateral are parallel and congruent, then the quadrilateral is a parallelogram.

Proof. Assigned as an exercise.

Theorem 7.34. If p and q are parallel lines, then all segments perpendicular to both p and q and having one endpoint on p and the other on q, have the same length.

Proof. Assigned as an exercise.

Definition. The *distance between two parallel lines* is the length of a segment which is perpendicular to both of the lines and which has one endpoint on each of the lines. The *distance between a line and itself* is zero.

The message of Theorem 7.34 is sometimes stated as "parallel lines are everywhere equidistant."

The relation of parallelism is useful not only for lines and segments but also for rays. We could define rays to be parallel if they lie on parallel lines. But it is useful for our purpose to distinguish between rays which lie on parallel lines and have the "same direction" and rays which lie on parallel lines and have "opposite directions."

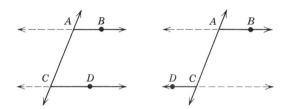

Definitions. Two noncollinear rays are *parallel* if and only if the lines which contain them are parallel and the line determined by their end-points is the edge of a halfplane containing their interiors. Two collinear rays are *parallel* if and only if one of them contains the other. Two non-collinear rays are *antiparallel* if and only if the lines which contain them are parallel and the interiors of the rays lie on opposite sides of the line determined by their endpoints. Two collinear rays are *antiparallel* if and only if neither is a subset of the other.

Exercises 7.8

1. Prove that opposite angles of a parallelogram are congruent.

2. Prove that the diagonals of a parallelogram bisect each other.

3. Prove Theorem 7.32.

4. Prove Theorem 7.33.

5. Prove Theorem 7.34.

6. Given two parallel lines and a transversal of them. Prove that the angle bisectors of two alternate interior angles are antiparallel rays.

7. Given coplanar angles $\angle ABC$ and $\angle DEF$, $\overrightarrow{BA}$ and $\overrightarrow{ED}$ are parallel and non-collinear, $\overrightarrow{BC}$ and $\overrightarrow{EF}$ are parallel and collinear. Prove that $\angle ABC \cong \angle DEF$.

Exercise 7

8. Given coplanar angles $\angle ABC$ and $\angle DEF$, $\overrightarrow{BA}$ and $\overrightarrow{ED}$ are parallel and non-collinear, $\overrightarrow{BC}$ and $\overrightarrow{EF}$ are parallel and noncollinear. Prove that $\angle ABC \cong \angle DEF$.

Exercise 8

9. Given coplanar angles $\angle ABC$ and $\angle DEF$, $\overrightarrow{BA}$ and $\overrightarrow{ED}$ are parallel and non-collinear, $\overrightarrow{BC}$ and $\overrightarrow{EF}$ are antiparallel and collinear. Prove that $\angle ABC$ and $\angle DEF$ are supplementary angles.

Exercise 9

10. Given coplanar angles $\angle ABC$ and $\angle DEF$, $\overrightarrow{BA}$ and $\overrightarrow{ED}$ are parallel and non-collinear, $\overrightarrow{BC}$ and $\overrightarrow{EF}$ are antiparallel and noncollinear. Prove that $\angle ABC$ and $\angle DEF$ are supplementary angles.

Exercise 10

11. Given coplanar angles $\angle ABC$ and $\angle DEF$, $\overrightarrow{BA}$ and $\overrightarrow{ED}$ are antiparallel and noncollinear, $\overrightarrow{BC}$ and $\overrightarrow{EF}$ are antiparallel and noncollinear. Prove that $\angle ABC \cong \angle DEF$.

Exercise 11

12. Given coplanar angles $\angle ABC$ and $\angle DEF$, $\overrightarrow{BA}$ and $\overrightarrow{ED}$ are antiparallel and noncollinear, $\overrightarrow{BC}$ and $\overrightarrow{EF}$ are antiparallel and collinear. Prove that $\angle ABC$ and $\angle DEF$ are congruent angles.

Exercise 12

13. Given coplanar angles $\angle ABC$ and $\angle DEF$, $\overrightarrow{BA}$ and $\overrightarrow{ED}$ are antiparallel and collinear, $\overrightarrow{BC}$ and $\overrightarrow{EF}$ are antiparallel and collinear. Draw an appropriate figure and prove that $\angle ABC \cong \angle DEF$.

14. Given noncoplanar angles $\angle ABC$ and $\angle DEF$, $\overrightarrow{BA}$ and $\overrightarrow{ED}$ are parallel and noncollinear, $\overrightarrow{BC}$ and $\overrightarrow{EF}$ are parallel and noncollinear. Prove that $\angle ABC \cong \angle DEF$. (*Hint:* Use several of the theorems regarding parallelograms and the S.S.S. congruence theorem.)

7.9 The Triangle Angle Measure Sum Theorem

Theorem 7.35. The sum of the measures of the angles of any triangle is 180.

Proof. Let $\triangle ABC$ be given. Let $\overleftrightarrow{DE}$ be a line in the plane of $\triangle ABC$ such that A is between D and E, $\overleftrightarrow{DE} \parallel \overleftrightarrow{BC}$, and D and C are on opposite sides of $\overleftrightarrow{AB}$. Then $\angle B \cong \angle DAB$, $\angle C \cong \angle EAC$ and $m\angle A + m\angle B + m\angle C = m\angle A + m\angle DAB + m\angle EAC = 180$. Since $\triangle ABC$ is an arbitrary triangle, the proof is complete.

Alternate Proof. Use Theorems 7.21 and 7.19.

Exercises 7.9

1. Prove: The sum of the measures of the angles of a convex quadrilateral is 360.

2. Prove: The sum of the measures of the angles of a convex n-gon is $(n-2)180$.

3. Given $\triangle ABC$. D is the midpoint of $\overline{AB}$, E is between A and C, and $\overline{DE} \parallel \overline{BC}$. L is a line through E and parallel to $\overline{AB}$. Prove that L intersects $\overleftrightarrow{BC}$ in an interior point of $\overline{BC}$.

4. Given $\triangle ABC$. D is the midpoint of $\overline{AB}$, E is between A and C, and $\overline{DE} \parallel \overline{BC}$. Prove that E is the midpoint of $\overline{AC}$.

7.10 Similarity

Definition. Let n be a natural number. A one-to-one correspondence between the vertices of two convex polygons, each with n sides (or between the vertices of a convex polygon and themselves), such that corresponding angles are congruent and such that the measures of corresponding sides are proportional is called a *similarity*, and the two polygons are said to be *similar* to each other.

Notation. If $A_1 A_2 \ldots A_n$ and $B_1 B_2 \ldots B_n$ are polygons with n sides, then the statement that "$A_1 A_2 \ldots A_n \leftrightarrow B_1 B_2 \ldots B_n$ is a similarity" is written $A_1 A_2 \ldots A_n \sim B_1 B_2 \ldots B_n$.

Definition. A similarity between two convex polygons is called a *congruence* if and only if the constant of proportionality for the measures of the corresponding sides is 1 (that is, if and only if the corresponding sides are congruent).

Theorem 7.36. The relation of similarity for convex polygons is reflexive, symmetric, and transitive.

Proof. Assigned as an exercise.

Theorem 7.37. If a line parallel to one side of a triangle bisects a second side, then it also bisects the third side.

Proof. Let $\triangle ABC$ and line L parallel to $\overline{BC}$ and bisecting $\overline{AB}$ at D be given. Since L is parallel to $\overline{BC}$, and $\overline{AB}$ is not, it follows that L is

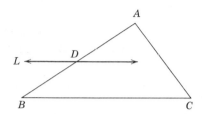

distinct from $\overleftrightarrow{AB}$. But a line in the plane of a triangle which intersects one side of a triangle also intersects another side of the triangle (Theorem 6.5). Since L does not contain A and since it does not intersect $\overleftrightarrow{BC}$, it follows that L contains an interior point of $\overline{AC}$, call it E. Let M be a line in the plane of $\triangle ABC$ through E and parallel to $\overleftrightarrow{AB}$. By an argument similar to that just applied to L, it follows that M intersects $\overline{BC}$ in an

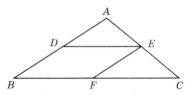

interior point, call it F. Then $BFED$ is a parallelogram and it follows that $EF = DB = AD$. Also $\angle EAD \cong \angle CEF$, $\angle ADE \cong \angle DBF \cong \angle EFC$. Therefore $\triangle ADE \cong \triangle EFC$ and $AE = EC$. This completes the proof.

Theorem 7.38. If lines parallel to one side of a triangle intersect a second side in interior points which divide that side into n congruent segments, then those parallel lines also divide the third side into n congruent segments.

Proof. We write the proof for $n = 3$ using the labeled figure. Suppose B_1 and B_2 are trisection points of $\overline{AB}$, that $\overline{B_1C_1}$ and $\overline{B_2C_2}$ are parallel to $\overline{BC}$, and that C_1 and C_2 are on $\overleftrightarrow{AC}$. It follows from Theorem 6.5 that

C_1 and C_2 are interior points of $\overline{AC}$. Since $\overline{B_1C_1}$ and $\overline{B_2C_2}$ are both parallel to $\overline{BC}$, it follows that they are parallel to each other. It then

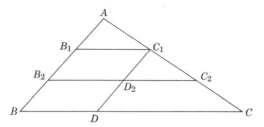

follows from Theorem 7.37 that $AC_1 = C_1C_2$. Let $\overleftrightarrow{C_1D}$ be the line in the plane of $\triangle ABC$, passing through C_1 parallel to $\overrightarrow{AB}$ and containing a point D on $\overrightarrow{BC}$. Then D is an interior point of $\overline{BC}$. Also $\overline{C_1D}$ intersects $\overline{B_2C_2}$ in a point; call it D_2. Then $C_1D_2 = B_1B_2 = B_2B = D_2D$, and it follows from Theorem 7.37 that $C_1C_2 = C_2C$. Therefore C_1 and C_2 are trisection points of $\overline{AC}$ and the proof is complete.

Theorem 7.39. Given $\triangle ABC$, D is an interior point of $\overline{AB}$, E is an interior point of $\overline{AC}$, and $\overline{DE} \parallel \overline{BC}$. If $(AD, DB, AB) \underset{p}{=} (m, n, m + n)$, where m and n are natural numbers, then $(AE, EC, AC) \underset{p}{=} (m, n, m + n)$, that is, the lengths of the segments into which $\overline{AB}$ is divided by the point D are proportional to the lengths of the segments into which $\overline{AC}$ is divided by the point E.

Proof. Assigned as an exercise.

Theorem 7.40. Given $\triangle ABC$, D is an interior point of $\overline{AB}$, and E is an interior point of $\overline{AC}$. If $\overline{DE} \parallel \overline{BC}$, then $(AD, AB) \underset{p}{=} (AE, AC)$.

Proof. The case in which AD/AB is a rational number follows from Theorem 7.39. Suppose, then, that AD/AB is an irrational number x.

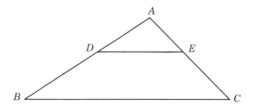

Suppose, contrary to the assertion of the theorem, that $AE/AC = y \neq x$. Suppose, to be definite, that $y > x$. Let m and n be natural numbers such that $x < m/(m + n) < y$. Let $m + n = p + 1$. Let $D_1, D_2, D_3, \ldots, D_p$ be the p interior points of $\overline{AB}$ which divide it into $m + n$ congruent segments, and $E_1, E_2, \ldots, E_p$ the p interior points of $\overline{AC}$ which divide it into $m + n$ congruent segments. Now $AD_m/AB = m/(m + n) = AE_m/AC$. Then $\overline{D_mE_m}$ is parallel to $\overline{BC}$. If it were not, then there would be a point E' between A and C, different from E_m such that $\overline{D_mE'} \parallel \overline{BC}$. Then $AE'/AC = m/(m + n)$, $AE' = [m/(m + n)] \cdot AC = AE_m$ and $E' = E_m$. (Contradiction.) Therefore $\overline{D_mE_m} \parallel \overline{BC}$.

Now $AD = x \cdot AB < [m/(m + n)] \cdot AB = AD_m$, and $AE = y \cdot AC > [m/(m + n)] \cdot AC = AE_m$. It follows that E is on the C-side of $\overleftrightarrow{D_mE_m}$ and that D is on the A-side of $\overleftrightarrow{D_mE_m}$. Therefore $\overline{DE}$ intersects $\overleftrightarrow{D_mE_m}$ and is not contained in it. Therefore $\overline{DE}$ is not parallel to $\overline{BC}$. Since this contradicts one of the hypotheses of the theorem, it follows that $AE/AC = AD/AB$. Then $AD = [AB/AC] \cdot AE$ and $AB = [AB/AC] \cdot AC$. It follows that $(AD, AB) \underset{\mathrm{p}}{=} (AE, AC)$ and the proof is complete.

Theorem 7.41. If coplanar and parallel lines $L, M, N, \ldots$, are cut by two transversals T_1 and T_2, the lengths of the segments formed on T_1 are proportional to the lengths of the corresponding segments on T_2.

Proof. We write a proof for the special case suggested by the figure.

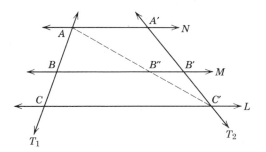

Using Theorem 7.40 we have $(AB, AC) \underset{\mathrm{p}}{=} (AB'', AC')$ and $(C'B'', C'A) \underset{\mathrm{p}}{=} (C'B', C'A')$. Let $k_1 = AC/AC'$, $k_2 = C'A/C'A'$. Then

$$AB = k_1 \cdot AB'' = k_1 \cdot (AC' - C'B'') = k_1(k_2 \cdot C'A' - k_2 \cdot C'B'),$$

$$AB = k_1k_2 \cdot (C'A' - C'B') = k_1k_2 \cdot A'B'.$$

Similarly $BC = k_1k_2 \cdot B'C'$ and $AC = k_1k_2 \cdot A'C'$. It follows that $(AB, BC, AC) \underset{\mathrm{p}}{=} (A'B', B'C', A'C')$.

Theorem 7.42. If a triangle and a positive number k are given, there is a triangle similar to the given triangle with proportionality constant k.

Proof. Let a positive number k and a triangle, $\triangle ABC$, be given. Let D be the unique point on $\overrightarrow{AB}$ such that $AD/AB = k$. Let E be the point in which the line through D and parallel to $\overline{BC}$ meets $\overrightarrow{AC}$. Then $AE/AC = k$ (Theorem 7.40). Let F be the unique point on $\overrightarrow{BA}$ such that $BF/AB = k$.

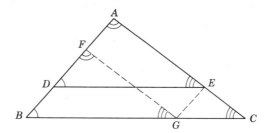

Let G be the unique point on $\overrightarrow{BC}$ in which the line through F and parallel to $\overline{AC}$ meets $\overrightarrow{BC}$. Then $BG/BC = k$.

Consider now $ADE \leftrightarrow FBG$. It follows from the A.S.A. theorem that $\triangle ADE \cong \triangle FBG$. Therefore $DE = BG$. Then

$$AD = k \cdot AB, \quad AE = k \cdot AC,$$

$$DE = BG = k \cdot BC, \quad \text{and} \quad (AD, DE, AE) \underset{p}{=} (AB, BC, CA).$$

Also $\angle A \cong \angle A$, $\angle ADE \cong \angle ABC$, $\angle AED \cong \angle ACB$. Therefore $\triangle ADE \sim \triangle ABC$ with proportionality constant k.

Theorem 7.43 (*The S.S.S. Similarity Theorem*). If there is a correspondence between two triangles such that lengths of corresponding sides are proportional, then that correspondence is a similarity.

Proof. Let $\triangle ABC$ and $\triangle A'B'C'$ be given. Suppose there is a number k such that $AB = k \cdot A'B'$, $BC = k \cdot B'C'$, $CA = k \cdot C'A'$. Let $\triangle A''B''C''$ be a

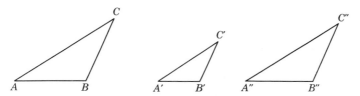

triangle similar to $A'B'C'$ with constant of proportionality k. Then $A''B'' = k \cdot A'B'$, $B''C'' = k \cdot B'C'$, $C''A'' = k \cdot C'A'$, $\angle A'' \cong \angle A'$, $\angle B'' \cong \angle B'$, $\angle C'' \cong \angle C'$. Also it follows from the S.S.S. congruence theorem that $\triangle ABC \cong A''B''C''$. Then $\angle A \cong \angle A'$, $\angle B \cong \angle B'$, $\angle C \cong \angle C'$. Why? Therefore $\triangle ABC \sim \triangle A'B'C'$.

Theorem 7.44 (*The S.A.S. Similarity Theorem*). If there is a correspondence between two triangles such that an angle of one triangle is congruent to the corresponding angle of the other triangle, and the lengths of the two sides which include that angle in the first triangle are proportional to the lengths of the corresponding sides of the other triangle, then that correspondence is a similarity.

Proof. Let $\triangle ABC$, $\triangle A'B'C'$ and $ABC \leftrightarrow A'B'C'$ be given. Suppose $\angle A \cong \angle A'$, $AB = k \cdot A'B'$, $AC = k \cdot A'C'$. Let $\triangle A''B''C''$ be a triangle such that $A''B''C'' \leftrightarrow A'B'C'$ is a similarity with constant of proportionality k. Then $\triangle ABC \cong \triangle A''B''C''$. It follows that $\angle B \cong \angle B'$, $\angle C \cong \angle C'$, $(AB, AC, BC) \underset{p}{=} (A'B', A'C', B'C')$, and that $\triangle ABC \sim \triangle A'B'C'$.

Theorem 7.45 (*The A.A. Similarity Theorem*). If there is a correspondence between two triangles such that two angles of one triangle are congruent to two angles of the other triangle, then that correspondence is a similarity.

Proof. Let $\triangle ABC$, $\triangle A'B'C'$, and the correspondence $ABC \leftrightarrow A'B'C'$ be given. Suppose $\angle A \cong \angle A'$, $\angle B \cong \angle B'$. Let $\triangle A''B''C''$ be a triangle such that $A''B''C'' \leftrightarrow A'B'C'$ is a similarity with proportionality constant $k = AB/A'B'$. Then $A''B'' = k \cdot A'B'$, $AB = k \cdot A'B'$, and it follows from the A.S.A. theorem that $\triangle ABC \cong \triangle A''B''C''$. Then

$$(AB, BC, CA) \underset{p}{=} (A''B'', B''C'', C''A'') \underset{p}{=} (A'B', B'C', C'A'),$$

$$\angle A \cong \angle A'' \cong \angle A', \quad \angle B \cong \angle B'' \cong \angle B', \quad \angle C \cong \angle C'' \cong \angle C',$$

and the proof is complete.

Theorem 7.46. If $\triangle ABC$ is a right triangle with $m\angle ACB = 90$, and if D is the foot of the perpendicular from C to $\overleftrightarrow{AB}$, then $\triangle ABC \sim \triangle ACD \sim \triangle CBD$.

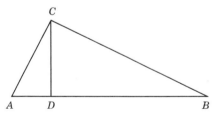

Proof. It follows from the triangle angle measure sum theorem that $\angle A$ and $\angle B$ are acute angles. Therefore $D \neq A$ and $D \neq B$. We assert that D is between A and B. (If A were between D and B, then $\triangle ADC$ would be a triangle with an exterior angle whose measure is less than the measure of one of the nonadjacent interior angles. This would contradict the exterior angle theorem. Similarly, it may be shown that B is not between A and D.)

Consider $ABC \leftrightarrow ACD$, a correspondence between the vertices of $\triangle ABC$ and the vertices of $\triangle ACD$. Since $\angle A \cong \angle A$ and $\angle ACB \cong \angle ADC$, it follows from the A.A. similarity theorem that $\triangle ABC \sim \triangle ACD$. Similarly, since $\angle B \cong \angle B$ and $\angle ACB \cong \angle CDB$, it follows that $\triangle ABC \sim \triangle CBD$.

Theorem 7.47 (*Pythagorean Theorem*). If $\triangle ABC$ is a right triangle with $m\angle ACB = 90$, then $(AC)^2 + (CB)^2 = (AB)^2$.

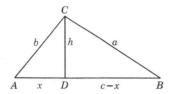

Proof. Let $\triangle ABC$ with $m\angle C = 90$ be given. Let D be the foot of the perpendicular from C to $\overline{AB}$. Let $AB = c$, $BC = a$, $CA = b$, $CD = h$, $AD = x$. Then $BD = c - x$. It follows from Theorem 7.46 that $\triangle ADC \sim \triangle ACB \sim \triangle CDB$. Therefore $(x, h, b) \underset{\overline{p}}{=} (b, a, c) \underset{\overline{p}}{=} (h, c - x, a)$. Then $(x, b) \underset{\overline{p}}{=} (b, c)$ and $xc = b^2$. Also $(a, c) \underset{\overline{p}}{=} (c - x, a)$ and $c(c - x) = a^2$. Adding, we get $xc + c(c - x) = a^2 + b^2$, or $a^2 + b^2 = c^2$.

Theorem 7.48 (*Converse of the Pythagorean Theorem*). If $\triangle ABC$ is a triangle such that $(AC)^2 + (CB)^2 = (AB)^2$, then $\triangle ABC$ is a right triangle with $m\angle ACB = 90$.

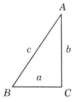 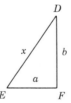

Proof. Let $\triangle ABC$ be given. Let $a = BC$, $b = AC$, $c = AB$. Suppose $a^2 + b^2 = c^2$. We are to prove that $m\angle C = 90$.

Let $\triangle DEF$ be a right triangle with $m\angle F = 90$, $EF = a$, $FD = b$, and $DE = x$. (The fact that there is such a triangle follows easily from the incidence, ruler, and protractor postulates.) It follows from the Pythagorean theorem that $a^2 + b^2 = x^2$. Then $x^2 = c^2$ and $x = c$. It follows from the S.S.S. congruence theorem that $\triangle ABC \cong \triangle DEF$. Then $\angle C \cong \angle F$ and $m\angle C = 90$.

Exercises 7.10

1. Given parallel lines $\overleftrightarrow{AP}$, $\overleftrightarrow{BQ}$, $\overleftrightarrow{CR}$, $\overleftrightarrow{DS}$ such that A, B, C, D are collinear in the order named, and P, Q, R, S are collinear in the order named. If $AB = 3$, $BC = 4$, $CD = 5$, $QR = 6$, find PQ and RS.

2. Given $\triangle ABC$ with $m\angle C = 90$ and D the foot of the perpendicular from C to $\overline{AB}$. If $BC = 6$ and $AC = 8$, find CD.

3. Given real numbers u and v such that $0 < v < u$. Prove that there is a right triangle with sides of length $2uv$, $u^2 - v^2$, $u^2 + v^2$.

4. Given $\triangle ABC$ with $AC = BC = 10$ and $AB = 5$. Find the distance from C to $\overleftrightarrow{AB}$.

5. Given $\triangle ABC$ with $m\angle A = 30$, $m\angle B = 60$. Prove that $(AC, BC, AB) \underset{p}{=} (\sqrt{3}, 1, 2)$.

6. Prove Theorem 7.36.

7. Prove Theorem 7.39.

CHAPTER 8

Affine Geometry

8.1 Introduction

Euclid's parallel postulate has played an important role in the development of non-Euclidean geometry, indeed, in the development of the modern point of view toward the entire field of mathematics. The modern mathematician recognizes the existence of several algebras and several geometries, each based on its own set of postulates.

In this chapter we shall consider affine geometry. By affine geometry we mean geometry based on the incidence postulates of Chapter 2 and the Euclidean parallel postulate (Postulate 19). In a sense Euclidean geometry is an affine geometry. The postulational basis of Euclidean geometry includes the affine geometry postulates and other postulates which provide a basis for ordering points on a line and for measuring segments and angles. The study of affine geometry involves the familiar qualitative properties of parallel lines and planes in Euclidean geometry. Since the postulational basis for this chapter includes all of the incidence postulates of Chapter 2, it should be clear that all of the theorems of that chapter are affine geometry theorems. There are no figures in this chapter. The reader should have paper and pencil at hand and should sketch at least one figure for each theorem.

8.2 Parallel and Intersecting Lines

We begin by adopting a modern definition of parallel lines and re-stating the parallel postulate.

Definition. If L and M are lines (distinct or not), then L is parallel to M, and we write $L \parallel M$, if and only if L and M are coplanar lines and the intersection of L and M is not a set consisting of a single point.

According to this definition, every line is parallel to itself. This, of course, is a departure from traditional geometry. We adopt this definition at this point since its advantages seem to outweigh its disadvantages.

Postulate 19 (*Euclidean Parallel Postulate; Alternate Form*). If P is a point and L is a line, then there is one and only one line through P and parallel to L.

For the purposes of Chapter 8 there are ten postulates, the nine postulates of Chapter 2 and Postulate 19.

Postulate 19 differs from Postulate 18 in that Postulate 19 makes an assertion about a point P and a line L when P is on L, whereas Postulate 18 does not. Considered as an assumption, Postulate 19 assumes more than Postulate 18. The "extra assumption" is, however, not significant. For if P is a point on a line L, then it follows from the incidence postulates of Chapter 2 that there is one and only one line through P and parallel to L.

Theorem 8.1. If L is a line, P is a point, and Q is a plane containing L and P, then there is one and only one line M in Q such that M contains P and is parallel to L.

Proof. If $P \notin L$, then Q is the unique (one and only one) plane containing P and L, and M is the unique line through P and parallel to L. Since $M \parallel L$, it follows that M and L are coplanar, and hence that they are subsets of a plane R. Since R contains L and P, it follows that $R = Q$ and $M \subset Q$.

If $P \in L$, then Q may be any plane containing L. If M is any line containing P, and if $M \neq L$, then M is not parallel to L. Since L is parallel to itself, it follows that L is the unique line through P which is parallel to L, and it lies in the given plane Q.

Theorem 8.2. If L, M, N are three distinct lines which are neither coplanar nor concurrent, and if each pair of these lines are coplanar, then each pair of them are parallel.

Proof. Suppose L and M lie in plane P, M and N lie in plane Q, and N and L lie in plane R. Since L, M, N are noncoplanar, it follows that P, Q, R are three distinct planes. The intersection of P and Q is the line M. The intersection of Q and R is the line N. The intersection of R and P is the line L.

Suppose that two of these three lines, say L and M, meet in a point X. Since $X \in L$, it follows that $X \in P$, $X \in R$; since $X \in M$, it follows that $X \in P$, $X \in Q$. It follows that if two of the three lines L, M, N intersect, then all three of them are concurrent. Therefore, if L, M, N are three distinct lines which are neither coplanar nor concurrent, and if each pair of them are coplanar, then each pair of them are parallel.

Theorem 8.3. If L and M are distinct parallel lines, and if X is a point not in the plane of L and M, then there is a unique line N through X and parallel to L and M.

Proof. Let P, Q, R be the planes determined by L and M, L and X, and M and X, respectively. Since $X \notin P$, $X \in Q$, $X \in R$, it follows that $P \neq Q$ and $P \neq R$. Since L and M do not lie in the same plane with X, it follows that $Q \neq R$. Since Q and R are distinct planes which intersect, it follows that their intersection is a line. Call that line N. Then L, M, N are three distinct lines which are neither coplanar nor concurrent, and each pair of these three lines are coplanar. It follows from Theorem 8.2 that $N \parallel L$ and $N \parallel M$.

To prove uniqueness, suppose N' is a line through X such that $N' \parallel L$ and $N' \parallel M$. Since $X \in N'$ and $N' \parallel L$, it follows that N' lies in Q. Since $X \in N'$ and $N' \parallel M$, it follows that N' lies in R. It follows that N' is the line of intersection of Q and R. Therefore $N' = N$ and this proves the uniqueness of the line N.

Theorem 8.4. If L, M, N are lines such that $L \parallel M$ and $M \parallel N$, then $L \parallel N$.

Proof. If L, M, N are not distinct lines, the conclusion of the theorem is immediate.

Suppose, then, that L, M, N are three distinct lines. We consider first the case in which L, M, N are coplanar lines. Suppose L is not parallel to N. Since L and N are distinct coplanar lines, it follows that L intersects N in some point P. Then L and N are two distinct lines through P and parallel to M. Since this contradicts the parallel postulate, our supposition that L is not parallel to N is untenable. Therefore, if L, M, N are distinct coplanar lines satisfying the hypotheses of the theorem, then $L \parallel N$.

Suppose, next, that L, M, N are distinct, noncoplanar lines such that $L \parallel M$ and $M \parallel N$, and that, contrary to the assertion of the theorem, L is not parallel to N. Let X be any point of N which is not on L. Let N' be the unique line containing X and parallel to L and M (Theorem 8.3). It follows from the parallel postulate that $N' = N$ and hence that $N \parallel L$. This completes the proof.

We note at this point that parallelism for lines is an equivalence relation. If L is any line, then it follows immediately from our definition of parallel lines that $L \parallel L$. If L and M are lines such that $L \parallel M$, then it follows immediately from our definition of parallel lines that $M \parallel L$. The transitive property of parallelism for lines follows from Theorem 8.4.

Theorem 8.5. If L, M, N are distinct coplanar lines such that L intersects M, and $M \parallel N$, then L intersects N.

Proof. Let L, M, N, lines satisfying the hypotheses of the theorem, be given. Let X be the point in which L intersects M. If L does not intersect N, then $L \parallel N$ and there are two distinct lines, L and M, through X and parallel to N. Since this contradicts the parallel postulate, it follows that L intersects N, and the proof is complete.

8.3   *Parallel and Intersecting Lines and Planes*

Definition. A line L and a plane P are *parallel* to each other, and we write $L \parallel P$, or $P \parallel L$, if and only if the intersection of L and P is not a set consisting of a single point.

Definition. A plane P and a plane Q are *parallel* if and only if $P = Q$ or $P \cap Q = \varnothing$.

It follows immediately from this definition and our incidence postulates that if L is a line and P is a plane, then either (1) $L \cap P = \varnothing$, in which case $L \parallel P$, or (2) $L \subset P$, in which case $L \parallel P$, or (3) the intersection of L and P is a set which contains one and only one point, in which case L is not parallel to P.

Theorem 8.6. If L and M are distinct parallel lines and P is a plane, then P is parallel to L if and only if P is parallel to M.

Proof. Let Q be the unique plane which contains L and M. Suppose P is parallel to L. There are two possibilities. The intersection of P and L is either the null set or it is the line L. Suppose P contains L. There are two possibilities. Either $P = Q$ or $P \neq Q$. If P contains L and $P = Q$, then P contains M, and P is parallel to M. If P contains L and $P \neq Q$, then the intersection of P and Q is the line L. Why? Then the intersection of P and M is the null set and P is parallel to M.

Suppose, next, that the intersection of P and L is the null set. There are two possibilities. The intersection of P and M is the null set or it is not. If the intersection of P and M is the null set, then P is parallel to M, as we wanted to prove. If the intersection of P and M is not the null set, then it is either a set consisting of a single point, say X, or it is the entire line M. If the intersection is the line M, then P contains M and is parallel to it, as we wanted to prove.

Suppose, then, contrary to the assertion of the theorem, that the intersection of P and L is the null set and that the intersection of P and M is a set consisting of a single point, call it X. Then P and Q are distinct planes whose intersection contains the point X but does not contain the line M. It follows that the intersection of P and Q is a line N, that $N \neq M$, and that $N \neq L$. Since N lies in Q, it follows from Theorem 8.5 that N intersects L. Since N is a subset of P, it follows that P intersects L, which is a contradiction.

This completes the proof that if P is parallel to L it is also parallel to M. Similarly, it may be proved that if P is parallel to M it is also parallel to L. Therefore P is parallel to L if and only if it is parallel to M.

Theorem 8.7. If L and M are distinct parallel lines and if P is a plane, then P intersects L and does not contain it if and only if P intersects M and does not contain it.

Proof. Assigned as an exercise.

Theorem 8.8. If P and Q are distinct parallel planes and if L is a line which intersects P but is not contained in it, then L intersects Q and is not contained in it.

Proof. Let distinct parallel planes P and Q be given. Let L be a line which is not contained in P but which intersects P in a point X. Let Y be any point of Q. If Y is a point of L, then L intersects Q and there is no more to prove. If Y is not a point of L, let M be the unique line through Y and parallel to L. Then it follows from Theorem 8.7 that M intersects P in some point Z. Since M intersects Q and is not contained in it, it follows from Theorem 8.7 that L intersects Q, and the proof is complete.

Theorem 8.9. Let P, Q, R be three distinct planes such that P is parallel to Q. The intersection of P and R is a line if and only if the intersection of Q and R is a line.

Proof. Let distinct planes P, Q, R be given such that P is parallel to Q and such that the intersection of P and R is a line L. Suppose, contrary to the assertion of the theorem, that the intersection of Q and R is not a line. Then Q is parallel to R. Why? Let X be any point of L. Let M be a line different from L which passes through X and lies in R. Then the intersection of M and P is the point X. Since M is a line which intersects P and is not contained in it, it follows from Theorem 8.8 that M is a line which intersects Q and is not contained in it. Since M is a subset of R, it follows that R intersects Q. Since R contains X and Q does not contain

X, it follows that $R \neq Q$. Therefore the intersection of R and Q is a line. Similarly, it may be shown that if the intersection of Q and R is a line, then the intersection of P and R is also a line.

Theorem 8.10. Let P, Q, R be three distinct planes such that P is parallel to Q. If the intersection of P and R is not a line, then the intersection of Q and R is not a line.

Proof. This follows immediately from Theorem 8.9.

Theorem 8.11. Let P, Q, R be planes such that $P \parallel Q$. Then $P \parallel R$ if and only if $Q \parallel R$.

Proof. This follows immediately from Theorem 8.9.

Theorem 8.12. Parallelism for planes is an equivalence relation.

Proof. This follows immediately from Theorem 8.11 and our definition of parallel planes.

Theorem 8.13. Two distinct intersecting planes are not both parallel to the same plane.

Proof. Assigned as an exercise.

Theorem 8.14. If two distinct intersecting lines are parallel to a given plane, then the plane determined by the intersecting lines is parallel to the given plane.

Proof. Let L and M be distinct intersecting lines, each parallel to a plane P. Let Q be the unique plane containing L and M. If $Q = P$, then $Q \parallel P$ as asserted in the theorem.

Suppose, then, that $Q \neq P$ and that Q is not parallel to P. Then the intersection of P and Q is a line N. Then L, M, N are coplanar lines. Why? Since L and M are distinct intersecting lines, it follows that N is not parallel to both of them. Why? If N is not parallel to L, then it intersects it in one and only one point. If N intersects L in a unique point, then L intersects P in a unique point and L is not parallel to P. Since $L \parallel P$, it follows that if $Q \neq P$, then $Q \parallel P$, and the proof is complete.

Theorem 8.15. Let P and Q be planes. Let L and M be distinct lines in P which intersect in a point X which is not in Q. If L' and M' are lines in Q, and if $L' \parallel L$, $M' \parallel M$, then $P \parallel Q$.

Proof. Let L, M, P, Q, L', M', as in the statement of the theorem, be given. Then it follows from Theorem 8.6 that $L' \parallel P$ and $M' \parallel P$. Since $L' \parallel L$, $M' \parallel M$, and L and M are distinct intersecting lines, it follows from the parallel postulate that $L' \neq M'$. If L' were parallel to M', then it would follow from the transitive property of parallelism for lines that L is parallel to M. But L and M are distinct intersecting lines. Therefore L'

and M' are distinct intersecting lines, each parallel to P. It follows from Theorem 8.14 that Q is parallel to P.

Theorem 8.16. If P is a plane and X is a point, there is a unique plane Q containing X and parallel to P.

Proof. If P is a plane containing X, then P is a plane containing X and parallel to P. If P is a plane containing X and Q is any plane distinct from P and containing X, then the intersection of P and Q is a line and Q is not parallel to P. Therefore if P is a plane containing X, there is a unique plane R containing X and parallel to P. The unique plane R is the plane P.

Let P be a plane and X a point not in P. Let Y be a point in P. Let L and M be lines in P which intersect at Y. Let L' and M' be the unique lines through X which are parallel to L and M, respectively. Let Q be the unique plane determined by L' and M'. Then it follows from Theorem 8.15 that Q is parallel to P.

Let Q' be any plane distinct from Q and containing X. Then the intersection of Q and Q' is a line and Q' is not parallel to Q. It follows that Q' is not parallel to P. (For if $Q' \parallel P$ and $P \parallel Q$, then $Q' \parallel Q$, a contradiction. See Theorem 8.12.) It follows that there is a unique plane Q containing X and parallel to P.

Exercises 8.3

1. Prove Theorem 8.7.

2. Prove Theorem 8.13.

3. Prove: If L and M are distinct lines in a plane P, and if every line in P which intersects L and is distinct from it also intersects M and is distinct from it, then $L \parallel M$.

4. Given a plane P and a point X not in P. Prove that there is a plane Q which contains all the lines which pass through X and are parallel to P.

5. Given a plane P, a line L parallel to P, and a line M parallel to L. Prove that if M intersects P, then M is contained in P.

6. Given two distinct planes P and Q. Prove that if every line which intersects P and does not lie in it also intersects Q and does not lie in it, then $P \parallel Q$.

7. Given a plane P and a line L which intersects P and is not contained in it. Prove that if Q is any plane which contains L, then P and Q are distinct intersecting planes.

8. Given a plane P, a line L which is parallel to P and is not contained in it, and a plane Q which intersects L but does not contain it. Prove that P and Q are distinct intersecting planes.

9. Given skew lines L and M. Prove that there is a unique plane which contains L and is parallel to M.

10. Given skew lines L and M. Prove that there is a unique pair of parallel planes P and Q with P containing L and Q containing M.

CHAPTER 9

Coordinates in a Plane

9.1 Introduction

Let a plane be given and suppose unless we specify otherwise that all sets of points under consideration are subsets of this plane. Let a unit-pair $\{A, A'\}$ be given and suppose that all distances are relative to this unit-pair unless otherwise indicated.

Let $\overleftrightarrow{OX}$ and $\overleftrightarrow{OY}$ be perpendicular lines intersecting in the point O. Let I and J be points on $\overleftrightarrow{OX}$ and $\overleftrightarrow{OY}$, respectively, such that $OI = OJ = 1$. There is a unique coordinate system on $\overrightarrow{OX}$ with origin O and unit-point I. We call this the x-coordinate system. There is a unique coordinate system on $\overrightarrow{OY}$ with origin O and unit-point J. We call this the y-coordinate system. Let P be an arbitrary point. There is a unique line m_1 through P and parallel to $\overleftrightarrow{OY}$ and a unique line m_2 through P and parallel to $\overleftrightarrow{OX}$. Let P_1 be the unique point in which m_1 intersects $\overleftrightarrow{OX}$ and P_2 the unique point in which m_2 intersects $\overleftrightarrow{OY}$. The x-coordinate or abscissa of P is by definition the coordinate of P_1 in the x-coordinate system on $\overleftrightarrow{OX}$. The y-coordinate or ordinate of P is by definition the coordinate of P_2 in the y-coordinate system on $\overleftrightarrow{OY}$. We sometimes write $P(a, b)$ to indicate that the abscissa and ordinate of P are a and b, respectively. Since there is a one-to-one correspondence between the set of all ordered pairs of real numbers and the set of all points in the given plane, it is clear that symbols used to denote the ordered pairs may be used also to denote the corresponding points. Thus the point $(3, 4)$ is the point whose abscissa is 3 and whose ordinate is 4.

The lines $\overleftrightarrow{OX}$ and $\overleftrightarrow{OY}$ are called the coordinate axes. The plane containing these lines is called the xy-plane. The one-to-one correspondence which matches each point in the plane with an ordered pair of real numbers is called the xy-coordinate system. If $P = (a, b)$, then a and b, or (a, b), are the xy-coordinates of P.

The coordinate axes separate the rest of the xy-plane into four mutually disjoint sets called quadrants. It is customary to number them as I, II, III, IV. Quadrant I is the set of all points (x, y) such that $x > 0$ and $y > 0$. Quadrant II is the set of all points (x, y) such that $x < 0$ and $y > 0$. Quadrant III is the set of all points (x, y) such that $x < 0$ and $y < 0$. Quadrant IV is the set of all points (x, y) such that $x > 0$ and $y < 0$.

9.2 *Graphs*

A *graph* is a set of points. To draw a graph, or to plot a graph, is to draw a picture that suggests which points belong to the graph. If the graph contains only a few points, it may be desirable to write the coordinates of each point beside the dot which represents it. If there are infinitely many points in the graph, the picture may contain segments or curves, sometimes shaded regions or arrows, to indicate which points belong to the graph. Sometimes a small open circle is used to indicate that the endpoint of a segment does not belong to a graph.

Example 1. Plot the points $A(2, 0)$, $B(-3, 2)$, $C(-1, -3)$.

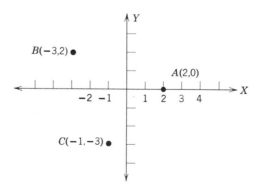

Example 2. Draw the graph of the set $\{(x, y): x = 3 \text{ and } -1 \leqslant y < 2\}$.

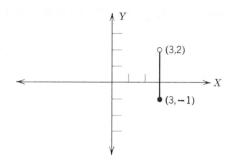

Example 3. Draw the graph of the set $\{(x, y): 2 \leqslant x \leqslant 3 \text{ or } 1 \leqslant y \leqslant 2\}$.

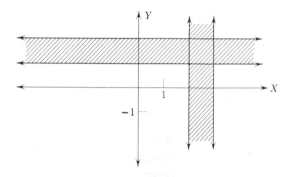

9.3   *A Distance Formula*

Theorem 9.1. If $P(x_1, y_1)$ and $Q(x_2, y_2)$ are points in the xy-plane, then
$$PQ = \sqrt{(x_2 - x_1)^2 + (y_2 - y_1)^2}.$$

Proof.

Case 1. $P = Q$. In this case $x_1 = x_2$, $y_1 = y_2$ and the distance formula yields 0 as it should.
$$PQ = \sqrt{(x_2 - x_1)^2 + (y_2 - y_1)^2} = \sqrt{0^2 + 0^2} = 0.$$

Case 2. $x_1 = x_2$ and $y_1 \neq y_2$. In this case P and Q are distinct points on a vertical line (that is, a line parallel to $\overleftrightarrow{O\,Y}$). Then $P_1(0, y_1)$ and $Q_1(0, y_2)$ are either the points P and Q, or they are the feet of the perpendiculars from P and Q to $\overleftrightarrow{O\,Y}$. If $P_1 = P$ and $Q_1 = Q$, we obtain the following by using our knowledge of the relationship of distance to coordinates in the y-coordinate system:
$$PQ = P_1Q_1 = |y_2 - y_1| = \sqrt{(x_2 - x_1)^2 + (y_2 - y_1)^2}.$$

If P and Q do not lie on the y-axis, then PQQ_1P_1 is a rectangle and we get the desired result by using the fact that its opposite sides are congruent.

$$PQ = P_1Q_1 = |y_2 - y_1| = \sqrt{(x_2 - x_1)^2 + (y_2 - y_1)^2}.$$

Case 3. $x_1 \neq x_2$ and $y_1 = y_2$. This case is similar to Case 2.

Case 4. $x_1 \neq x_2$ and $y_1 \neq y_2$. In this case $\overline{PQ}$ is parallel to neither $\overleftrightarrow{OX}$ nor $\overleftrightarrow{OY}$. Let R be the point (x_2, y_1). Then $\triangle PQR$ is a right triangle with R the vertex of the right angle. It follows from the Pythagorean theorem and Cases 2 and 3 above that

$$PQ = \sqrt{(PR)^2 + (RQ)^2} = \sqrt{(x_2 - x_1)^2 + (y_2 - y_1)^2}.$$

Exercises 9.3

1. Write out Case 3 in the proof of Theorem 9.1.

2. Draw the graph of the set $\{(x, y): x = 3 \text{ or } y = 3\}$.

3. Draw the graph of the set $\{(x, y): x = 3 \text{ and } y = 3\}$.

4. Draw the graph of the set $\{(x, y): (x - 1)^2 + (y - 1)^2 = 2\}$.

5. Draw the graph of the set $\{(x, y): x + y = 2 \text{ and } xy > 0\}$.

6. Draw the graph of the set $\{(x, y): x = 3 \text{ and } 0 \leqslant y \leqslant 4\}$.

7. Draw the graph of the set $\{(x, y): x = y\}$.

8. Draw the graph of the set $\{(x, y): x \geqslant 2 \text{ and } y \leqslant -2\}$.

9. Compute the distance from P to Q if $P = (5, -3)$ and $Q = (-3, 5)$.

10. Find the perimeter of the quadrilateral $ABCD$ if $A = (0, 0)$, $B = (10, 0)$, $C = (10, -10)$, $D = (0, -20)$.

11. Given $P = (5, 0)$, $Q = (10, 0)$. Find the coordinates of the point R on $\overrightarrow{PQ}$ if $PR = 2 \cdot PQ$.

12. Given $P = (5, 0)$, $Q = (10, 0)$. Find the coordinates of the point R on the ray opposite to $\overrightarrow{PQ}$ if $PR = 2 \cdot PQ$.

13. Given $P = (0, 5)$, $Q = (0, 10)$. Find the coordinates of the point R on $\overrightarrow{PQ}$ if $PR = 2 \cdot PQ$.

14. Given $P = (5, 5)$, $Q = (10, 10)$. Find the coordinates of the point R on $\overrightarrow{PQ}$ if $PR = 2 \cdot PQ$.

15. Draw the graph of the set $\{(x, y): x = 2 + 3k, y = 4, 0 \leqslant k \leqslant 1\}$.

16. Draw the graph of the set $\{(x, y): x = 4, y = 3 + 2k, 0 \leqslant k \leqslant 1\}$.

17. Draw the graph of the set $\{(x, y): x = 2 + 3k, y = 3 + 2k, 0 \leqslant k \leqslant 1\}$.

18. If $A = (4, 3)$, $B = (-2, 1)$, find the numbers a and b so that $\overrightarrow{AB} = \{(x, y): x = 4 + ak, y = 3 + bk, 0 \leqslant k \leqslant 1\}$.

19. Given points A and B as in Exercise 18. Find the coordinates of the point C if B is the midpoint of $\overline{AC}$.

20. Find the coordinates of the point on the x-axis which is equidistant from $(3, 4)$ and $(0, 7)$.

9.4 *Parametric Linear Equations*

Definition. If P is a point and L is a line, the *projection* of P on L is (1) the point P if P is a point of L, (2) the foot of the perpendicular from P to L if P is not on L.

Let two distinct points $A(x_1, y_1)$ and $B(x_2, y_2)$ be given. Then $A_1(x_1, 0)$ and $B_1(x_2, 0)$ are the projections on the x-axis of A and B, respectively. Let $P(x, y)$ be an arbitrary point on $\overleftrightarrow{AB}$. Then $P_1(x, 0)$ is its projection on the x-axis and $P_2(0, y)$ is the projection on the y-axis.

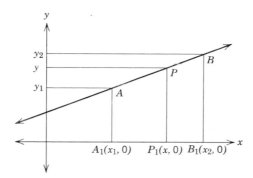

Suppose, first, that $\overleftrightarrow{AB}$ is a nonvertical line. Then $x_1 \neq x_2$. Also $x = x_1 + k(x_2 - x_1)$ where $k = A_1P_1/A_1B_1$ if P_1 is a point of $\overrightarrow{A_1B_1}$, and $-k = A_1P_1/A_1B_1$ if P_1 is a point of Opp $\overrightarrow{A_1B_1}$. Since P is a point of $\overrightarrow{AB}$ if and only if P_1 is a point of $\overrightarrow{A_1B_1}$, and since $(AP, AB) \overset{=}{_P} (A_1P_1, A_1B_1)$, it follows that $x = x_1 + k(x_2 - x_1)$ where $k = AP/AB$ if P is a point of $\overrightarrow{AB}$, and $-k = AP/AB$ if P is a point of Opp $\overrightarrow{AB}$. If $\overleftrightarrow{AB}$ is a vertical line, then $x_1 = x = x_2$ and $x = x_1 + k(x_2 - x_1)$ for every real number k.

Suppose, next, that $\overleftrightarrow{AB}$ is a nonhorizontal line. Then $y_1 \neq y_2$, and it follows by an argument similar to that for the x-coordinate that $y = y_1 + k(y_2 - y_1)$ where $k = AP/AB$ if P is a point of $\overrightarrow{AB}$ and $-k = AP/AB$ if P is a point of Opp $\overrightarrow{AB}$. If $\overleftrightarrow{AB}$ is a horizontal line, then $y_1 = y = y_2$ and $y = y_1 + k(y_2 - y_1)$ for every real number k.

It follows for all three cases (vertical, horizontal, oblique) that $x = x_1 + k(x_2 - x_1)$ and $y = y_1 + k(x_2 - x_1)$ where $k = AP/AB$ if $P \in \overrightarrow{AB}$, $-k = AP/AB$ if $P \in \mathrm{Opp}\ \overrightarrow{AB}$.

Note that the correspondence between the set of all points P on $\overleftrightarrow{AB}$ and the set of all real numbers k is a one-to-one correspondence. If $P = A$, then $k = 0$. If $P = B$, then $k = 1$. If P is the midpoint of $\overline{AB}$, then $k = \frac{1}{2}$. If P is in the ray opposite to $\overrightarrow{AB}$ and if $AP = 3 \cdot AB$, then $-k = 3$ and $k = -3$.

We shall show that the correspondence between the points P on line $\overleftrightarrow{AB}$ and the real numbers k is a coordinate system on $\overleftrightarrow{AB}$ with origin A and unit-point B. We call it the k-coordinate system on $\overleftrightarrow{AB}$. Let $P_3(x_3, y_3)$ and $P_4(x_4, y_4)$ be any two points of $\overleftrightarrow{AB}$. Let k_3 and k_4 be the real numbers which satisfy the following equations

$$x_3 = x_1 + k_3(x_2 - x_1), \quad y_3 = y_1 + k_3(y_2 - y_1),$$

$$x_4 = x_1 + k_4(x_2 - x_1), \quad y_4 = y_1 + k_4(y_2 - y_1).$$

Then

$$x_3 - x_4 = (k_3 - k_4)(x_2 - x_1), \quad y_3 - y_4 = (k_3 - k_4)(y_2 - y_1),$$

and

$$P_3P_4 = \sqrt{(k_4 - k_3)^2(x_2 - x_1)^2 + (k_4 - k_3)^2(y_2 - y_1)^2}$$

$$= |k_4 - k_3| \cdot AB.$$

It follows that P_3P_4 (relative to $\{A, B\}$) $= |k_4 - k_3|$, and that the correspondence between k and P is a coordinate system on $\overleftrightarrow{AB}$.

We consolidate our results into the following theorem.

Theorem 9.2. If $A(x_1, y_1)$ and $B(x_2, y_2)$ are any two distinct points, then

$$\overleftrightarrow{AB} = \{(x, y): x = x_1 + k(x_2 - x_1), \quad y = y_1 + k(y_2 - y_1), \quad k \text{ is real}\}.$$

If $P = (x_1 + k(x_2 - x_1), \quad y_1 + k(y_2 - y_1))$, then

$$AP = k \cdot AB \quad \text{and} \quad P \in \overrightarrow{AB} \quad \text{if } k \geqslant 0;$$

$$AP = -k \cdot AB, \quad \text{and} \quad P \in \mathrm{Opp}\ \overrightarrow{AB} \quad \text{if } k \leqslant 0.$$

The equations $x = x_1 + k(x_2 - x_1)$ and $y = y_1 + k(y_2 - y_1)$ are called *parametric equations*; the variable k is the *parameter*.

According to Theorem 9.2 every line can be represented with set-builder notation using parametric equations. Note in the statement of this theorem that A and B are distinct points and hence that the co-efficients of k in the parametric equations cannot both be zero. A converse of Theorem 9.2 is our next theorem.

Theorem 9.3. If a, b, c, d are real numbers, if b and d are not both zero, and if $S = \{(x, y): x = a + bk, y = c + dk, k$ is real$\}$, then S is a line.

Proof. Taking $k = 0$ and $k = 1$ we get two points in S, namely $A(a, c)$ and $B(a + b, c + d)$. From Theorem 9.2 it follows that $\overleftrightarrow{AB} = \{(x, y): x = a + bk, y = c + dk, k$ is real$\}$. Therefore $S = \overleftrightarrow{AB}$, and S is a line.

Example 1. Given $A = (5, 2)$, $B = (1, -3)$, express $\overline{AB}$ using coordinates and parametric equations.

Solution. $\overline{AB} = \{(x, y): x = 5 - 4k, y = 2 - 5k, 0 \leqslant k \leqslant 1\}$.

Example 2. Given $A = (5, 2)$, $B = (1, -3)$. Find P on $\overrightarrow{AB}$ such that $AP = 5 \cdot AB$.

Solution. Taking $k = 5$ in the parametric equations of Example 1 we get $P = (x, y) = (-15, -23)$.

Example 3. Given $A = (5, 2)$, $B = (1, -3)$. Find Q on Opp $\overrightarrow{AB}$ such that $AP = 5 \cdot AB$.

Solution. Taking $k = -5$ in the parametric equations of Example 1 we get $P = (x, y) = (25, 27)$.

Example 4. Given $A = (5, 2)$, $B = (1, -3)$. Find the points of trisection to $\overline{AB}$.

Solution. Take $k = \frac{1}{3}$ and $k = \frac{2}{3}$. The points of trisection are $C(\frac{11}{3}, \frac{1}{3})$ and $D(\frac{7}{3}, -\frac{4}{3})$. Note that $A = (\frac{15}{3}, \frac{6}{3})$ and $B = (\frac{3}{3}, -\frac{9}{3})$, that the abscissas of A, C, D, B are $\frac{15}{3}, \frac{11}{3}, \frac{7}{3}, \frac{3}{3}$, respectively, and that the ordinates of A, C, D, B, are $\frac{6}{3}, \frac{1}{3}, -\frac{4}{3}, -\frac{9}{3}$, respectively. The abscissas form an arithmetic progression, as do the ordinates. This is as it should be. For if A, C, D, B are "evenly spaced" on $\overleftrightarrow{AB}$, then their projections on the x-axis should be "evenly spaced" also. Why?

Exercises 9.4

1. Using parametric equations and set-builder notation express the three segments $\overline{AB}, \overline{BC}, \overline{CA}$, if $A = (0, 0)$, $B = (5, 1)$, $C = (-1, 6)$.

2. Given $A = (5, 7)$, $B = (-2, 1)$. Find C on $\overrightarrow{AB}$ such that $AC = 5 \cdot AB$.

3. Given $A = (5, 7)$, $B = (-2, 1)$. Find all positions for D on $\overleftrightarrow{AB}$ if $AD = 2 \cdot AB$.

4. Given $A = (5, 7)$, $B = (-2, 1)$. Express the ray opposite to $\overrightarrow{AB}$ using set-builder notation.

5. Find the coordinates of the midpoints of the three segments in Exercise 1.

6. Given A, B, C as in Exercise 1. Find the coordinates of the point which is two-thirds of the way from A to the midpoint of $\overline{BC}$.

7. Given lines:

$$S = \{(x, y): x = 1 + 2k, y = 2 + 3k, k \text{ is real}\},$$

$$T = \{(x, y): x = 5 - 4k, y = 8 - 6k, k \text{ is real}\}.$$

Show that $k = 2$ in the equations for S and that $k = 0$ in the equations for T yield the same point. Find another point which lies on both S and T. Does this show that $S = T$?

8. Given lines:

$$L = \{(x, y): x = 1 + k, y = 3 - 2k, k \text{ is real}\},$$

$$M = \{(x, y): x = 2 - h, y = 5 - 2h, h \text{ is real}\}.$$

Show that L and M are distinct intersecting lines.

9. Given lines:

$$m = \{(x, y): x = -1 + 5k, y = 3 + 4k, k \text{ is real}\},$$

$$n = \{(x, y): x = -6 - 5h, y = -1 - 4h, h \text{ is real}\}.$$

Show that $m = n$. Find the x and y coordinates of the origin P and unit-point Q of the k-coordinate system on m. Find the x and y coordinates of the origin P' and the unit-point Q' of the h-coordinate system on m. If A and B are any two distinct points on m, what is the value of

$$\frac{AB \text{ (relative to } \{P, Q\})}{AB \text{ (relative to } \{P', Q'\})} ?$$

10. Given lines:

$$m = \{(x, y): x = 3 + 2k, y = -2 + 4k, k \text{ is real}\},$$

$$n = \{(x, y): x = 3 + 6h, y = -2 + 12h, h \text{ is real}\}.$$

Show that $m = n$. The k-distance between two points on m is the absolute value of the difference between their k-coordinates. The h-distance is defined similarly in terms of the h-coordinates. How does the k-distance between any two points on m compare with the h-distance between them?

11. Given $A = (0, 2)$, $B = (-3, 1)$. Complete the following parametric representation of $\overline{AB}$:

$$\overline{AB} = \{(x, y): \qquad\qquad \}.$$

12. Given $A = (0, 2)$, $B = (-3, 1)$. Complete the following parametric representation of $\overrightarrow{AB}$:

$$\overrightarrow{AB} = \{(x, y): \qquad\qquad \}.$$

13. Given $A = (0, 2)$, $B = (-3, 1)$. Express $\overleftrightarrow{AB}$ using a parameter k in such a way that the k-coordinate of B is 0 and the k-coordinate of A is 1.

14. Given $A = (0, 2)$, $B = (-4, 0)$. Express $\overleftrightarrow{AB}$ using a parameter k in such a way that the k-coordinate of A is 3 and the k-coordinate of B is 5.

Hint : First find P and Q on the ray opposite to $\overrightarrow{AB}$ such that $AP = \frac{3}{2} \cdot AB$, $AQ = AB$. Use P and Q as the origin and unit-point of the k-coordinate system.

15. Given $A = (0, 2)$, $B = (-4, 0)$. Express $\overline{AB}$ using a parameter k in such a way that the k-coordinate of A is 5 and the k-coordinate of B is 1.

16. Given $A = (5, 2)$, $B = (100, 20)$. Find the three points which divide $\overline{AB}$ into four congruent nonoverlapping segments.

17. Given lines:

$$A = \{(x, y): x = -3 + 4h, y = 5 + 2h, h \text{ is real}\},$$

$$B = \{(x, y): x = 11 - 2k, y = 12 - k, k \text{ is real}\}.$$

Show that $A = B$. The Two Coordinate Systems Theorem implies that there are two numbers a and b, with $a \neq 0$, such that if (x, y) is any point on line A, and if h and k are the corresponding parameter values (in the parametric equations above), then $k = ah + b$. Find the numbers a and b.

18. Given lines:

$$A = \{(x, y): x = 4h, y = 5 + 2h, h \text{ is real}\},$$

$$B = \{(x, y): x = 11 - 2k, y = 12 - k, k \text{ is real}\}.$$

Show that A and B are distinct parallel lines.

19. Plot the graphs of sets A and B given as follows.

$$A = \{(x, y): x = 2 + h; y = 3 + 2h; h = 0, 1, 2, 3, 4\},$$

$$B = \{(x, y): x = 2 + 2k; y = 3 + 4k; k = 0, 1, 2, 3, 4\}.$$

20. Plot the graph of the sets S and T given as follows:

$$S = \{(x, y): x = 1 + h, y = 2 + 2h, 0 \leqslant h \leqslant 1\},$$

$$T = \{(x, y): x = 1 + h, y = 2 + 2k, 0 \leqslant h \leqslant 1, 0 \leqslant k \leqslant 1\}.$$

9.5 *Slope*

The steepness of an inclined plane may be expressed as a number, the number which results when the "rise" is divided by the "run." This

is the same as the tangent of the angle of inclination θ in the figure. Using this idea we could express the slope of a segment in the xy-plane in terms of the coordinates of its endpoints. Thus, if $P = (x_1, y_1)$ and $Q = (x_2, y_2)$ where $x_1 \neq x_2$, then $|y_2 - y_1|/|x_2 - x_1|$ is the number which expresses the rise divided by the run for the segment $\overline{PQ}$. We might define the

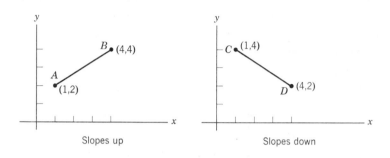

Slopes up   Slopes down

slope as this number, *but we do not*. The same formula without the absolute value symbols is easier to handle, and it turns out to be more useful. The sign of the slope indicates whether the segment "slopes up or down" as indicated in the figure. If $A = (1, 2)$ and $B = (4, 4)$, then the slope of $\overline{AB}$ is $(4 - 2)/(4 - 1) = \frac{2}{3}$. If $C = (1, 4)$ and $D = (4, 2)$, then the slope of $\overline{CD}$ is $(2 - 4)/(4 - 1) = -\frac{2}{3}$.

Definition. If $A(x_1, y_1)$ and $B(x_2, y_2)$ are two distinct points and if $x_1 \neq x_2$, then the *slope* of $\overline{AB}$ is $(y_2 - y_1)/(x_2 - x_1)$.

If $A(x_1, y_1)$ and $B(x_2, y_2)$ are two distinct points with $x_1 = x_2$, then $\overline{AB}$ is a vertical segment and no slope is defined for it. If $A(x_1, y_1)$ and $B(x_2, y_2)$ are two distinct points and if $y_1 = y_2$, then $\overline{AB}$ is a horizontal segment and its slope is zero. Note that the definition of slope is symmetric in A and B, that is, that the slopes of $\overline{AB}$ and $\overline{BA}$ are equal for every nonvertical segment $\overline{AB}$.

The concept of the slope of a line is based on the concept of the slope of a segment. In the following theorem we shall show that the slopes of all segments of a nonvertical line are equal.

Theorem 9.4. The slopes of all segments of a nonvertical line are equal.

Proof. Let an arbitrary nonvertical line $\overleftrightarrow{AB}$ be given parametrically as follows: $\overleftrightarrow{AB} = \{(x, y): x = a + bk, y = c + dk, k \text{ is real}\}$. Note that $P(a, c)$ and $Q(a + b, c + d)$ are two distinct points of $\overleftrightarrow{AB}$ and that the slope of $\overline{PQ}$ is d/b. Let R and S be any two distinct points of $\overleftrightarrow{AB}$. Then there are two distinct parameter values k_1 and k_2 such that $R = (a + bk_1,$

$c + dk_1$) and $S = (a + bk_2, c + dk_2)$. The slope of $\overline{RS}$ is

$$\frac{(c + dk_2) - (c + dk_1)}{(a + bk_2) - (a + bk_1)} = \frac{d}{b}.$$

Therefore all segments of $\overleftrightarrow{AB}$ have the same slope and the proof is complete.

Definition. *The slope of a nonvertical line* is the slope of any one of its segments; *the slope of a nonvertical ray* is the slope of the line which contains it.

According to this definition we can compute the slope of a nonvertical line by computing the slope of any one of its segments. The result is independent of which segment is used since the slopes of all segments of a nonvertical line are equal. In the following theorem we shall prove that a nonvertical line is "determined" by a point on it and its slope.

Theorem 9.5. Given a point A and a real number m, there is one and only one line through A with slope m.

Proof. Let $A = (x_1, y_1)$ and $B = (x_1 + 1, y_1 + m)$. Then $\overleftrightarrow{AB}$ is a line through A with slope m.

Let $\overleftrightarrow{PQ}$ be any line through A with slope m. Since $\overleftrightarrow{PQ}$ is a nonvertical line, it intersects the vertical line through $(x_1 + 1, y_1 + m)$ in some point $(x_1 + 1, y_2)$. Since $\overleftrightarrow{PQ}$ contains the two points (x_1, y_1) and $(x_1 + 1, y_2)$, its slope is $y_2 - y_1$. But $\overleftrightarrow{PQ}$ has slope m. Therefore $y_2 - y_1 = m$ and $y_2 = y_1 + m$. It follows that $\overleftrightarrow{PQ}$ contains A and B and that $\overleftrightarrow{PQ} = \overleftrightarrow{AB}$. Therefore there is one and only one line through A with slope m.

Using Theorem 9.2 we can write parametric equations for a line if we know the coordinates of two points on it. Using our next theorem we can write parametric equations for a line if we know its slope and the coordinate of one point on it.

Theorem 9.6. If p is a line through (x_1, y_1) with slope $m = f/g$, then
1. $p = \{(x, y): x = x_1 + k, y = y_1 + mk, k \text{ is real}\}$,
2. $p = \{(x, y): x = x_1 + gk, y = y_1 + fk, k \text{ is real}\}$.

Proof. Taking $k = 0$ and $k = 1$ in the first expression we get (x_1, y_1) and $(x_1 + 1, y_1 + m)$, two points on p. Since the slope of the segment joining these two points is $(y_1 + m - y_1)/(x_1 + 1 - x_1) = m$, it follows that p as given in (1) is the line through (x_1, y_1) with slope m.

Taking $k = 0$ and $k = 1$ in (2) we get (x_1, y_1) and $(x_1 + g, y_1 + f)$. Since the slope of the segment joining these two points is

$$\frac{y_1 + f - y_1}{x_1 + g - x_1} = \frac{f}{g},$$

it follows that p as given in (2) is the line through (x_1, y_1) with slope m. This completes the proof.

If two lines are vertical, then they are parallel. Why? If one of two lines is vertical and the other is not, then the two lines are not parallel. Why? In the following theorem we shall show that two nonvertical lines are parallel if and only if their slopes are equal.

Theorem 9.7. Two nonvertical lines are parallel if and only if their slopes are equal.

Proof. Let p and q be nonvertical lines and suppose that there is a number m which is the slope of both p and q. If $p = q$, then p is parallel to q. Suppose $p \neq q$. Then p and q are either parallel or they have exactly one point in common. If they have a point in common, it follows from Theorem 9.5 that they are the same line. So if $p \neq q$, it is impossible for p and q to have one and only one point in common. It follows that p is parallel to q.

Next, let p and q be nonvertical parallel lines. If $p = q$, then their slopes are equal. Suppose $p \neq q$. Let $P_1(x_1, y_1)$ and $P_2(x_2, y_2)$ be two distinct points of p. Then there are real numbers h and k such that $Q_1(x_1, y_1 + h)$ and $Q_2(x_2, y_2 + k)$ are points of q. Note that h and k are both positive or both negative and that $P_1 P_2 Q_2 Q_1$ is a parallelogram. Therefore $P_1 Q_1 = P_2 Q_2$. But $P_1 Q_1 = |h|$, $P_2 Q_2 = |k|$. Therefore $h = k$. Since the slope of p is $(y_2 - y_1)/(x_2 - x_1)$ and the slope of q is

$$\frac{(y_2 + k) - (y_1 + h)}{x_2 - x_1} = \frac{y_2 - y_1}{x_2 - x_1},$$

it follows that the slopes of p and q are equal.

Theorem 9.8. Three distinct points A, B, C are collinear if and only if they lie on a vertical line or the slopes of $\overline{AB}$ and $\overline{BC}$ are equal.

Proof. Suppose A, B, C are distinct collinear points, and that the line which contains them is not a vertical line. Then it follows from Theorem 9.4 that the slopes of $\overline{AB}$ and $\overline{BC}$ are equal.

Suppose, next, that A, B, C are distinct points such that the slopes of $\overline{AB}$ and $\overline{BC}$ are equal. Then the slopes of lines $\overleftrightarrow{AB}$ and $\overleftrightarrow{BC}$ are equal. It follows from Theorem 9.7 that $\overleftrightarrow{AB}$ and $\overleftrightarrow{BC}$ are parallel lines. Since they have point B in common, it follows that $\overleftrightarrow{AB} = \overleftrightarrow{BC}$ and hence that A, B, C are collinear.

Exercises 9.5

1. Write parametric equations for the vertical line through $(3, 5)$.

2. Write parametric equations for the line through $(3, 5)$ with slope 0.

3. Write parametric equations for the line through $(3, 5)$ with slope 10.

4. Write parametric equations for the line through $(3, 5)$ with slope $\frac{1}{10}$.

5. Given $A = (5, 1)$, $B = (-1, 6)$, $C = (16, -9)$, $D = (-7, 11)$, $E = (10, -4)$. Use slopes to determine which of the points C, D, E, if any, lie on the line $\overleftrightarrow{AB}$.

6. If L is the line through $(3, 4)$ with slope $\frac{2}{3}$, find the ordinates of the points of L whose abscissas are 6, 9, 12, 15, 18, and 21, respectively.

7. Given $\overleftrightarrow{AB} = \{(x, y): x = 1 + 2k, y = 3 + 4k, k \text{ is real}\}$. Write parametric equations for the line which contains $(0, 0)$ and is parallel to $\overleftrightarrow{AB}$.

8. Given:

$$a = \{(x, y): x = 1 + 4h, y = 3 - 6h, h \text{ is real}\},$$

$$b = \{(x, y): x = 1 - 2k, y = 4 + 3k, k \text{ is real}\}.$$

Show that a and b are distinct parallel lines.

9. Given $A(0, 0)$, $B(3, -4)$, $C(4, 4)$, $D(1, 8)$. Show using slopes that $ABCD$ is a parallelogram.

10. Given $P(a, 1)$, $Q(b, c)$, $R(4, 2)$, $S(2, 2)$. Show that $PQRS$ is a parallelogram if and only if $b = a + 2$ and $c = 1$.

9.6 *Other Equations of Lines*

In this section we shall develop several nonparametric forms of equations to represent lines. Theorems 9.9 and 9.10 follow immediately from the definitions of horizontal and vertical and the definition of the x- and y-coordinates of a point.

Theorem 9.9. If L is the horizontal line through (x_1, y_1), then $L = \{(x, y): y = y_1\}$.

Theorem 9.10. If M is the vertical line through (x_2, y_2), then $M = \{(x, y): x = x_2\}$.

Theorem 9.11 (*The Two-Point Form*). If $A = (x_1, y_1)$ and $B = (x_2, y_2)$ are distinct points, and if $\overleftrightarrow{AB}$ is an oblique line, then

$$\overleftrightarrow{AB} = \left\{(x, y): \frac{x - x_1}{x_2 - x_1} = \frac{y - y_1}{y_2 - y_1}\right\}.$$

Proof. $P(x, y)$ is a point of $\overleftrightarrow{AB}$ if and only if $P = A$ or the slope of $\overline{AP}$ is equal to the slope of $\overline{AB}$. If $A = P$, then $x = x_1$, $y = y_1$, and $(x - x_1)/(x_2 - x_1) = (y - y_1)/(y_2 - y_1)$. If $A \neq P$, then setting the slope of $\overline{AB}$ equal to the slope of $\overline{AP}$, we get $(y_2 - y_1)/(x_2 - x_1) = (y - y_1)/(x - x_1)$. Multiplying both members of this equation by

$(x - x_1)/(y_2 - y_1)$, we get $(x - x_1)/(x_2 - x_1) = (y - y_1)/(y_2 - y_1)$. It follows that P is an element of $\overleftrightarrow{AB}$ if and only if $(x - x_1)/(x_2 - x_1) = (y - y_1)/(y_2 - y_1)$.

Theorem 9.12. If $A = (x_1, y_1)$ and $B = (x_2, y_2)$ are distinct points and if $\overleftrightarrow{AB}$ is an oblique line, then

$$\overleftrightarrow{AB} = \left\{ (x, y): y - y_1 = \frac{y_2 - y_1}{x_2 - x_1}(x - x_1) \right\}.$$

Proof. This follows from Theorem 9.11 by multiplying both sides of the two-point form by $y_2 - y_1$.

Theorem 9.13 (*The Point Slope Form*). If L is the line through $A(x_1, y_1)$ with slope m, then $L = \{(x, y): y - y_1 = m(x - x_1)\}$.

Proof. Let (x_2, y_2) be any point of L different from (x_1, y_1). Then $m = (y_2 - y_1)/(x_2 - x_1)$ and the result follows immediately from Theorem 9.12.

Definition. If line L contains the point $(a, 0)$, then a is the *x-intercept* of L; if line L contains the point $(0, b)$, then b is the *y-intercept* of L.

Theorem 9.14 (*The Intercept Form*). If a and b are nonzero numbers, and if L is the line which passes through $(a, 0)$ and $(0, b)$, then

$$L = \left\{ (x, y): \frac{x}{a} + \frac{y}{b} = 1 \right\}.$$

Proof. Assigned as an exercise.

Theorem 9.15 (*The Slope y-Intercept Form*). If L is the line through $(0, b)$ with slope m, then

$$L = \{(x, y): y = mx + b\}.$$

Proof. Assigned as an exercise.

Theorem 9.16 (*The General Linear Equation*). Every line has an equation of the form $Ax + By + C = 0$ in which A, B, C are real numbers and A and B are not both zero. Conversely, every equation $Ax + By + C = 0$ in which A, B, C are real numbers and A and B are not both zero is the equation of a line.

Proof. Let L be a line and (x_1, y_1) a point on L. If L is a vertical line, then $L = \{(x, y): x = x_1\}$ and $L = \{(x, y): 1 \cdot x + 0 \cdot y + (-x_1) = 0\}$. If L is a nonvertical line, then it has a slope, say m. Then

$$L = \{(x, y): y - y_1 = m(x - x_1)\},$$
$$= \{(x, y): mx + (-1)y + (y_1 - mx_1) = 0\}.$$

This completes the proof that every line has an equation of the form $Ax + By + C = 0$ with A and B not both zero.

We proceed to prove the converse, that is, that every equation $Ax + By + C = 0$, with A and B not both zero, is the equation of a line. We consider two cases: $B = 0$ and $B \neq 0$. If $B = 0$, then $A \neq 0$, and if

$$S = \{(x, y): Ax + By + C = 0\},$$

$$= \left\{(x, y): x = -\frac{C}{A}\right\},$$

then S is a vertical line.

If $B \neq 0$, let

$$S = \{(x, y): Ax + By + C = 0\}$$

$$= \left\{(x, y): y = -\frac{A}{B}x - \frac{C}{B}\right\}.$$

Let L be the unique line through $(0, -C/B)$ and $(1, -A/B - C/B)$. Then L has slope $-A/B$ and y-intercept $-C/B$. It follows from Theorem 9.15 that

$$L = \left\{(x, y): y = -\frac{A}{B}x - \frac{C}{B}\right\}.$$

Therefore $L = S$ and $Ax + By + C = 0$ is the equation of a line.

Exercises 9.6

1. Prove Theorem 9.14.

2. Prove Theorem 9.15.

3. Write an equation in two-point form for the line which passes through $(5, 3)$ and $(6, 5)$.

4. Write an equation in point-slope form for the line which passes through $(5, 3)$ and $(6, 5)$.

5. Write an equation in intercept-form for the line which passes through $(5, 3)$ and $(6, 5)$.

6. Find the slope of line L given as follows:

$$L = \left\{(x, y): \frac{x - 1}{3} = \frac{y - 2}{5}\right\}.$$

7. Find the x- and y-intercepts of line M given as follows:

$$M = \left\{(x, y): \frac{x-5}{7} = \frac{y-2}{4}\right\}.$$

8. Find the slope of the line N given as follows:

$$N = \{(x, y): 3x + 4y = 5\}.$$

9. Given line L with equation $7x - 6y + 8 = 0$. Write an equation for the line M which is parallel to L and passes through $(0, 5)$.

10. Are points $(5, 8)$, $(5, 15)$, $(5, -7)$ collinear?

9.7 *Perpendicular Lines*

We have seen that two nonvertical lines are parallel if and only if their slopes are equal. Our next theorem provides a test for perpendicularity using slopes.

Theorem 9.17. Two nonvertical lines are perpendicular if and only if the product of their slopes is -1.

Proof. Let p_1 and p_2 be two nonvertical lines with slopes m_1 and m_2, respectively. Let q_1 and q_2 be the lines through the origin which are parallel to p_1 and p_2, respectively. Then the slopes of q_1 and q_2 are m_1 and m_2, respectively, and $p_1 \perp p_2$ if and only if $q_1 \perp q_2$. Since neither q_1 nor q_2 is vertical, they both intersect the line $L = \{(x, y): x = 1\}$. Let $R(1, y_1)$ be the point of intersection of q_1 with L. Let $S(1, y_2)$ be the point of intersection of q_2 with L. Then $m_1 = (y_1 - 0)/(1 - 0) = y_1$, $m_2 = (y_2 - 0)/(1 - 0) = y_2$, and $R = (1, m_1)$, $S = (1, m_2)$. Then $q_1 \perp q_2$
 if and only if $(RS)^2 = (OR)^2 + (OS)^2$,
 if and only if $(m_1 - m_2)^2 = (m_1^2 + 1) + (m_2^2 + 1)$,
 if and only if $-2m_1m_2 = 2$,
 if and only if $m_1m_2 = -1$.

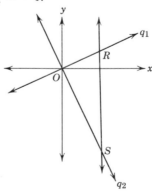

Exercises 9.7

1. Given $\triangle ABC$ with $A = (0, 0)$, $B = (3, 2)$, $C = (-2, 3)$. Use slopes to show that this is a right triangle.

2. Write parametric equations for the line M which contains $(5, 3)$ and is perpendicular to the line L given as follows:

$$L = \{(x, y): x = 7 + 3k, y = 5 - 2k, k \text{ is real}\}.$$

3. Write parametric equations for the line A, which contains the origin and which is perpendicular to the following parallel lines:

$$B = \{(x, y): x = 1 + k, y = 3 + 4k, k \text{ is real}\},$$

$$C = \{(x, y): x = -5 + k, y = 3 + 4k, k \text{ is real}\}.$$

4. Given the lines A, B, C as in Exercise 3. Find the points in which A intersects B and C. Then find the distance between the lines B and C.

5. Determine which pairs of the following lines, L, M, N, are perpendicular to each other:

$$L = \left\{(x, y): \frac{x - 1}{3} = \frac{y - 2}{4}\right\},$$

$$M = \left\{(x, y): \frac{x + 1}{4} = \frac{y + 3}{3}\right\},$$

$$N = \left\{(x, y): \frac{x - 5}{3} = \frac{y - 1}{-4}\right\}.$$

6. Write an equation in point-slope form for the line which contains $(3, 4)$ and is perpendicular to the line given by the equation $y = 3x - 7$.

7. Write an equation in point-slope form for the line which contains $(3, 4)$ and is parallel to the line given by the equation $y = 3x - 7$.

8. Write an equation in two-point form for the line which contains $(0, 2)$ and is perpendicular to the line L given by

$$L = \left\{(x, y): \frac{x - 0}{1} = \frac{y - 2}{2}\right\}.$$

9. Write an equation in intercept form for the line which contains $(0, 2)$ and is perpendicular to the line L given in Exercise 8.

10. Write an equation in slope y-intercept form for the line which contains $(0, 2)$ and is perpendicular to the line L given in Exercise 8.

9.8   *Proofs Using Coordinates*

In preceding paragraphs of this chapter we have defined an xy-coordinate system in a plane and have used coordinates as tools in our study of geometry. Given a plane, there are many xy-coordinate systems in that plane. In using coordinate systems as tools, it is natural to select an xy-coordinate which seems to fit the problem. The amount and difficulty of the work involved are usually less if one uses a "picked" coordinate system rather than a "random" coordinate system, as we shall now illustrate with our next theorem.

Theorem 9.18. A line segment which joins the midpoints of two sides of a triangle is parallel to the third side and its length is half the length of the third side.

Proof I. Let $\triangle ABC$ in an xy-plane be given. Suppose $A = (x_1, y_1)$, $B = (x_2, y_2)$, $C = (x_3, y_3)$. Let D, E, F be the midpoints of $\overline{BC}$, $\overline{CA}$,

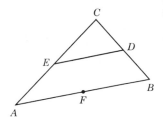

$\overline{AB}$, respectively. Then

$$D = \left(\frac{x_2 + x_3}{2}, \frac{y_2 + y_3}{2} \right), \quad E = \left(\frac{x_1 + x_3}{2}, \frac{y_1 + y_3}{2} \right),$$

$$(DE)^2 = \left(\frac{x_2 + x_3}{2} - \frac{x_1 + x_3}{2} \right)^2 + \left(\frac{y_2 + y_3}{2} - \frac{y_1 + y_3}{2} \right)^2,$$

$$(DE)^2 = \tfrac{1}{4}[(x_2 - x_1)^2 + (y_2 - y_1)^2],$$

$$(DE)^2 = \tfrac{1}{4}(AB)^2, \quad \text{and} \quad DE = \tfrac{1}{2} \cdot AB.$$

To prove that $\overline{DE}$ is parallel to $\overline{AB}$ we consider two cases. Suppose first that $\overline{AB}$ is a vertical segment. Then $x_1 = x_2, (x_2 + x_3)/2 = (x_1 + x_3)/2$, and $\overline{DE}$ is also a vertical segment. Suppose, next, that $\overline{AB}$ is not a vertical segment. Then the slope of $\overline{AB}$ is $(y_2 - y_1)/(x_2 - x_1)$, the slope of $\overline{DE}$ is

$$\frac{\dfrac{y_2 + y_3}{2} - \dfrac{y_1 + y_3}{2}}{\dfrac{x_2 + x_3}{2} - \dfrac{x_1 + x_3}{2}} = \frac{y_2 - y_1}{x_2 - x_1},$$

and $\overline{AB} \| \overline{DE}$.

This completes the proof as far as the segment $\overline{DE}$ is concerned. The assertion of the theorem as it applies to $\overline{EF}$ and $\overline{FD}$ may be proved in a similar manner.

Proof II. Let $\triangle ABC$ be given. In the plane of this triangle there is an xy-coordinate system with the origin at A, with $\overleftrightarrow{AB}$ as the x-axis, with the x-coordinate of B positive, and with the y-coordinate of C positive. Let x_1, x_2, y_2 be real numbers such that $B = (2x_1, 0)$, $C = (2x_2, 2y_2)$. Let D, E, F be the midpoints of $\overline{BC}$, $\overline{CA}$, $\overline{AB}$, respectively. Then

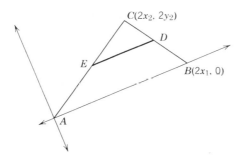

$C(2x_2, 2y_2)$

D

E

$B(2x_1, 0)$

A

$D = (x_1 + x_2, y_2)$, $E = (x_2, y_2)$, slope $\overline{DE} = 0$, slope $\overline{AB} = 0$, $DE = x_1$, and $AB = 2x_1$. Therefore $\overline{DE} \| \overline{AB}$ and $DE = \frac{1}{2} \cdot AB$.

This completes the proof as far as $\overline{DE}$ is concerned, and this is all we need to prove. For $\overline{DE}$ might be any other of the three segments which join the midpoints of two sides of the given triangle. To prove the assertion for the segment which joins the midpoints of two sides we first label the triangle so that $\overline{AC}$ and $\overline{CB}$ are those two sides, then proceed as above. This means that each of the three parts of the proof uses a different set of labels and a different coordinate system. But what we write in each case is the same.

Proof I is not recommended. Proof II is simpler and is to be preferred. It is a proof in which we play the role of master with respect to the coordinate system we choose.

The next three theorems are useful in solving many problems regarding parallelograms. Following them are several theorems, some proved using coordinates, some proved without using coordinates, and some with proofs assigned as exercises.

Theorem 9.19. Given quadrilateral $ABCD$ with $A = (0, 0)$, $B = (a, 0)$, $D = (b, c)$. $ABCD$ is a parellelogram if and only if $C = (a + b, c)$.

Proof. Suppose $C = (a + b, c)$. Then slope $\overline{DC} = 0 = $ slope $\overline{AB}$ and $\overline{DC} \| \overline{AB}$. Also $AB = |a| = CD$. Therefore $ABCD$ is a parallelogram.

Suppose, next, that $ABCD$ is a parallelogram. Then $\overline{AB} \parallel \overline{CD}$. Slope $\overline{AB} = 0$. Therefore slope $\overline{CD} = 0$. If $C = (x, y)$, then slope $\overline{CD} = (y - c)/(x - b) = 0$, and $y = c$. If $a > 0$, then $x > b$. If $a < 0$ then $x < b$. (Otherwise, C and B would lie on opposite sides of $\overleftrightarrow{AD}$ and $ABCD$ would not be a parallelogram.) But $AB = CD$. It follows that $|a| = |x - b|$ and that $x = a + b$. Therefore $C = (a + b, c)$.

Theorem 9.20. If the vertices of a parallelogram are $A(0, 0)$, $B(a, 0)$, $C(a + b, c)$, $D(b, c)$, then it is a rectangle if and only if $b = 0$.

Proof. If $b = 0$, then $\overline{AD}$ lies on the y-axis, $\overline{AD} \perp \overline{AB}$, and $ABCD$ is a rectangle. If $ABCD$ is a rectangle, then $\overline{AD} \perp \overline{AB}$, $\overline{AD}$ lies on y-axis, and $b = 0$.

Definition. A *rhombus* is a parallelogram with two adjacent sides which are congruent. (Necessarily, then, it is equilateral.)

Theorem 9.21. If the vertices of a parallelogram are $A(0, 0)$, $B(a, 0)$, $C(a + b, c)$, $D(b, c)$, then it is a rhombus if and only if $a^2 = b^2 + c^2$.

Proof. If $a^2 = b^2 + c^2$, then $AD = \sqrt{b^2 + c^2} = a = AC$ and $ABCD$ is a rhombus. If $ABCD$ is a rhombus, then

$$|a| = AC = AD = \sqrt{b^2 + c^2}, \quad \text{and} \quad a^2 = b^2 + c^2.$$

Theorem 9.22. A quadrilateral is a parallelogram if and only if its diagonals bisect each other.

Proof. Let $A(0, 0)$, $B(a, 0)$, $C(x, y)$, $D(b, c)$ be the vertices of a quadrilateral and suppose its diagonals bisect each other. Since the midpoints of $\overline{AC}$ and $\overline{BD}$ are $(x/2, y/2)$ and $[(a + b)/2, c/2]$, it follows that $x = a + b$ and $y = c$. From Theorem 9.19 it follows that $ABCD$ is a parallelogram.

If $ABCD$ is a parallelogram, then there is a coordinate system so that $A = (0, 0)$, $B = (a, 0)$, $C = (a + b, c)$, $D = (b, c)$. Since $[(a + b)/2, c/2]$ is the midpoint of both $\overline{AC}$ and $\overline{BD}$, it follows that the diagonals bisect each other.

Theorem 9.23. A parallelogram is a rectangle if and only if its diagonals are congruent.

Theorem 9.24. A parallelogram is a rhombus if and only if its diagonals are perpendicular.

Theorem 9.25. A parallelogram is a rhombus if and only if one of its diagonals bisects one of its angles.

Proof. Let $ABCD$ be a parallelogram and suppose that $\angle DAC \cong \angle CAB$. Then $\angle DAC \cong \angle BCA$, $\angle BAC \cong \angle DCA$, $\angle DCA \cong \angle BCA$, $\overline{AC} \cong \overline{AC}$, and $\triangle DAC \cong \triangle BAC$. Therefore $AD = AB$ and $ABCD$ is a rhombus.

Next, let $ABCD$ be a rhombus with $AB = AD$. Since the opposite sides of a parallelogram are congruent, it follows that $ABCD$ is equilateral. It

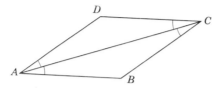

follows from the isosceles triangle theorem that $\angle DAC \cong \angle DCA$ and $\angle BAC \cong \angle BCA$. But $\angle DAC \cong \angle BCA$. It follows that $\angle DAC \cong \angle BAC$ and hence that $\overline{AC}$ bisects $\angle BAD$.

Several theorems pertaining to trapezoids come next. For the purpose of this section a *trapezoid* is considered as a quadrilateral with one pair of sides parallel and the other pair not parallel. (Some authors do not require that one pair of sides be not parallel. They consider a parallelogram as a special case of a trapezoid.) The parallel sides are called its *bases.* The other pair of sides are its *legs.* If $\overline{AB}$ is a base of a trapezoid, then $\angle A$ and $\angle B$ are a *pair of base angles* of the trapezoid. In other words, two distinct angles of a trapezoid are a pair of base angles if and only if one base is a subset of both angles. A segment which is perpendicular to both bases and which has its endpoints on the lines containing these bases is called an *altitude* of the trapezoid. The segment which joins the midpoints of the legs of a trapezoid is called the *median* of a trapezoid. A trapezoid whose legs are congruent is called an *isosceles* trapezoid.

Theorem 9.26. The median of a trapezoid is parallel to its bases and its length is half the sum of the lengths of its bases.

Theorem 9.27. A trapezoid is isosceles if and only if a pair of its base angles are congruent.

Theorem 9.28. A trapezoid is isosceles if and only if diagonals are congruent.

Theorem 9.29. The midpoints of the diagonals of a trapezoid are distinct points.

Theorem 9.30. The segment joining the midpoints of the diagonals of a trapezoid is parallel to the bases and its length is half the difference of their lengths.

Exercises 9.8

1. Prove Theorem 9.23.

2. Prove Theorem 9.24.

3. Prove Theorem 9.26.

4. Prove Theorem 9.27.

5. Prove Theorem 9.28.

6. Prove Theorem 9.29.

7. Prove Theorem 9.30.

8. Let L and $\triangle ABC$ be a line and a triangle lying in the same plane. Using co-ordinates, prove that if L contains an interior point of $\overline{AC}$ and is parallel to $\overline{AB}$, then L contains an interior point of $\overline{BC}$.

9. Let L and $\triangle ABC$ be a line and triangle lying in the same plane. Using co-ordinates, prove that if L is perpendicular to $\overline{AC}$ at an interior point of $\overline{AC}$, then L intersects $\overline{AB}$ or $\overline{BC}$.

10. Using coordinates prove that the segment which joins the midpoints of the bases of an isosceles trapezoid is an altitude of the trapezoid.

11. Complete the following proof that the medians of a triangle are concurrent in a point (centroid) which is two-thirds of the way from any vertex of the triangle to the midpoint of the opposite side.
    Proof: Let $A = (0,0)$, $B = (6a, 0)$, $C = (6b, 6c)$. Then the midpoint of $\overline{AB}$ is $D(3a, 0)$, $\overleftrightarrow{CD} = \{(x, y): x = 6b + (3a - 6b)k, y = 6c + (0 - 6c)k, 0 \leqslant k \leqslant 1\}$, and the point G on $\overleftrightarrow{CD}$ such that $CG = \frac{2}{3}$. CD is obtained by setting $k = \frac{2}{3}$. So $G = (2a + 2b, 2c)$. (Now find the point G' which is two-thirds of the way from B to the midpoint of $\overline{AC}$, and the point G'' which is two-thirds of the way from C to the midpoint of $\overline{AB}$.)

12. Complete the following proof that the lines which contain the altitudes of a triangle are concurrent. (Their common point is the *orthocenter* of the triangle.)
    Proof: Let $A = (a, 0)$, $B = (b, 0)$, $C = (0, c)$, and suppose that $a < b, 0 < c$. Let A', B', C' be the feet of the perpendiculars from A, B, C to $\overleftrightarrow{BC}$, $\overleftrightarrow{CA}$, $\overleftrightarrow{AB}$, respectively. We are to prove that $\overleftrightarrow{AA'}$, $\overleftrightarrow{BB'}$, $\overleftrightarrow{CC'}$ are concurrent. $\overleftrightarrow{AA'} = \{(x, y): y = (b/c)(x - a)\}$. (Now write equations for $\overleftrightarrow{BB'}$ and $\overleftrightarrow{CC'}$ and solve "simultaneously" with the equation for $\overleftrightarrow{AA'}$.)

13. Complete the following proof that the set of all points in a plane which are equidistant from two given points in the plane is the perpendicular bisector of the segment joining those two points.
    Proof: Let $A(0, a)$ and $B(0, -a)$ be the two given points and the xy-plane the given plane. (Now prove: (1) if $P(x, y)$ is equidistant from A and B, then P lies on the y-axis; and (2) if $P(x, y)$ lies on the y-axis, then $AP = PB$.)

14. Complete the following proof that the perpendicular bisectors of the sides of a triangle are concurrent. (Their common point is the *circumcenter* of the triangle. It is the center of the *circumscribed circle* of the triangle.)

Proof: Let $\triangle ABC$ be given. Let D, E, F be the midpoints of $\overline{BC}$, $\overline{CA}$, $\overline{AB}$, respectively. Let $\overleftrightarrow{DD'}$, $\overleftrightarrow{EE'}$, $\overleftrightarrow{FF'}$ be the perpendicular bisectors of $\overline{BC}$, $\overline{CA}$, $\overline{AB}$, respectively. If $\overleftrightarrow{DD'} \parallel \overleftrightarrow{EE'}$, then $\overleftrightarrow{EC} \parallel \overleftrightarrow{CD}$. Since $\overleftrightarrow{EC}$ is not parallel to $\overleftrightarrow{CD}$, then $\overleftrightarrow{DD'}$ intersects $\overleftrightarrow{EE'}$ in some point S. Then $SB = SC$. Why? $SB = SA$. Why? (Now finish the proof.)

15. Complete the following proof that the rays which bisect the angles of a triangle are concurrent. (Their common point is the *incenter* of the triangle.)

    Proof: Let $\overrightarrow{AA'}$, $\overrightarrow{BB'}$, $\overrightarrow{CC'}$ be bisectors of $\angle A$, $\angle B$, $\angle C$, respectively, of $\triangle ABC$. If $\overrightarrow{AA'} \parallel \overrightarrow{BB'}$, then $\frac{1}{2}m\angle A + \frac{1}{2}m\angle B = 180$ and $m\angle A + m\angle B = 360$. Since $m\angle A + m\angle B < 180$, it follows that $\overrightarrow{AA'}$ is not parallel to $\overrightarrow{BB'}$. Also $\overrightarrow{AA'}$ is not antiparallel to $\overrightarrow{BB'}$. For A' and B' lie on the same side (the C-side) of $\overleftrightarrow{AB}$. Therefore $\overrightarrow{AA'}$ intersects $\overrightarrow{BB'}$ in some point I. (Now prove that I lies on $\overrightarrow{CC'}$.)

9.9 *Coordinates and Circle Geometry*

Recall that a circle is a plane figure. Given a point $C(a, b)$ and a positive number r, the circle with center C and radius r is the set of all points $P(x, y)$ such that $PC = r$. Since $PC = \sqrt{(x - a)^2 + (y - b)^2}$, and since $\sqrt{(x - a)^2 + (y - b)^2} = r$ if and only if $(x - a)^2 + (y - b)^2 = r^2$, it follows that the circle with center C and with radius r is the set $\{(x, y): (x - a)^2 + (y - b)^2 = r^2\}$.

Definition. The *interior* of the circle $\{(x, y): (x - a)^2 + (y - b)^2 = r^2\}$ is the set $\{(x, y): (x - a)^2 + (y - b)^2 < r^2\}$; its *exterior* is the set $\{(x, y): (x - a)^2 + (y - b)^2 > r^2\}$.

Theorem 9.31. Let C be a circle of radius r, L a line in the plane of the circle, and d the (perpendicular) distance from the center of the circle to L. The line L intersects C in 0, 1, or 2 points according to whether $d > r$, $d = r$, or $d < r$.

Proof. Set up a coordinate system with the origin at the center of the circle, and with the x-axis parallel to L, and with L intersecting the y-axis in the point $(0, d)$. Then

$$C = \{(x, y): x^2 + y^2 = r^2\} \quad \text{and} \quad L = \{(x, y): y = d\}.$$

A point $P(x, y)$ lies on both L and C if $y = d$ and $x^2 + d^2 = r^2$. If $d < r$, there are two and only two such points, namely $(\sqrt{r^2 - d^2}, d)$ and $(-\sqrt{r^2 - d^2}, d)$. If $d = r$, there is one and only one such point, namely $(0, r)$. If $d > r$, there is no such point.

Theorem 9.32. If P is an interior point and Q is an exterior point of a given circle C, then the intersection of $\overline{PQ}$ and C is a set which contains one and only one point.

Proof. Set up a coordinate system so that $C = \{(x, y): x^2 + y^2 = r^2\}$, so that $\overleftrightarrow{PQ}$ is parallel to the x-axis, and so that the abscissa of Q is positive. Then there are real numbers a, b, c such that $b > 0$, $c < r$, $P = (a, c)$, $Q = (b, c)$, $a^2 + c^2 < r^2$, and $b^2 + c^2 > r^2$. $\overleftrightarrow{PQ} = \{(x, y): y = c\}$ and $\overleftrightarrow{PQ}$ intersects C in the two distinct points $A(-\sqrt{r^2 - c^2}, c)$ and $B(\sqrt{r^2 - c^2}, c)$. Since $-\sqrt{r^2 - c^2} < a < \sqrt{r^2 - c^2} < b$, it follows that B is between P and Q and that A is not between P and Q. Therefore the intersection of $\overline{PQ}$ and C is a set consisting of exactly one point.

Theorem 9.33. If C is a circle of radius r and if P is a point at distance a, $0 < a < r$, from the center Q of C, then the longest chord of C through P is the diameter containing P, and the shortest chord of C through P is the one which is perpendicular to the diameter through P.

Proof. Set up a coordinate system so that $P = (0, 0)$ and $Q = (0, a)$. Then $C = \{(x, y): x^2 + (y - a)^2 = r^2\}$. Let $A = (-\sqrt{r^2 - a^2}, 0)$, $B = (\sqrt{r^2 - a^2}, 0)$, $D = (0, a - r)$, $E = (0, a + r)$. Then $DE = 2r$. $AB =$

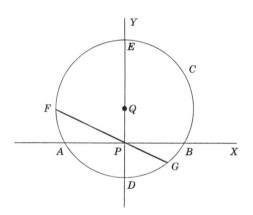

$2\sqrt{r^2 - a^2}$, and $\overline{AB} \perp \overline{DE}$. Let $\overline{FG}$ be any chord through P except $\overline{AB}$ and $\overline{DE}$. Then there is a number $m, m \neq 0$, such that $\overleftrightarrow{FG} = \{(x, y): y = mx\}$. Solving the equations for $\overleftrightarrow{FG}$ and C simultaneously, the coordinates of F and G may be expressed in terms of a, m, and r, and it can be shown that $(FG)^2 - (AB)^2 = (4a^2m^2)/(1 + m^2)$ and $(DE)^2 - (FG)^2 = 4a^2/(1 + m^2)$. Since $4a^2m^2/(1 + m^2)$ and $4a^2/(1 + m^2)$ are positive, it follows that $(DE)^2 > (FG)^2 > (AB)^2$ and hence that $DE > FG > AB$.

Theorem 9.34. A line L in the plane of a circle C is tangent to the circle at the point P if and only if L is perpendicular to the diameter of C which contains P.

Proof. Set up a coordinate system so that $C = \{(x, y): x^2 + y^2 = r^2\}$ and $P = (r, 0)$. Let $Q = (-r, 0)$. Then $\overline{PQ}$ is a diameter of C. First we assume that L is perpendicular to $\overline{PQ}$ at P. Then $L = \{(x, y): x = r\}$. Solving $x = r$ and $x^2 + y^2 = r^2$ simultaneously we find that L intersects C in one and only one point, the point P. This means that L is tangent to C.

We assume next that L is tangent to C at P. Then L intersects C in one and only one point, the point P. If L were any line through P except the vertical one, there would be a number m such that $L = \{(x, y): y = m(x - r)\}$, and L would intersect C in two distinct points, namely $P(r, 0)$ and $(r(m^2 - 1)/(m^2 + 1), (-2mr)/(m^2 + 1))$. It follows that L is the vertical line through P and hence that L is perpendicular to $\overline{PQ}$ at P.

Theorem 9.35. If A, B, C are three noncollinear points, there is one and only one circle containing them.

Proof. Set up a coordinate system so that $A = (0, 0)$, $B = (a, 0)$, and $C = (b, c)$. Then $a \neq 0$ and $c \neq 0$. There is one and only one circle containing A, B, C if there is one and only one point $P(x, y)$ such that $PA = PB = PC$, or, equivalently, that $(PA)^2 = (PB)^2 = (PC)^2$. $(PA)^2 = x^2 + y^2$, $(PB)^2 = (x - a)^2 + y^2$, $(PC)^2 = (x - b)^2 + (y - c)^2$. (Now complete the proof.)

Exercises 9.9

1. See the proof of Theorem 9.33. Express the coordinates of F and G in terms of a, m, r.

2. See the proof of Theorem 9.33. Show that $(FG)^2 - (AB)^2 = 4a^2m^2/(1 + m^2)$ and that $(DE)^2 - (FG)^2 = 4a^2/(1 + m^2)$.

3. Write an equation for the circumcircle of $\triangle ABC$ if $A = (0, 0)$, $B = (5, 0)$, $C = (0, 8)$.

4. Given $C = \{(x, y): (x - 1)^2 + (y - 3)^2 = 16\}$, $P = (0, 10)$. Find two distinct points on circle C which are at a distance of 10 from point P.

5. Given two circles

$$C = \{(x, y): x^2 + y^2 = 25\} \quad \text{and} \quad C' = \{(x, y): (x - 10)^2 + y^2 = 16\}$$

and a line L which is tangent to C at A and to C' at B. If L intersects the x-axis at D and if A and B are on the same side of the x-axis, find AD and BD.

6. Same as Exercise 5 except that A and B are on opposite sides of the x-axis.

7. Prove that the midpoint of the hypotenuse of a right triangle is the circumcenter of the triangle.

8. Complete the proof of Theorem 9.35.

CHAPTER 10

Space Geometry

10.1 Introduction

An informal treatment of some basic solid geometry may be found in Appendix 1. In this chapter we extend our formal treatment of geometry, giving primary attention to space, or solid, geometry. We begin with a consideration of perpendicularity for planes and for planes and lines.

10.2 Perpendicularity

Definition. A line L and a plane P are *perpendicular* to each other if and only if they intersect in one and only one point and every line lying in P and passing through the point of intersection is perpendicular to L.

Theorem 10.1. If A, B, C, D are four distinct points such that $AC = CB$ and $AD = DB$, then $AE = EB$ for every point E on $\overleftrightarrow{CD}$.

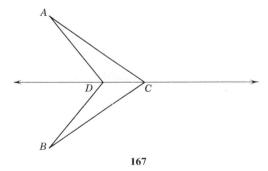

Proof. From the S.S.S. congruence theorem it follows that $\triangle ACD \cong \triangle BCD$. Let E be any point on $\overleftrightarrow{CD}$ except C or D. Since $\angle ACE$ and $\angle BCE$ are corresponding parts of congruent triangles, or supplements of corresponding parts, it follows that $\triangle ACE \cong \triangle BCE$. Therefore $AE = EB$.

Theorem 10.2. If $\overleftrightarrow{OX}$ and $\overleftrightarrow{OY}$ are perpendicular lines, there is a line $\overleftrightarrow{OZ}$ which is perpendicular to both of them.

Proof. Let I and I' be distinct points on $\overrightarrow{OX}$ such that $OI = OI'$. Let J and J' be distinct points on $\overrightarrow{OY}$ such that $OJ = OJ'$. Let p be the plane determined by $\overleftrightarrow{OX}$ and $\overleftrightarrow{OY}$. Let R be a point not in p, and let q be the plane determined by R and $\overleftrightarrow{OX}$. Let P be a point in q, on the R-side of p, and such that $\overrightarrow{OP} \perp \overrightarrow{OX}$. (How do you know there is such a point?) Let r be the plane determined by P and $\overleftrightarrow{OY}$. Let Q be a point in r, on the

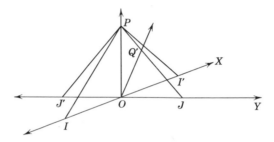

R-side of p, and such that $\overrightarrow{OQ} \perp \overleftrightarrow{OY}$. If $\overrightarrow{OQ} = \overrightarrow{OP}$, then $\overrightarrow{OP}$ is perpendicular to both $\overleftrightarrow{OX}$ and $\overleftrightarrow{OY}$. If $\overrightarrow{OQ} \neq \overrightarrow{OP}$, then $\overrightarrow{OQ}$ intersects $\overline{PJ'}$ or $\overline{PJ}$. Suppose, to be definite, that $\overrightarrow{OQ}$ intersects $\overline{PJ}$ at the point Q'. Then $PI = PI'$, $JI = JI'$, and it follows from Theorem 10.1 that $Q'I = Q'I'$. It then follows from the S.S.S. congruence theorem that $\triangle IOQ' \cong \triangle I'OQ'$, and hence that $\overleftrightarrow{OQ} \perp \overleftrightarrow{OX}$. Then $\overleftrightarrow{OQ}$ qualifies as a line $\overleftrightarrow{OZ}$ whose existence we were to prove.

Theorem 10.3. If a line is perpendicular to two distinct intersecting lines at their point of intersection, then it is perpendicular to the plane which contains them.

Proof. Let L, M, N be three distinct lines intersecting at a point O. Let p be the plane determined by M and N. Let R be any line in p and passing through O. Suppose $L \perp M$ and $L \perp N$. We shall show that $L \perp R$. From this it follows that $L \perp p$.

Let P and Q be distinct points of L such that $OP = OQ$. Let A and B be distinct points of M such that $OA = OB$. Let C be any point of N other than O. Then R intersects $\overline{AC}$ or $\overline{BC}$. Suppose to be definite that

R intersects $\overrightarrow{AC}$ at the point D. Since $QA = PA$, $QC = PC$, it follows from Theorem 10.1 that $QD = PD$, and from this it follows easily that $L \perp R$.

Theorem 10.4. If p is a plane and P is a point in p, then there is a line L containing P and perpendicular to p.

Proof. Let M and N be perpendicular lines intersecting at P and lying in p. It follows from Theorems 10.2 and 10.3 that there is a line L perpendicular to p and containing P.

Theorem 10.5. If p is a plane and P is a point not in p, then there is a line L containing P and perpendicular to p.

Proof. Let Q' be any point in p and $\overleftrightarrow{QQ'}$ a line perpendicular to p. If $\overleftrightarrow{QQ'}$ contains P, the conclusion of the theorem is established. Suppose, then, that $\overleftrightarrow{QQ'}$ does not contain P. Let L be the unique line through P parallel to $\overleftrightarrow{QQ'}$. Then it follows from Theorem 8.7 that L intersects p.

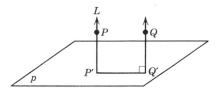

Suppose P' is the point of intersection. Since $\angle P'Q'Q$ is a right angle, and since $\overleftrightarrow{P'Q'}$ is a transversal of the parallel lines $\overleftrightarrow{PP'}$ and $\overleftrightarrow{QQ'}$, it follows that $\angle Q'P'P$ is also a right angle.

Let R' be any point of p not on $\overleftrightarrow{P'Q'}$. Then it follows as above that $\angle R'P'P$ is a right angle. It follows from Theorem 10.3 that $\overleftrightarrow{PP'} \perp p$.

Theorem 10.6. If p is a plane and P is a point, there is only one line L through P and perpendicular to p.

Proof. Suppose first that P is not a point of p. Suppose Q and Q' are distinct points of p such that $\overleftrightarrow{PQ} \perp p$ and $\overleftrightarrow{PQ'} \perp p$. Since this implies the existence of a right triangle with two right angles, it follows that there cannot be two such points Q and Q', and hence there is at most one line through P and perpendicular to p.

Suppose next that P is a point of p. Suppose Q and Q' are points not in p such that $\overleftrightarrow{PQ} \perp p$, $\overleftrightarrow{PQ'} \perp p$, and $\overleftrightarrow{PQ} \neq \overleftrightarrow{PQ'}$. Then P, Q, Q' determine a plane q which intersects p in a line L. Since this implies that $\overleftrightarrow{PQ}$, $\overleftrightarrow{PQ'}$ and L are distinct coplanar lines such that $\overleftrightarrow{QP} \perp L$, $\overleftrightarrow{Q'P} \perp L$, and since this contradicts the protractor postulate, it follows that there cannot be two such points Q and Q', and hence there is at most one line through P and perpendicular to L.

Our next theorem follows immediately from Theorems 10.4, 10.5, and 10.6.

Theorem 10.7. There is a unique line which contains a given point and is perpendicular to a given plane.

Theorem 10.8. If a line is perpendicular to a given plane at a given point, then that plane contains every line perpendicular to the given line at the given point.

Proof. Let L, p, and P be a line, a plane, and a point. Suppose L contains P, p contains P, and $L \perp p$. We know that every line through P and in p is perpendicular to L. We must show that every line through P and perpendicular to L lies in p.

Let L' be any line through P and perpendicular to L. Let p' be the plane determined by L and L', and let L'' be the line in which p and p' intersect. Now L, L', L'' are concurrent and coplanar, $L \perp L'$ and $L \perp L''$. (Why?) Therefore $L' = L''$. But L'' lies in p. Therefore L' lies in p. Since L' is an arbitrary line through P and perpendicular to L, the proof is complete.

Theorem 10.9. Two lines which are perpendicular to the same plane are parallel.

Proof. Let L and M be distinct lines each perpendicular to plane p. Let P and Q be the points in which L and M intersect p, respectively.

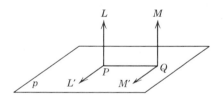

Let L' and M' be lines in p through P and Q, respectively, and perpendicular to $\overleftrightarrow{PQ}$. Let M'' be the line which contains Q and is parallel to L. Then $M'' \perp \overline{PQ}$ (Why?), $M \perp \overline{PQ}$, $M \perp M'$. Let q be the plane determined by M and M'. Since $\overline{PQ} \perp M$, $\overline{PQ} \perp M'$, it follows that $\overline{PQ} \perp q$. Since $\overline{PQ} \perp M''$, it follows from Theorem 10.8 that q contains M''. Now M, M', M'' are coplanar and concurrent, $M \perp M'$, $M'' \perp M'$. Therefore $M = M''$. But $M'' \parallel L$. Therefore $M \parallel L$.

Theorem 10.10. There is a unique plane which is perpendicular to a given line at a given point on it.

Proof. Let a line L and a point P on it be given. Let Q be any point not on L. Let q be the plane determined by L and Q. Let R be a point in q such that $L \perp \overline{PR}$. Let S be a point not in q such that $\overleftrightarrow{PS}$ is perpendicular to q. Let p be the plane determined by $\overleftrightarrow{PR}$ and $\overleftrightarrow{PS}$. Then $L \perp p$, and there is at least one plane perpendicular to L at P.

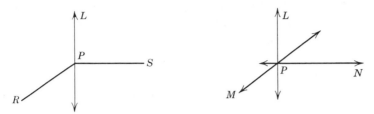

Let t be any plane perpendicular to L at P. Suppose $t \neq p$. Then t intersects p in some line M. Let N be perpendicular to both L and M at P. Then M and N are both in t and in p. Since there is only one plane which contains both M and N it follows that $t = p$. (Contradiction.) Therefore there is one and only one plane which is perpendicular to a given line at a given point on it.

Theorem 10.11. Given a line L and a point P, there is one and only one plane perpendicular to L and containing P.

Proof. If $P \in L$, the assertion follows from Theorem 10.10. Suppose then that $P \notin L$. Let M be the unique line through P and parallel to L. Let p be the unique plane through P and perpendicular to M. Then it follows from Theorem 8.7 that p intersects L in one and only one point. Call it Q. From Theorem 10.7 it follows that there is one and only one line L' through Q and perpendicular to p. From Theorem 10.9 it follows

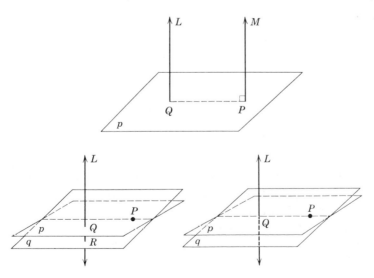

that $L' \parallel M$. But $L \parallel M$ and L contains Q. Therefore $L = L'$ and $L \perp p$. Therefore there is at least one plane p through P and perpendicular to L.

Suppose now that p and q are planes both containing P and both perpendicular to L. Let Q and R be the points in which L intersects p and q, respectively. Then $L \perp p$ at Q and $L \perp q$ at R. Since $R \neq Q$ implies the existence of a triangle with two right angles, it follows that $R = Q$. Then $L \perp p$ at Q and $L \perp q$ at Q. It follows from Theorem 10.10 that $p = q$. Therefore there is at most one plane through P and perpendicular to L.

Theorem 10.12. A line which is perpendicular to one of two parallel planes is perpendicular to the other also.

Proof. Let p and q be distinct parallel planes. Suppose L is a line which is perpendicular to p at point P. It follows from Theorem 8.8 that the intersection of L and q is a point. Call it Q. Let M and M' be two distinct lines through P in p. Let N and N' be the unique lines through Q which are parallel to M and M', respectively. It follows from Theorems 8.14 and 8.16 that N and N' lie in q. Since $L \perp N$, $L \perp N'$, it follows that $L \perp q$.

Theorem 10.13. Planes which are perpendicular to the same line are parallel.

Proof. Let p and q be planes and L a line. If $p = q$ then $p \parallel q$. Suppose then that $p \neq q$ and that $p \perp L$, $q \perp L$. It follows from Theorem 10.11 that p and q do not intersect. Therefore $p \parallel q$.

Theorem 10.14. If a plane is perpendicular to one of two parallel lines, then it is perpendicular to the other one also.

Proof. Let M and N be parallel lines and suppose p is a plane which is perpendicular to M at point P. It follows from Theorem 8.7 that the

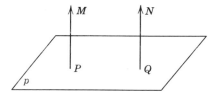

intersection of N and p is a point. Call it Q. Let N' be the unique line through Q and perpendicular to p. It follows from Theorem 10.9 that $N' \parallel M$. Then $N' = N$ and $N \perp p$.

Theorem 10.15. The shortest segment joining a given point P to a point of a given plane p which does not contain P is the segment which is perpendicular to p.

Proof. Assigned as an exercise.

Definition. The *distance between a point and a plane not containing it* is the length of the segment joining the given point to a point of the given plane and perpendicular to the given plane.

Theorem 10.16. All segments which are perpendicular to each of two distinct parallel planes and which have their endpoints in these planes have the same length.

Proof. Let p and q be distinct parallel planes. Let A, B, C, D, be four distinct points, A and C in p, B and D in q, such that $\overline{AB} \perp p$, $\overline{CD} \perp p$, $\overline{AB} \perp q$, $\overline{CD} \perp q$. It follows from Theorem 10.9 that $\overline{AB} \parallel \overline{CD}$. Then $\overleftrightarrow{AC}$ and $\overleftrightarrow{BD}$ are coplanar, and since they do not intersect (Why?), they are parallel. Therefore $ABDC$ is a parallelogram and $AB = CD$. Since $\overline{AB}$ and $\overline{CD}$ are arbitrary segments satisfying the hypotheses of the theorem the proof is complete.

Definition. The *distance between two distinct parallel planes* is the length of a segment with endpoints in these planes and perpendicular to them.

Definition. A *dihedral angle* is the union of a line and two halfplanes having this line as edge and not lying in the same plane. The edge of these halfplanes is called the *edge of the dihedral angle.* The halfplanes are called the *faces* of the dihedral angle.

Definition. The intersection of a dihedral angle and a plane perpendicular to its edge is called a *plane angle of the dihedral angle.*

Theorem 10.17. Any two plane angles of a dihedral angle are congruent.

Proof. Let $\angle BAC$ and $\angle B'A'C'$ be two distinct plane angles of a given dihedral angle. We may suppose that B and B' are points in one

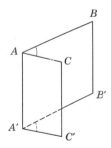

face, that C and C' are points in the other face, and that $AB = A'B'$, $AC = A'C'$. Since the plane determined by A, B, C and the plane determined by A', B', C' are each perpendicular to $\overleftrightarrow{AA'}$, it follows that $ACC'A'$

and $ABB'A'$ are rectangles. Then $\overline{CC'} \parallel \overline{AA'} \parallel \overline{BB'}$, $CC' = AA' = BB'$. It follows that $BB'C'C$ is a parallelogram. Therefore $BC = B'C'$. From the S.S.S. congruence theorem it follows that $\triangle ABC \cong \triangle A'B'C'$. Therefore $\angle BAC \cong \angle B'A'C'$.

Definition. The measure of a dihedral angle is the measure of any one of its plane angles.

Definition. A right dihedral angle is a dihedral angle whose measure is 90.

Definition. Two planes are *perpendicular* if and only if their union contains a right dihedral angle.

Theorem 10.18. If a given line is perpendicular to a given plane, then any plane which contains the given line is perpendicular to the given plane.

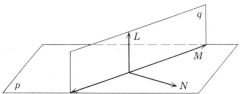

Proof. Let L be a line and p a plane such that $L \perp p$. Let q be any plane which contains L. Let M be the line in which p and q intersect, and let N be the line which is perpendicular to both L and M at their point of intersection. Then N lies in p. (Why?) Since $L \perp N$ and since the union of L and N contains a set of four plane angles, one for each of the dihedral angles formed by p and q, it follows that $p \perp q$.

Theorem 10.19. If two planes are perpendicular, then any line in one of the planes perpendicular to their line of intersection is perpendicular to the other plane.

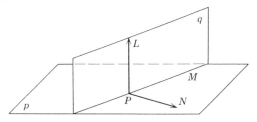

Proof. Let M be the line of intersection of two perpendicular planes p and q. Let L be any line in q and perpendicular to M. Let P be the point in which L intersects M. Let N be the line in p which is perpendicular to

M at P. Then $L \perp N$ (Why?) and $L \perp M$. Therefore L is perpendicular to p. (Why?)

Theorem 10.20. If two planes are perpendicular, then any line perpendicular to one of the planes at a point on their line of intersection lies in the other plane.

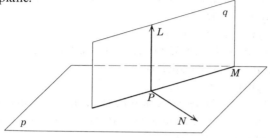

Proof. Let M be the line of intersection of two perpendicular planes p and q. Let P be a point of M, and N any line which is perpendicular to q at P. Let L be the line in q which is perpendicular to M at P. It follows from Theorem 10.19 that $L \perp p$. It follows from Theorem 10.8 that N lies in p.

Theorem 10.21. If two distinct intersecting planes are each perpendicular to a third plane, then their line of intersection is perpendicular to the plane.

Proof. Let L be the line of intersection of two distinct intersecting planes q and r, each of which is perpendicular to plane p. Let M and N be the lines in which r and q intersect p, respectively. Let P be the point in which M and N intersect. Let L' be the line in q which is perpendicular to N at P. It follows from Theorem 10.19 that $L' \perp p$. Let L'' be the line in r which is perpendicular to M at P. Then $L'' \perp p$. It follows from Theorem 10.7 that $L' = L''$. Therefore L' lies in both p and q. Therefore $L' = L$ and $L \perp p$.

Theorem 10.22. The set of all points equidistant from two given distinct points is the plane which is the perpendicular bisector of the segment joining the two given points.

Proof. Assigned as an exercise.

Theorem 10.23. If L, M, N are three mutually perpendicular lines, if L', M', N' are concurrent lines such that $L' \parallel L$, $M' \parallel N$, $N' \parallel N$, then L', M', N are also mutually perpendicular.

Proof. Assigned as an exercise.

Theorem 10.24. If a line L is parallel to a plane p, then the plane p is "simply covered" by a family of lines, each one of them parallel to the given line. (A family of lines *simply covers* a set if and only if every point of the set is an element of one and only one of the lines in the family.)

   Proof. Assigned as an exercise.

   Theorem 10.25. If *L*, *M*, *N* are three distinct lines such that *M* ‖ *N*, *L* intersects *M*, and *L* does not intersect *N*, then *N* is parallel to the plane determined by *L* and *M*.

   Proof. Assigned as an exercise.

   Theorem 10.26. If *L* and *M* are skew lines, there is one and only one plane containing *L* and parallel to *M*.

   Proof. Assigned as an exercise.

   Theorem 10.27. If a line *M* is parallel to a plane *p* and not contained in it, then there is a unique plane containing *M* and perpendicular to *p*.

   Proof. Assigned as an exercise.

   Theorem 10.28. If *L* and *M* are skew lines, there is a unique segment joining a point of *L* to a point of *M* and perpendicular to each of them.

   Proof. Let *p* be the unique plane containing *L* and parallel to *M*.

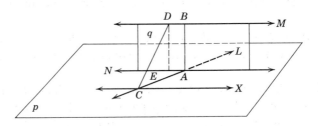

Let *q* be the unique plane containing *M* and perpendicular to *p*. Let *N* be the line in which *p* and *q* intersect. Now *N* and *L* are not parallel. (Why?) Since they are coplanar, their intersection is a point. Call it *A*. There is a unique line through *A* and perpendicular to *p*. It follows from Theorem 10.20 that this line lies in *q*. Since it is perpendicular to *N*, it is also perpendicular to *M*. Let *B* be the point in which it intersects *M*. Then $\overline{AB} \perp L$ (Why?) and $\overline{AB} \perp M$. Therefore there is at least one segment joining a point of *L* to a point of *M* and perpendicular to each of them.

   Suppose $\overline{CD}$ is another segment joining a point *C* of *L* to a point *D* of *M*, and perpendicular to both of them. Let *E* be the foot of the perpendicular from *D* to *N*. Let *X* be the unique line through *C* and parallel to *M*. Since $\overline{DC} \perp M$, it follows that $\overline{DC} \perp X$. Then $\overline{DC} \perp p$. (Why?) but $\overline{DE} \perp p$ (Theorem 10.19). Therefore $\overline{DE}$ and $\overline{DC}$ are perpendiculars from *D* to *p*.

If $D = B$ then $\overline{DE} = \overline{BA}$, $\overline{DC} = \overline{BC}$ and $\triangle ABC$ is a triangle with two right angles. Since this is impossible, it follows that $D \neq B$. Then $E \neq A$.

If $C = A$, then $\triangle BCD$ is a triangle with two right angles. Since this is impossible, it follows that $C \neq A$. Since $\overline{DE}$ contains a point of N, whereas $\overline{DC}$ does not, it follows that $\overline{DE} \neq \overline{DC}$. Therefore there are two distinct perpendiculars from D to p. Since this is impossible (Theorem 10.7), it follows that our supposition regarding the existence of the segment $\overline{CD}$ is untenable. Therefore there is one and only one segment joining a point of L to a point of M and perpendicular to each of them.

Exercises 10.2

1. Prove Theorem 10.15.

2. Prove Theorem 10.22.

3. Prove Theorem 10.23.

4. Prove Theorem 10.24.

5. Prove Theorem 10.25. *Hints:* Show that N does not lie in the plane of L and M. What is the intersection of the plane determined by L and M with the plane determined by M and N?

6. Prove Theorem 10.26. *Hints:* Let P be a point of L and let N be a line through P and parallel to M. Use Theorem 10.25 to prove the existence of a plane m with the required properties. This plane is simply covered by a family of lines parallel to M. Use Theorem 10.24 and the parallel postulate to prove uniqueness.

7. Prove Theorem 10.27. *Hints:* Drop a perpendicular from a point of M to p. Let P be the foot of that perpendicular. P and M determine a plane.

10.3 *Coordinates and Space Geometry*

Let $\{A, A'\}$ be a unit-pair of points and suppose that all distances are relative to this unit-pair unless otherwise stated.

Let $\overleftrightarrow{OX}$, $\overleftrightarrow{OY}$, $\overleftrightarrow{OZ}$ be three mutually perpendicular lines. Let I, J, K be points on $\overleftrightarrow{OX}$, $\overleftrightarrow{OY}$, $\overleftrightarrow{OZ}$, respectively, such that $OI = OJ = OK = 1$. There is a coordinate system on $\overleftrightarrow{OX}$ with origin O and with unit-point I. Call this the x-coordinate system. The y-coordinate system on $\overleftrightarrow{OY}$ and the z-coordinate system on $\overleftrightarrow{OZ}$ are defined similarly. The lines $\overleftrightarrow{OX}$, $\overleftrightarrow{OY}$, and $\overleftrightarrow{OZ}$ are referred to frequently as the x-axis, the y-axis, and the z-axis, respectively. Collectively they are referred to as the coordinate axes. The plane determined by the x- and y-axes is called the xy-plane. The xz-plane and the yz-plane are defined similarly. These planes are called the coordinate planes. The xy-coordinate system is the one-to-one correspondence between the set of all points in the xy-plane and the set of all ordered pairs of real numbers as described in Chapter 9. Similarly the xz-coordinate system is defined for the points in the xz-plane, and the yz-coordinate system is defined for the points in the yz-plane.

Let P be any point in space. Let P_{xy}, P_{xz}, P_{yz} be the feet of the perpendiculars from P to the xy-plane, to the xz-plane, and to the yz-plane, respectively. (If P lies in the xy-plane, then $P = P_{xy}$, etc.) Let p_{xy}, p_{xz}, p_{yz} be the planes through P and parallel to the xy-plane, to the xz-plane, and to the yz-plane, respectively. Then p_{xy} contains P, P_{xz}, and P_{yz}; p_{xz} contains P, P_{xy}, and P_{yz}; and p_{yz} contains P, P_{xz}, and P_{xy}.

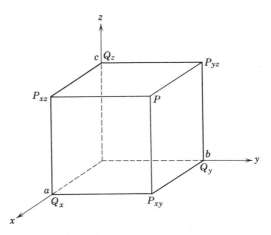

Let Q_x, Q_y, Q_z denote the points in which p_{yz}, p_{xz}, p_{xy} intersect the x-axis, the y-axis, and the z-axis, respectively. We are now ready to set up an xyz-coordinate system in space. The x-coordinate of P is the x-coordinate of Q_x; the y-coordinate of P is the y-coordinate of Q_y; the z-coordinate of P is the z-coordinate of Q_z. We write $P = P(a, b, c)$ to indicate that the x-, y-, and z-coordinates of P are a, b, and c, respectively.

If (a, b, c) is any ordered triple of real numbers, then there is one and only one point P such that $P = P(a, b, c)$. It is the intersection of three planes, one parallel to the yz-plane and cutting the x-axis at the point whose x-coordinate is a, etc. The correspondence between the set of all ordered triples of real numbers and the set of all points is a one-to-one correspondence. For if (a, b, c) and (d, e, f) are different triples, then one or more of the following is true: $a \neq d, b \neq e, c \neq f$. Suppose, for example, that $a \neq d$. Then $P(a, b, c)$ and $R(d, e, f)$ lie in distinct planes parallel to the yz-plane. Therefore $P \neq R$.

Definition. The one-to-one correspondence (described above) between the set of all points P and the set of all ordered triples of real numbers (a, b, c) is the *xyz-coordinate system*.

In view of the one-to-one correspondence in this definition, a system of names for the triples is a suitable system of names for the points. Thus $(3, 4, 5)$ is an ordered triple of real numbers. It is also a point; it is the unique point whose x-, y-, and z-coordinates are 3, 4, 5, respectively.

Exercises 10.3

1. Prove : Space is simply covered by the family of all planes parallel to the xy-plane.

2. Prove : Space is simply covered by the family of all lines parallel to the x-axis.

3. Prove : The z-axis is perpendicular to the xy-plane.

4. Prove : All lines perpendicular to the xy-plane are parallel.

5. Using the language of points, lines, planes, perpendicularity, parallelism, etc., describe the sets :
$$A = \{(x, y, z): x = 2\}, \quad B = \{(x, y, z): y = 2\}, \quad C = \{(x, y, z): z = 2\}.$$

6. Describe the sets :
$$A = \{(x, y, z): x = 2, y = 2\},$$
$$B = \{(x, y, z): x = 2, z = 2\},$$
$$C = \{(x, y, z): y = 2, z = 2\}.$$

7. Describe the sets :
$$A = \{(x, y, z): x = 0, y = 0, z = 0\},$$
$$B = \{(x, y, z): x = 0 \text{ or } y = 0, z = 0\},$$
$$C = \{(x, y, z): x = 0 \text{ or } y = 0 \text{ or } z = 0\}.$$

8. Describe the sets :
$$A = \{(x, y, z): x^2 + y^2 = 1, z = 0\},$$
$$B = \{(x, y, z): x^2 + y^2 = 1, z = 1\},$$
$$C = \{(x, y, z): x^2 + y^2 = 1, -1 \leqslant z \leqslant 1\}.$$

9. Use set-builder symbols and coordinates to express the following sets :

$A = $ the xy-plane $\qquad D = $ the x-axis

$B = $ the xz-plane $\qquad E = $ the y-axis

$C = $ the yz-plane $\qquad F = $ the z-axis

10. Use set-builder symbols and coordinates to express the following sets:

A = the plane containing $(1, 2, 7)$, $(1, 3, 5)$, and $(1, 9, 8)$.

B = the line parallel to the x-axis and containing $(3, 4, 7)$.

C = the plane containing the points $(0, 0, 0)$, $(5, 0, 0)$, and $(0, 5, 5)$.

10.4   *Distance and Coordinate Space Geometry*

Let points $P(x_1, y_1, z_1)$ and $Q(x_2, y_2, z_2)$ be given. Let $P_2 = (x_1, y_1, 0)$, $Q_1 = (x_2, y_2, z_1)$, $Q_2 = (x_2, y_2, 0)$, $Q_3 = (0, y_2, z_1)$, $Q_4 = (0, y_2, z_2)$. Since P and Q_1 are points in a plane parallel to the xy-plane it follows that

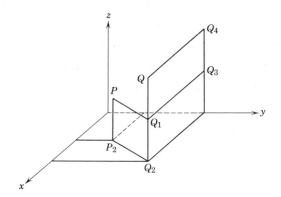

$\overleftrightarrow{PQ_1}$ is parallel to the xy-plane. Then either $P_2Q_2Q_1P$ is a rectangle, or $\overline{PQ_1} = \overline{P_2Q_2}$, or $P = Q_1$ and $P_2 = Q_2$. In all of these cases it is true that $(PQ_1)^2 = (P_2Q_2)^2 = (x_2 - x_1)^2 + (y_2 - y_1)^2$.

Similarly, $Q_1Q_3Q_4Q$ is a rectangle, or $\overline{QQ_1} = \overline{Q_3Q_4}$, or $Q = Q_1$ and $Q_4 = Q_3$. In all of these cases it is true that $(Q_1Q)^2 = (Q_3Q_4)^2 = (z_2 - z_1)^2$.

If $Q = Q_1$, then $z_2 = z_1$ and $(PQ)^2 = (PQ_1)^2 = (x_2 - x_1)^2 + (y_2 - y_1)^2 + (z_2 - z_1)^2$. If $P = Q_1$, then $x_2 = x_1$, $y_2 = y_1$, and $(PQ)^2 = (Q_1Q)^2 = (x_2 - x_1)^2 + (y_2 - y_1)^2 + (z_2 - z_1)^2$. If $P \neq Q_1$ and $Q \neq Q_1$, then $\overline{QQ_1} \perp \overline{PQ_1}$ and it follows from the Pythagorean theorem that $(PQ)^2 = (PQ_1)^2 + (QQ_1)^2 = (x_2 - x_1)^2 + (y_2 - y_1)^2 + (z_2 - z_1)^2$. Thus the distance formula as stated in the next theorem hold in all cases.

Theorem 10.29. If $P(x_1, y_1, z_1)$ and $Q(x_2, y_2, z_2)$ are points, then $PQ = \sqrt{(x_2 - x_1)^2 + (y_2 - y_1)^2 + (z_2 - z_1)^2}$.

As an immediate application of this formula we write an equation for a sphere in our next theorem.

Theorem 10.30. If S is the sphere with center (a, b, c) and radius r, then $S = \{(x, y, z) : (x - a)^2 + (y - b)^2 + (z - c^2) = r^2\}$.

10.5 *Parametric Equations for a Line in Space*

By an argument similar to the one we used to develop parametric equations for a line in the xy-plane we can prove the following theorem.

Theorem 10.31. If $P(x_1, y_1, z_1)$ and $Q(x_2, y_2, z_2)$ are two distinct points, then

$$\overleftrightarrow{PQ} = \left\{ (x, y, z) : \begin{array}{l} x = x_1 + k(x_2 - x_1), \\ y = y_1 + k(y_2 - y_1), \\ z = z_1 + k(z_2 - z_1). \end{array} \quad \text{and } k \text{ is real} \right\}$$

If $R = (x_1 + k(x_2 - x_1), y_1 + k(y_2 - y_1), z_1 + k(z_2 - z_1))$ is a point of $\overleftrightarrow{PQ}$, then

1. $R = P$ if $k = 0$.
2. $R \in \overrightarrow{PQ}$ and $PR = k \cdot PQ$ if $k > 0$.
3. $R \in \text{Opp } \overrightarrow{PQ}$, and $PR = -k \cdot PQ$ if $k < 0$.

Exercises 10.5

1. Describe the sets:

$$A = \{(x, y, z) : x^2 + y^2 + z^2 = 0\},$$
$$B = \{(x, y, z) : x^2 + y^2 + z^2 = 5\},$$
$$C = \{(x, y, z) : x^2 + y^2 + z^2 = 25\}.$$

2. Describe the sets:

$$A = \{(x, y, z) : x + y = 1 \text{ and } z = -1\},$$
$$B = \{(x, y, z) : x + z = 1 \text{ and } y = -1\},$$
$$C = \{(x, y, z) : y + z = 1 \text{ and } x = -1\}.$$

3. In the proof of Theorem 10.29 what authority might be given for the following statements?
   (a) $(P_2Q_2)^2 = (x_2 - x_1)^2 + (y_2 - y_1)^2$,
   (b) $(Q_3Q_4)^2 = (z_2 - z_1)^2$.

4. Determine the distance between P and Q if the coordinates are as given.
   (a) $P = (0, 0, 0)$, $Q = (5, 3, -4)$.
   (b) $P = (7, -3, 4)$, $Q = (-2, 5, 3)$.
   (c) $P = (-2, 5, 3)$, $Q = (7, -3, 4)$.
   (d) $P = (7, 8, 1)$, $Q = (7, 8, 1)$.

5. Use the distance formula to show that the following three points are collinear.
$$A = (3, -2, -4), \quad B = (-2, 5, -6), \quad C = (13, -16, 0).$$

6. Use the distance formula to show that the following three points are not collinear.

$$A = (3, 1, 4), \quad B = (2, 7, 5), \quad C = (1, -2, -3).$$

7. Determine for each of the points A, B, C whether it is inside the sphere S, on the sphere S, or outside the sphere S if S, A, B, C are given as follows:

$$S = \{(x, y, z) : (x - 1)^2 + (y - 2)^2 + (z + 3)^2 = 17\},$$

$$A = (1, 2, -2), \quad B = (1, 2, 1), \quad C = (2, 3, -5).$$

8. Compute $m\angle ABC$ if $A = (3, 7, 4)$, $B = (10, -3, 4)$, $C = (3, 7, -2)$.

9. Given $A = (5, 3, 2)$, $B = (7, 8, 1)$, $C = (5, 2, -7)$, $D = (5, 2, -3)$. Determine for each of the following triangles whether it is or is not a right triangle: $\triangle ABC$, $\triangle ABD, \triangle ACD, \triangle BCD$.

10. Express using set-builder symbols the interior and the exterior of the sphere S given as follows:

$$S = \{(x, y, z) : x^2 + y^2 + z^2 = 100\}.$$

11. Express using a set-builder symbol and parametric equations the line determined by the two points $A = (5, -1, 3)$ and $B = (-1, -2, 1)$.

12. Given points A and B as in Exercise 11. Find the coordinates of the point C on $\overrightarrow{AB}$ such that $AC = 5 \cdot AB$.

13. Given points A and B as in Exercise 11. Find the coordinates of the point D on Opp $\overrightarrow{AB}$ such that $AD = 5 \cdot AB$.

14. Given a line L and a sphere S as follows:

$$L = \{(x, y, z) : x = 1 + k, y = 2 - 3k, z = -1 + 2k, k \text{ is real}\},$$

$$S = \{(x, y, z) : (x - 1)^2 + (y - 2)^2 + (z + 1)^2 = 16\}.$$

Find the coordinates of the points in which L and S intersect.

15. Find the radius and the coordinates of the center of the circle which is the intersection of the sphere S of Exercise 14 and the plane whose equation is $z = 2$.

16. Determine whether or not lines L and M intersect, given that

$$L = \{(x, y, z) : x = k, y = 2 - 2k, z = -3 + 3k, k \text{ is real}\},$$

$$M = \{(x, y, z) : x = k + 1, y = 1 - 2k, z = 4 - 3k, k \text{ is real}\}.$$

17. Determine whether or not lines L and M intersect, given that:

$$L = \{(x, y, z) : x = k, y = 3 - 2k, z = -3 + 3k, k \text{ is real}\},$$

$$M = \{(x, y, z) : x = k + 1, y = 1 - 2k, z = 4 - k, k \text{ is real}\}.$$

18. Find the shortest distance between the skew lines L and M given as follows:

$$L = \{(x, y, z): x = u, y = u + 1, z = u + 2, u \text{ is real}\},$$

$$M = \{(x, y, z): x = 2v, y = 3v - 1, z = v + 3, v \text{ is real}\}.$$

Hint: Use calculus and minimize

$$(PQ)^2 = (u - 2v)^2 + \cdots.$$

19. For the lines L and M of Exercise 18 find the coordinates of the endpoints of the shortest segment joining a point of one of these lines to a point of the other.

10.6 *Symmetric Equations and Direction Numbers for a Line*

Let $A = (1, 2, 3)$ and $B = (-1, 4, -3)$. Then

$$\overleftrightarrow{AB} = \{(x, y, z): x = 1 - 2k, y = 2 + 2k, z = 3 - 6k, k \text{ is real}\}.$$

Solving each of the three parametric equations for k we get

$$(*) \qquad \frac{x - 1}{-2} = \frac{y - 2}{2} = \frac{z - 3}{-6}.$$

For every real number k there is a point (x, y, z) on $\overleftrightarrow{AB}$ with (x, y, z) satisfying (*). Conversely, if x, y, z satisfy (*), then there is a number, namely $(x - 1)/-2$, which upon substitution for k in the parametric equations for $\overleftrightarrow{AB}$, yields (x, y, z) as a point of $\overleftrightarrow{AB}$. Therefore

$$\overleftrightarrow{AB} = \left\{ (x, y, z): \frac{x - 1}{-2} = \frac{y - 2}{2} = \frac{z - 3}{-6} \right\}.$$

Note the form of equations (*). The numbers subtracted from x, y, z in the numerators are the coordinates of the point A. The numbers in the denominators are the coefficients of k in the parametric equations. Equations (*) are called *symmetric equations* for $\overleftrightarrow{AB}$. The ordered triple of numbers in the denominators, $[-2, 2, -6]$, are called *direction numbers* for $\overleftrightarrow{AB}$.

Definition. If $P(x_1, y_1, z_1)$ and $Q(x_2, y_2, z_2)$ are two distinct points and if a is any number different from zero, then $[a(x_2 - x_1), a(y_2 - y_1), a(z_2 - z_1)]$ is a triple of *direction numbers* for $\overline{PQ}$.

Since P and Q are distinct points, at least one of the numbers, $x_2 - x_1$, $y_2 - y_1$, $z_2 - z_1$, is not zero. If $[d, e, f]$ and $[g, h, i]$ are two triples of real numbers, and if $[d, e, f]$ is a set of direction numbers for $\overline{PQ}$, then $[g, h, i]$

is a set of direction numbers for $\overline{PQ}$ if and only if $(d, e, f) \neq (g, h, i)$. The set of all triples which serve as direction numbers for $\overline{PQ}$ is an equivalence class, where two triples are considered equivalent if they are proportional. Any one of these triples may be considered as the *direction* of the segment $\overline{PQ}$.

Theorem 10.32. All segments of a given line have the same direction.

Proof. Let A and B be two distinct points. Then there are real numbers a, b, c, a', b', c' such that

$$\overleftrightarrow{AB} = \{(x, y, z): x = a + ka', y = b + kb', z = c + kc', k \text{ is real}\}.$$

Let C and D be any two distinct points of $\overleftrightarrow{AB}$. Then there are distinct values of k, say k_1 and k_2, such that

$$C = (a + k_1 a', b + k_1 b', c + k_1 c') \quad \text{and} \quad D = (a + k_2 a', b + k_2 b', c + k_2 c').$$

A triple of direction numbers for $\overline{CD}$ is $[(k_2 - k_1)a', (k_2 - k_1)b', (k_2 - k_1)c']$. It follows that the equivalence class of direction numbers for $\overline{CD}$ is the set of all triples proportional to $[a', b', c']$. Since the same result would be obtained for every choice of two distinct points of $\overleftrightarrow{AB}$, it follows that all segments of $\overleftrightarrow{AB}$ have the same direction.

Definition. The *direction of a line* is the direction of any one of its segments.

If $A = (x_1, y_1, z_1)$ and $B = (x_2, y_2, z_2)$ are two distinct points, then $[x_2 - x_1, y_2 - y_1, z_2 - z_1]$ is a triple of direction numbers for the line $\overleftrightarrow{AB}$ (as well as for the segment $\overline{AB}$). If all three numbers in this triple are different from zero, then symmetric equations can be given for the line.

Theorem 10.33. If $A = (x_1, y_1, z_1)$ and $B = (x_2, y_2, z_2)$ are two distinct points and $x_2 \neq x_1, y_2 \neq y_1, z_2 \neq z_1$, then

$$\overleftrightarrow{AB} = \left\{(x, y, z): \frac{x - x_1}{x_2 - x_1} = \frac{y - y_1}{y_2 - y_1} = \frac{z - z_1}{z_2 - z_1}\right\}.$$

Proof.

$$\overleftrightarrow{AB} = \left\{(x, y, z): \begin{array}{l} x = x_1 + (x_2 - x_1)k, \\ y = y_1 + (y_2 - y_1)k, \quad k \text{ is real} \\ z = z_1 + (z_2 - z_1)k. \end{array}\right\}.$$

Solving each of the three parametric equations for k, we get

$$(*) \qquad \frac{x - x_1}{x_2 - x_1} = \frac{y - y_1}{y_2 - y_1} = \frac{z - z_1}{z_2 - z_1}.$$

If (x, y, z) is any point on $\overleftrightarrow{AB}$, there is one and only one number k which yields this point when used in the parametric equations. This number k yields the numbers x, y, z which satisfy (*). Conversely, if x, y, z satisfy (*), then there is exactly one number k, namely $(x - x_1)/(x_2 - x_1)$, which produces x, y, z in the parametric equations, and hence (x, y, z) is a point of $\overleftrightarrow{AB}$.

Exercises 10.6

1. Given $A = (1, 2, 3)$ and $B = (-1, 4, -3)$. Then

$$\overleftrightarrow{AB} = \left\{ (x, y, z) : \frac{x - 1}{-2} = \frac{y - 2}{2} = \frac{z - 3}{-6} \right\}.$$

What is the common value of the three members of the symmetric equations when (x, y, z) is the point A? When it is the point B? When it is the point C on $\overrightarrow{AB}$ such that $AC = 2 \cdot AB$?

2. Given A and B as in Exercise 1. Find the coordinates of the point P on $\overrightarrow{AB}$ such that $AP = 3 \cdot AB$.

3. Describe the set

$$\left\{ (x, y) : \frac{x - 1}{-2} = \frac{y - 2}{2} \right\}.$$

4. Describe the set

$$\left\{ (x, y, z) : \frac{x - 1}{-2} = \frac{y - 2}{2} \text{ and } z = 0 \right\}.$$

5. Describe the set

$$\left\{ (x, y, z) : \frac{x - 1}{-2} = \frac{y - 2}{2} \text{ and } z = 3 \right\}.$$

6. Describe the set

$$\left\{ (x, y, z) : \frac{x - 1}{-2} = \frac{y - 2}{2} \text{ and } 0 \leqslant z \leqslant 3 \right\}.$$

7. Describe the set

$$\left\{ (x, y, z) : \frac{x - 1}{-2} = \frac{y - 2}{2} = \frac{z - 3}{-6}, 1 \leqslant x \right\}.$$

8. Describe the set

$$\left\{ (x, y, z) : \frac{x - 1}{-2} = \frac{y - 2}{2} = \frac{z - 3}{-6}, 1 \leqslant x \leqslant 11 \right\}.$$

9. Compute a triple of direction numbers for $\overline{AB}$ if $A = (5, 3, 2)$ and $B = (3, 1, 4)$.

10. Given $P = (0, 0, 0)$, $Q = (1, 1, 1)$, and $R = (x, y, z)$. Express in terms of co-ordinates $(PQ)^2, (PR)^2, (QR)^2$. Set $(PQ)^2 + (PR)^2 = (QR)^2$ and simplify.

11. Given P, Q, R as in Exercise 10. Set $(PQ)^2 + (QR)^2 = (PR)^2$ and simplify.

12. Describe the set of all points R in Exercise 10.

13. Describe the set of all points R in Exercise 11.

14. Use a set-builder symbol and symmetric equations to express $\overleftrightarrow{AB}$ if $A = (5, 2, 3)$ and $B = (7, 1, 5)$.

15. Use a set-builder symbol and symmetric equations to express line M if $(3, 4, 7)$ is a point of M and $[4, 3, -2]$ is a set of direction numbers for M.

16. Use a set-builder symbol and parametric equations to express line L if $(5, 3, 7)$ is a point of L and $[3, 4, 0]$ is a set of direction numbers for L.

17. Given $A = (3, 4, 5)$, $B = (5, 4, 5)$, $C = (5, 8, 5)$, $D = (5, 8, 10)$. Find a set of direction numbers for each of the segments $\overline{AB}, \overline{BC}, \overline{CD}, \overline{AD}$.

18. Given a line L and a sphere S as follows:

$$L = \left\{ (x, y, z) : \frac{x - 2}{1} = \frac{y + 3}{-1} = \frac{z - 4}{-2} \right\},$$

$$S = \{(x, y, z) : x^2 + y^2 + z^2 = 29\}.$$

Find the coordinates of the points in which L and S intersect.

19. Given line L as in Exercise 18. Find a number t such that the sphere T given as follows is tangent to L. (There is one and only one such number t.)

$$T = \{(x, y, z) : x^2 + y^2 + z^2 = t\}.$$

20. Describe the intersection of T and L if t is replaced by a number which is larger than the answer to Exercise 19. Describe the intersection if it is replaced by a number smaller than the answer to Exercise 19.

21. Compute the distance from the origin to the line L in Exercise 18.

22. Given $A = (1, 1, 1)$, $B = (2, 7, 8)$, $C = (x, y, z)$. Express AC and BC in terms of coordinates. Set $AC = BC$ and simplify the resulting equation in x, y, z. Consider C as a variable point subject to the condition $AC = BC$. Describe the set of all points C.

23. Given $A = (1, 0, 0)$ and $B = (x, y, z)$. Express in terms of coordinates (a) the distance from B to the plane P given by $P = \{(x, y, z) : x = -1\}$, and (b) the distance AB. Set these distances equal and simplify. Describe the set of all points B.

24. Find the coordinates of a point on the x-axis which is equidistant from $(4, 2, 5)$ and $(7, 4, 8)$.

25. Given

$$L = \left\{(x, y, z): \frac{x-1}{2} = \frac{y-2}{-3} = \frac{z+1}{-1}\right\}.$$

Find the coordinates of the point on L which is equidistant from $(4, 2, 5)$ and $(7, 4, 8)$.

26. Given $A = (0, 0, 0)$, $B = (5, 5, 5)$,

$$L = \{(x, y, z): x = 1 + k, y = 1 - k, z = 1 - k, k \text{ is real}\}.$$

Find the coordinates of a point C on L such that $m\angle ACB = 90$.

27. Given skew lines L and M as follows:

$$L = \left\{(x, y, z): \frac{x-0}{2} = \frac{y-2}{-1} = \frac{z-3}{2}\right\},$$

$$M = \left\{(x, y, z): \frac{x-1}{-2} = \frac{y+3}{-2} = \frac{z-7}{5}\right\}.$$

Outline a procedure for finding the length of the shortest segment with one endpoint on L and one endpoint on M.

10.7 *Equation of a Plane*

Let $A = (0, 0, 0)$, $B = (3, 2, 5)$, P the unique plane which is perpendicular to $\overleftrightarrow{AB}$ at B, and Q the unique plane which is perpendicular to $\overleftrightarrow{AB}$ at A. Then $C(x, y, z)$ is a point of P if and only if $C = B$ or $\overline{AB} \perp \overline{BC}$. By using the Pythagorean theorem and its converse it follows that $C(x, y, z)$ is a point of P if and only if $C = B$ or $(AC)^2 = (AB)^2 + (BC)^2$. In terms of coordinates, $C \in P$ if and only if $(x, y, z) = (3, 2, 5)$ or $x^2 + y^2 + z^2 = 38 + (x-3)^2 + (y-2)^2 + (z-5)^2$, that is, if and only if $(x, y, z) = (3, 2, 5)$ or $3x + 2y + 5z = 38$. But $3^2 + 2^2 + 5^2 = 38$. Therefore C is a point of P if and only if $3x + 2y + 5z = 38$. Therefore $P = \{(x, y, z): 3x + 2y + 5z = 38\}$.

Similarly, $D = (x, y, z)$ is a point of Q if and only if $D = A$ or $(DB)^2 = (DA)^2 + (AB)^2$. Then $D \in Q$ if and only if $(x, y, z) = (0, 0, 0)$ or

$$(x-3)^2 + (y-2)^2 + (z-5)^2 = x^2 + y^2 + z^2 + 9 + 4 + 25.$$

Finally $D \in Q$ if and only if $3x + 2y + 5z = 0$. Therefore $Q = \{(x, y, z): 3x + 2y + 5z = 0\}$.

Note the similarity of the equations for P and Q. The coefficients of x, y, z in the equations for P and Q are a set of direction numbers for $\overleftrightarrow{AB}$, a line which is normal (perpendicular) to each of these planes. The number in the right member of the equation also has an interesting significance.

Plane Q passes the origin. In other words its distance from the origin is 0. The distance of P from the origin is $AB = \sqrt{38}$. Generalizing, it would seem that $ax + by + cz = a^2 + b^2 + c^2$ should be an equation for a plane which is normal to a line with direction $[a, b, c]$ and which is at a distance of $\sqrt{a^2 + b^2 + c^2}$ from the origin, and that $ax + by + cz = 0$ is the equation of a plane which is normal to the same line and passes through the origin.

Theorem 10.34. Let $[a, b, c]$ be a set of direction numbers. Then

$$P = \{(x, y, z): ax + by + cz = 0\}$$

is the unique plane through $(0, 0, 0)$ and normal to the segment from $(0, 0, 0)$ to $(a,\ b, c)$, and

$$Q = \{(x, y, z): ax + by + cz = a^2 + b^2 + c^2\}$$

is the unique plane through (a, b, c) and normal to the segment from $(0, 0, 0)$ to (a, b, c).

Proof. Let $[a, b, c]$ be a triple of direction numbers. Let $A = (0, 0, 0)$, $B = (a, b, c)$, $C = (x, y, z)$. Let P and Q be the unique planes perpendicular to the segment from $(0, 0, 0)$ to (a, b, c) which pass through $(0, 0, 0)$ and (a, b, c), respectively. Then $C \in P$ if and only if $C = A$ or $(CB)^2 = (CA)^2 + AB^2$; $C \in P$ if and only if $(x, y, z) = (0, 0, 0)$ or

$$(x - a)^2 + (y - b)^2 + (z - c)^2 = x^2 + y^2 + z^2 + a^2 + b^2 + c^2;$$

and $C \in P$ if and only if $ax + by + cz = 0$. Also, $C \in Q$ if and only if $C = B$ or $(CA)^2 = (CB)^2 + (BA)^2$; $C \in Q$ if and only if $(x, y, z) = (a, b, c)$ or

$$x^2 + y^2 + z^2 = (x - a)^2 + (y - b)^2 + (z - c)^2 + a^2 + b^2 + c^2;$$

and $C \in Q$ if and only if $ax + by + cz = a^2 + b^2 + c^2$.

Theorem 10.35. Every plane has an equation of the form $ax + by + cz = d$, where one or more of the coefficients $a, b, c,$ is different from zero; and every equation of this form is an equation of a plane.

Proof. Let $A = (0, 0, 0)$, $B = (a, b, c)$, $C = (x, y, z)$. We consider two cases: $d = 0$ or $d \neq 0$. Suppose first that $d = 0$. Then (x, y, z) satisfies $ax + by + cz = d$ if and only if

$$x^2 + y^2 + z^2 + a^2 + b^2 + c^2 = (x - a)^2 + (y - b)^2 + (z - c)^2,$$

if and only if $(CA)^2 + (AB)^2 = (CB)^2$, if and only if $C = A$ or $\overline{CA} \perp \overline{AB}$, that is, if and only if C lies in the plane through the origin and perpendicular to the line $\overleftrightarrow{AB}$.

Suppose next that $d \neq 0$. Let

$$a' = \frac{ad}{a^2 + b^2 + c^2}, \quad b' = \frac{bd}{a^2 + b^2 + c^2}, \quad c' = \frac{cd}{a^2 + b^2 + c^2},$$

$$d' = \frac{dd}{a^2 + b^2 + c^2}.$$

Let $D = (a', b', c')$. Then (x, y, z) satisfies $ax + by + cz = d$ if and only if $a'x + b'y + c'z = d'$, if and only if $a'x + b'y + c'z = (a')^2 + (b')^2 + (c')^2$, that is, if and only if C lies in the plane which contains D and is normal to the segment $\overline{AD}$.

Theorem 10.36. If $ax + by + cz = d$ is an equation of a plane P, then $|d|/\sqrt{a^2 + b^2 + c^2}$ is the distance from the origin to P, and

$$\left[\frac{a}{\sqrt{a^2 + b^2 + c^2}}, \quad \frac{b}{\sqrt{a^2 + b^2 + c^2}}, \quad \frac{c}{\sqrt{a^2 + b^2 + c^2}} \right]$$

is a set of direction numbers for a line which is normal to P.

Proof. Suppose $d = 0$. Then P passes through the origin, and the distance from P to the origin is $0 = d = |d|/\sqrt{a^2 + b^2 + c^2}$. As shown in the proof of Theorem 10.35, P is normal to the segment from the origin to (a, b, c). Hence $[a, b, c]$, or any triple proportional to them, is a set of direction numbers for a line normal to P.

Suppose next that $d \neq 0$. Then $P = \{(x, y, z): a'x + b'y + c'z = d'\}$ where a', b', c', d' are defined as in the proof of Theorem 10.35. Then P contains $D = (a', b', c')$ and is perpendicular to the segment $\overline{AD}$. It follows that the distance from the origin to P is

$$AD = \sqrt{(a')^2 + (b')^2 + (c')^2} = \sqrt{\frac{d^2}{a^2 + b^2 + c^2}} = \frac{|d|}{\sqrt{a^2 + b^2 + c^2}},$$

and that a triple of direction numbers for a line normal to P is $[a', b', c']$. Since $(a, b, c) \underset{p}{=} (a', b', c')$, it follows that $[a, b, c]$ is also a triple of direction numbers for a line normal to P.

10.8 *Perpendicularity and Parallelism*

Two *directions are perpendicular* if there are perpendicular lines with these directions. In advanced mathematics we consider lines as perpendicular if their directions are perpendicular (regardless of whether or not the lines intersect). Two *directions are parallel* if and only if there are parallel lines which have these directions. Following are two important theorems which give necessary and sufficient conditions for two directions to be perpendicular, or parallel.

Theorem 10.37. Given two directions d_1 and d_2 such that $d_1 = [a, b, c]$, $d_2 = [u, v, w]$. Then $d_1 \perp d_2$ if and only if $au + bv + cw = 0$.

Proof. Let $A = (0, 0, 0)$, $B = (a, b, c)$, $C = (u, v, w)$. If $au + bv + cw = 0$, then

$$a^2 + b^2 + c^2 + u^2 + v^2 + w^2 = (a - u)^2 + (b - v)^2 + (c - w)^2,$$

$$(AB)^2 + (AC)^2 = (BC)^2, \quad \overline{AB} \perp \overline{AC} \quad \text{and} \quad d_1 \perp d_2.$$

Conversely, if $d_1 \perp d_2$, then

$$\overline{AB} \perp \overline{AC}, \quad (AB)^2 + (AC)^2 = (BC)^2,$$

$$a^2 + b^2 + c^2 + u^2 + v^2 + w^2 = (a - u)^2 + (b - v)^2 + (c - w)^2,$$

and

$$au + bv + cw = 0.$$

Theorem 10.38. Two lines are parallel if and only if they have the same direction.

Proof. Let lines L and M be given:

$$L = \{(x, y, z) : x = x_1 + ah, y = y_1 + bh, z = z_1 + ch, h \text{ is real}\},$$

$$M = \{(x, y, z) : x = x_2 + uk, y = y_2 + vk, z = z_2 + wk, k \text{ is real}\}.$$

Suppose first that L and M have the same direction. Then $(a, b, c) \overline{\overline{p}}$ (u, v, w) and there is a number t, $t \neq 0$, such that $u = ta$, $v = tb$, $w = tc$. We consider two cases: (1) $L \cap M \neq \varnothing$ and (2) $L \cap M = \varnothing$.

Case 1. $L \cap M \neq \varnothing$. There is a point (x_0, y_0, z_0) on both L and M. There are numbers h_0 and k_0 such that

$$x_0 = x_1 + ah_0 = x_2 + uk_0 = x_2 + tak_0, \quad x_2 = x_1 + a(h_0 - tk_0),$$

$$y_0 = y_1 + bh_0 = y_2 + vk_0 = y_2 + tbk_0, \quad y_2 = y_1 + b(h_0 - tk_0),$$

$$z_0 = z_1 + ch_0 = z_2 + wk_0 = z_2 + tck_0, \quad z_2 = z_1 + c(h_0 - tk_0).$$

Then

$$M = \{(x, y, z) : x = x_1 + a(h_0 - tk_0 + tk),$$

$$y = y_1 + b(h_0 - tk_0 + tk),$$

$$z = z_1 + c(h_0 - tk_0 + tk), k \text{ is real}\}.$$

Since there is a one to one correspondence between the set of all real numbers h and the set of all real numbers $h_0 - tk_0 + tk$ (h_0, k_0, and t are fixed and k is variable), it follows that

$$M = \{(x, y, z): x = x_1 + ah, y = y_1 + bh, z = z_1 + ch, h \text{ is real}\}.$$

Therefore $L = M$ and $L \parallel M$.

Case 2. $L \cap M = \emptyset$. $A = (x_1, y_1, z_1)$ and $C = (x_1 + a, y_1 + b, z_1 + c)$ are two distinct points of L. $B = (x_2, y_2, z_2)$ and $D = (x_2 + u, y_2 + v, z_2 + w)$ are two distinct points of M. Since L and M do not intersect, and since $a, b,$ and c are not all zero, it follows that A, B, C are three noncollinear points, and hence they determine a plane P. Then there are numbers a', b', c', d', with a', b', c' not all zero, such that

$$P = \{(x, y, z): a'x + b'y + c'z = d'\}.$$

We shall show that D lies in P. Since A, B, C lie in P we have

1. $a'x_1 + b'y_1 + c'z_1 = d'$.
2. $a'(x_1 + a) + b'(y_1 + b) + c'(z_1 + c) = d'$.
3. $a'x_2 + b'y_2 + c'z_2 = d'$.

From (1) and (2) we get (4), from (4) we get (5), and from (3) and (5) we get (6):

4. $a'a + b'b + c'c = 0$.
5. $a'at + b'bt + c'ct = 0$.
6. $a'(x_2 + u) + b'(y_2 + v) + c'(z_2 + w) = d'$.

Therefore D is a point of P. It follows that L and M are coplanar nonintersecting lines, and hence they are parallel. This completes the proof of the "if" part of the theorem : If two lines have the same direction, they are parallel.

Suppose now that lines L and M as given at the beginning of the proof are parallel. Let

$$L' = \{(x, y, z): x = ah, y = bh, z = ch, h \text{ is real}\},$$

$$M' = \{(x, y, z): x = uk, y = vk, z = wk, k \text{ is real}\}.$$

Since L' and L have the same direction, and M' and M have the same direction, it follows from the first part of this proof that $L' \parallel L$ and $M' \parallel M$. Since $L \parallel M$, it follows from the transitive property of parallelism for lines that $L' \parallel M'$. But L' and M' each contains the origin. Therefore

$L' = M'$. Let h_1 be any number different from zero. Then (ah_1, bh_1, ch_1) is a point of L'. Since it is also a point of M', there is a number k_1 such that $ah_1 = uk_1$, $bh_1 = vk_1$, $ch_1 = wk_1$. Therefore $(a, b, c) \mathrel{\overline{\parallel}} (u, v, w)$. This completes the proof of the "only if" part of the theorem: Two lines are parallel only if they have the same direction.

Theorem 10.39. Given planes P and Q as follows:

$$P = \{(x, y, z): ax + by + cz = d\},$$

$$Q = \{(x, y, z): a'x + b'y + c'z = d'\}.$$

Then $P \parallel Q$ if and only if $[a, b, c] = [a', b', c']$.

Proof. Suppose $[a, b, c] = [a', b', c']$. Since P is perpendicular to a line L with direction $[a, b, c]$ and Q is perpendicular to a line M with direction $[a', b', c']$, it follows from Theorem 10.38 that $L \parallel M$, and from Theorem 10.14 that P and Q are perpendicular to the same line, and from Theorem 10.13 that $P \parallel Q$.

Suppose next that $P \parallel Q$. Since P is perpendicular to a line L with direction $[a, b, c]$ and Q is perpendicular to a line M with direction $[a', b', c']$, it follows from Theorem 10.12 that L is perpendicular to Q, and from Theorem 10.9 that $L \parallel M$, and from Theorem 10.38 that $[a, b, c] = [a', b', c']$.

Theorem 10.40. Given planes P and Q as in Theorem 10.39. Then $P \perp Q$ if and only if $aa' + bb' + cc' = 0$.

Proof. Suppose $aa' + bb' + cc' = 0$. Then it is false that $[a, b, c] = [a', b', c']$. For if $[a', b', c] = [a, b, c]$, there is a number $t \neq 0$ such that $a' = at$, $b' = bt$, $c' = ct$, and $aa' + bb' + cc' = (a^2 + b^2 + c^2)t \neq 0$. It follows that P and Q are intersecting planes. Let L be their line of intersection. Let $\overline{AB}$ be a segment in P which is perpendicular to L at A. Let $\overline{AD}$ be a segment in Q which is perpendicular to L at A. Let C be the intersection of the normal to Q at D and the normal to P at B. Since the direction of $\overline{DC}$ is $[a', b', c']$, the direction of $\overline{BC}$ is $[a, b, c]$, and $aa' + bb' + cc' = 0$, it follows that $m\angle BCD = 90$. But $m\angle ABC = 90 = m\angle ADC$. It follows that $m\angle DAB = 90$ and hence that $P \perp Q$.

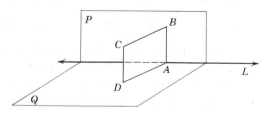

Suppose next that $P \perp Q$. Then, using a figure labeled as the one above, we see that $ABCD$ is a quadrilateral with right angles at A, B, and D. It follows that $m\angle C = 90$ and hence that $aa' + bb' + cc' = 0$.

Theorem 10.41. Three distinct points P, Q, R are collinear if and only if the segments $\overline{PQ}$ and $\overline{PR}$ have the same direction.

Proof. Assigned as an exercise.

Theorem 10.42. Three distinct points (x_i, y_i, z_i), $i = 1, 2, 3$, are collinear if and only if

$$(x_3 - x_1, y_3 - y_1, z_3 - z_1) \underset{\overline{P}}{=} (x_2 - x_1, y_2 - y_1, z_2 - z_1).$$

Proof. Assigned as an exercise.

Theorem 10.43. Four points (x_i, y_i, z_i), $i = 1, 2, 3, 4$, are coplanar if and only if

$$\begin{vmatrix} x_1 & y_1 & z_1 & 1 \\ x_2 & y_2 & z_2 & 1 \\ x_3 & y_3 & z_3 & 1 \\ x_4 & y_4 & z_4 & 1 \end{vmatrix} = 0$$

Proof. Let four points be given in terms of their coordinates as in the statement of the theorem. These four points are coplanar if and only if there are four numbers a, b, c, d, with a, b, c, not all zero, such that $ax_i + by_i + cz_i = d$, for $i = 1, 2, 3, 4$, or equivalently, that $ax_i + by_i + cz_i + d(-1) = 0$ for $i = 1, 2, 3, 4$.

We consider these equations as a system of four equations in the four unknowns (a, b, c, d). This system has the trivial solutions $a = 0$, $b = 0$, $c = 0$, $d = 0$. It has a nontrivial solution if and only if the determinant Δ

$$\Delta = \begin{vmatrix} x_1 & y_1 & z_1 & -1 \\ x_2 & y_2 & z_2 & -1 \\ x_3 & y_3 & z_3 & -1 \\ x_4 & y_4 & z_4 & -1 \end{vmatrix}$$

of the coefficients is zero. It is clear that there is no solution with $a = b = c = 0$ and $d \neq 0$. For this would imply that $-1 = 0$. Therefore the system of four equations has a solution for a, b, c, d, with a, b, c, not all zero, if and only if $\Delta = 0$. Since the determinant in the statement of the theorem is $-\Delta$, it follows that the four points are coplanar if and only if the determinant in the statement of the theorem is zero.

Theorem 10.44. Given two distinct points $P = (x_1, y_1, z_1)$ and $Q = (x_2, y_2, z_2)$. Then

$$\overleftrightarrow{PQ} = \{(x, y, z): (x - x_1, y - y_1, z - z_1) \underset{\overline{p}}{=} (x_2 - x_1, y_2 - y_1, z_2 - z_1)$$

$$\text{or} \quad (x, y, z) = (x_1, y_1, z_1)\}.$$

Proof. Assigned as an exercise.

Theorem 10.45. Given three noncollinear points $P(x_1, y_1, z_1)$, $Q(x_2, y_2, z_2)$, $R(x_3, y_3, z_3)$. Then an equation for the plane p determined by these points is as follows:

$$\begin{vmatrix} x & y & z & 1 \\ x_1 & y_1 & z_1 & 1 \\ x_2 & y_2 & z_2 & 1 \\ x_3 & y_3 & z_3 & 1 \end{vmatrix} = 0$$

Proof. Assigned as an exercise.

Theorem 10.46. An equation for the plane p which passes through the point (x_0, y_0, z_0) and is perpendicular to a line with directions $[a, b, c]$ is $a(x - x_0) + b(y - y_0) + c(z - z_0) = 0$.

Proof. Assigned as an exercise.

Exercises 10.8

1. Write an equation for the plane which passes through $(0, 0, 0)$ and is normal to the segment from the origin to $(5, -7, 2)$.

2. Write an equation for the plane which passes through $(5, -7, 2)$ and is normal to the segment from the origin to $(5, -7, 2)$.

3. Write an equation for the plane determined by the three points $(1, 2, 3)$, $(0, 0, 0)$ and $(2, 2, 3)$.

4. Write an equation for the plane determined by the point $P = (0, 0, 0)$ and the line L given by

   $$L = \{(x, y, z): x = 2 + k, y = 3 - 2k, z = -1 + k, k \text{ is real}\}.$$

5. Write symmetric equations for the line which passes through the origin, intersects the line L of Exercise 4, and is perpendicular to it. *Hint:* Find a value of k so that the direction from the origin to the point determined by that value of k is perpendicular to the direction of L.

6. Determine whether or not the points $(1, 0, 0)$, $(-1, 2, 5)$, $(7, -4, 3)$ are collinear. If they are collinear, express the line containing them using a set-builder symbol

and parametric equations. If they are not collinear, write an equation in "determinant form" for the plane determined by them.

7. Same as Exercise 6 for the three points $(5, 2, 8)$, $(5, 3, 12)$, and $(5, 9, 36)$.

8. Find the distance of the plane p from the origin where p is given by

$$p = \{(x, y, z): 3x - 4y - 7z = 8\}.$$

9. Given three points $P = (7, 3, 0)$, $Q = (1, 1, 1)$, $R = (0, 4, 7)$. Show that these points are noncollinear and that the plane determined by them contains the origin. *Hint :* The system of three equations in the three unknowns a, b, c obtained by substituting in turn the coordinates of P, Q, R in the equation $ax + by + cz = 0$ has a nontrivial solution if and only if the determinant of the coefficients is zero.

10. Following are pairs of equations for planes. Determine which pairs of planes are perpendicular, which pairs are parallel, and which pairs are neither.
    (a) $3x - 7y + 5z = 8$ and $3x - 7y + 5z = 9$.
    (b) $14x - 49y + 21z = 4$ and $10x - 35y + 15z = 7$.
    (c) $8x - 7y + 4z = 2$ and $7x + 8y = 0$.
    (d) $8x - 7y + 4z = 2$ and $4x + 4y - z = 103$.
    (e) $8x - 7y + 4z = 2$ and $x - 2z = 17$.
    (f) $8x - 7y + 4z = 2$ and $x + y - 2z = 17$.
    (g) $x - 3y + z - 0$ and $x + y + 2z = 0$.
    (h) $x - 3y + z = 0$ and $x - y + z = 1$.

11. Write an equation for the plane p determined by the distinct parallel lines L and M given as follows:

$$L = \{(x, y, z): x = k, y = 2k, z = 3 + 3k, k \text{ is real}\},$$

$$M = \{(x, y, z): x = 1 + k, y = 1 + 2k, z = 4 + 3k, k \text{ is real}\}.$$

Hint : Find the coordinates of a point P on L and a point Q on M. A normal to the required plane is perpendicular to L as well as to $\overline{PQ}$.

12. Write parametric equations for the line L which passes through $(5, 2, -3)$ and is parallel to the line M given by

$$M = \{(x, y, z): x = -k, y = 2 + 3k, z = 4 - 2k\}.$$

13. Write symmetric equations for the line L which passes through $(7, 8, 1)$ and is parallel to the line M given by

$$M = \left\{(x, y, z): \frac{x}{5} = \frac{y - 3}{7} - \frac{z - 8}{2}\right\}.$$

14. Write an equation for the plane which passes through $(0, 3, 8)$ and is perpendicular to the line M of Exercise 13.

15. In each part of this exercise there is an equation of a plane and a set of symmetric equations for a line. Determine for each part whether the line and the plane are perpendicular, parallel, or neither.

(a) $3(x - 1) + 4(y - 5) + 6(z + 2) = 0$,

$$\frac{x - 1}{3} = \frac{y - 5}{4} = \frac{z + 2}{6}.$$

(b) $3(x - 1) + 4(y - 5) + 6(z + 2) = 0$,

$$\frac{x - 1}{6} = \frac{y - 5}{3} = \frac{z + 2}{-5}.$$

(c) $3(x - 7) + 4(y + 2) - 6(z + 2) = 0$,

$$\frac{x}{6} = \frac{y}{3} = \frac{z}{5}.$$

(d) $x + 3y - 5z = 75$,

$$\frac{x - 7}{2} = \frac{y - 7}{6} = \frac{z - 7}{-10}.$$

(e) $x + 3y - 5z = 75$,

$$\frac{x - 7}{2} = \frac{y - 7}{6} = \frac{z - 7}{-9}.$$

16. Prove that the intersection of a sphere and a plane is either the null set, or a point, or a circle. *Hint :* Select a coordinate system so that the sphere S and the plane p are given as follows for some numbers r and z_0, where $r > 0$.

$$S = \{(x, y, z): x^2 + y^2 + z^2 = r^2\},$$

$$p = \{(x, y, z): z = z_0\}.$$

17. Given S and p as in Exercise 16 and $-r < z_0 < r$. Let C be the circle in which S and p intersect. Express the coordinates of the center of C, and the radius of C, in terms of r and z_0.

18. Prove that the intersection of two distinct spheres is either the null set, or a point, or a circle. *Hint :* Set up a coordinate system so that the given spheres S_1 and S_2 are given as follows for some numbers r_1, r_2, z_0:

$$S_1 = \{(x, y, z): x^2 + y^2 + z^2 = r_1^2\},$$

$$S_2 = \{(x, y, z): x^2 + y^2 + (z - z_0)^2 = r_2^2\}.$$

19. Given

$$S = \{(x, y, z): x^2 + y^2 + z^2 \leqslant 25\},$$

$$L = \left\{(x, y, z): \frac{x}{3} = \frac{y}{4} = \frac{z}{5}\right\}.$$

Show that $S \cap L$ is a segment. Find the length of this segment and the co-ordinates of its endpoints.

20. Given

$$T = \{(x, y, z): x^2 + y^2 + z^2 = 25\},$$

$$P = \{(x, y, z): 3x + 4y + 5z = 50\}.$$

Show that $T \cap P$ is the null set. *Hint:* Find the distance from the origin to P.

21. Prove Theorem 10.41.

22. Prove Theorem 10.42.

23. Prove Theorem 10.44.

24. Prove Theorem 10.45.

25. Prove Theorem 10.46.

10.9 *Summary*

In this chapter we developed the concepts of perpendicularity and parallelism. We introduced coordinates as a tool in space geometry and used them in the development of the distance formula, the concept of direction for a line, and the conditions for perpendicularity and parallelism. Coordinates may be used to advantage in the development of geometry, particularly in metric considerations. This concludes our study of the foundations of geometry. We shall go on to consider selected topics in Euclidean geometry.

Exercises 10.9

1. Write symmetric equations for the line L in which the planes p and q given as follows intersect:

$$p = \{(x, y, z): 2x + 4y + 5z = 10\},$$

$$q = \{(x, y, z): 2x - y + 4z = 5\}.$$

Hint: L is perpendicular to every line which is perpendicular to p. Same for L and q.

2. Given $r = \{(x, y, z): x + y + z = 5\}$ and p and q as in Exercise 1. Find the point in which the planes p, q, r intersect.

3. Find an equation for the plane determined by the following three points: $(0, 0, 0), (1, 1, 1), (0, 1, 0)$.

4. Describe the set of all points (x, y, z) such that

$$3(x - 1) + 4(y + 2) + 5(z + 1) = 0.$$

5. Describe the set of all points (x, y, z) such that $x + y + z = 10$ and $x^2 + y^2 + z^2 \leqslant 100$.

6. Describe the set of all points (x, y, z) such that

$$x = 1 + k, \quad y = 2 + 2k, \quad z = 3 - k, \qquad \text{and} \quad 1 \leqslant k \leqslant 3.$$

7. Describe the set

$$\left\{ (x, y, z): \frac{x - 1}{2} = \frac{y - 2}{3} \right\}.$$

8. Describe the set

$$\left\{ (x, y, z): \frac{x - 1}{2} = \frac{z - 2}{3} \right\}.$$

9. Describe the intersection of the sets S and T where

$$S = \{(x, y, z): 2x - 3y + 4z = 5\},$$

$$T = \{(x, y, z): 2x - 3y + 4z = 6\}.$$

10. Describe the intersection of the sets L and M where

$$L = \{(x, y, z): x = 1 + k, y = -2 + k, z = 3 + k, 0 \leqslant k \leqslant 1\},$$

$$M = \{(x, y, z): x = 5 + k, y = -2 + k, z = 3 + k, 0 \leqslant k \leqslant 1\}.$$

CHAPTER 11

Further Geometry of Triangles

11.1 Introduction

In Chapters 11 to 14 we assume that the student has a background of elementary plane geometry and trigonometry. This chapter is a collection of theorems on the geometry of the triangle, including the classical theorems of Ceva and Menelaus and the nine-point circle theorem. Following chapters include more circle geometry and several topics selected from modern geometry.

11.2 Notation

In this chapter items associated with a triangle will be denoted as follows:

A, B, C	Vertices, angles, measures of angles
D, E, F	Feet of altitudes (D opposite A, etc.)
A', B', C'	Midpoints of sides (A' opposite A, etc.)
X, Y, Z	Points of contact of incircle (X opposite A, etc.)
a, b, c	Lengths of sides ($a = BC$, etc.)
s	Semiperimeter ($2s = a + b + c$)
R	Circumradius, either number or segment
r	Inradius, either number or segment
r_1, r_2, r_3	Exradii
K	Area of triangle

S	Circumcenter
H	Orthocenter
G	Centroid
I	Incenter
I_1, I_2, I_3	Excenters
N	Nine-point center
P, Q, T	Midpoints of $\overline{HA}, \overline{HB}, \overline{HC}$

11.3   *Inscribed Angles*

The degree-measure of an arc of a circle was defined in Section 1.6. According to that definition the degree-measure of a minor arc of a circle is the measure of the central angle subtended by the arc; the degree-measure of a semicircle is 180; and the degree-measure of a major arc is $360 - m$, where m is the measure of the corresponding minor arc.

Definition. If A, B, C, D are four distinct points of a circle arranged in the order named, then $\angle ABC$ is an *inscribed* angle of that circle, and $\overarc{ADC}$ is the arc intercepted by that angle.

Theorem 11.1. The measure of an inscribed angle is half the measure of its intercepted arc.

Proof. Assigned as an exercise. *Hint:* Use the exterior angle theorem and the isosceles triangle theorem. Consider three cases suggested by the following three figures.

11.4   *Some Triangle Theorems*

Theorem 11.2. $K = \frac{1}{2}ab \sin C = \frac{1}{2}bc \sin A = \frac{1}{2}ca \sin B$.

Proof. Assigned as an exercise.

Theorem 11.3 (*Law of Sines*). $a/\sin A = b/\sin B = c/\sin C = 2R$.

Proof. It follows from Theorem 11.2, multiplying by $2/abc$, that $\sin C/c = \sin A/a = \sin B/b$. Since each of the numbers $\sin A, \sin B, \sin C$ is different from zero, it follows that $a/\sin A = b/\sin B = c/\sin C$.

Let V be the point in which $\overrightarrow{CS}$ intersects the circumcircle. If $V = B$, then $m\angle A = 90$. (Why?) and $a/\sin A = 2R$. (Why?) Suppose $V \neq B$. Then CBV is a right triangle and $\sin \angle BVC = a/2R$. But $\angle BVC$ and

$\angle BAC$ are either congruent or supplementary. Therefore $\sin \angle BVC = \sin A$. It follows that $a/\sin A = 2R$.

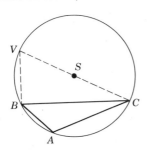 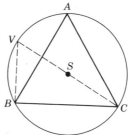

Theorem 11.4. $R = abc/4K$.

Proof. Assigned as an exercise.

Theorem 11.5. The bisector of any angle of a triangle divides the opposite side into two segments whose lengths are proportional to the lengths of the sides which include the angle.

Proof. Assigned as an exercise. *Hint :* Apply Theorem 11.3 to triangles AWB and AWC in the figure.

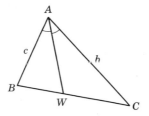

Theorem 11.6 (*Law of Cosines*).

$$a^2 = b^2 + c^2 - 2bc \cos A,$$

$$b^2 = c^2 + a^2 - 2ca \cos B,$$

$$c^2 = a^2 + b^2 - 2ab \cos C.$$

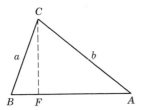 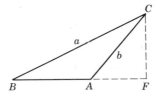

Proof.

If $m\angle A \leqslant 90$:	If $m\angle A \geqslant 90$:
$a^2 = (BF)^2 + (FC)^2$	$a^2 = (BF)^2 + (FC)^2$
$\quad = (BF)^2 + b^2 - (AF)^2$	$\quad = (BF)^2 + b^2 - (AF)^2$
$\quad = (c - AF)^2 + b^2 - (AF)^2$	$\quad = (c + AF)^2 + b^2 - (AF)^2$
$\quad = b^2 + c^2 - 2c \cdot AF$	$\quad = b^2 + c^2 + 2c \cdot AF$
$\quad = b^2 + c^2 - 2c \cdot b \cos A$	$\quad = b^2 + c^2 + 2c \cdot b \cos(180 - A)$
$\quad = b^2 + c^2 - 2bc \cos A.$	$\quad = b^2 + c^2 - 2bc \cos A.$

Theorem 11.7 (*Apollonius*). $(AC)^2 + (BC)^2 = 2(AC')^2 + 2(CC')^2.$

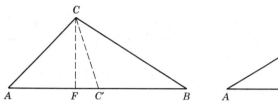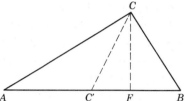

Proof.

$$(AC)^2 = (CC')^2 + (AC')^2 - 2(CC')(AC') \cos \angle AC'C,$$

$$(BC)^2 = (CC')^2 + (BC')^2 - 2(CC')(BC') \cos \angle BC'C,$$

$$BC' = AC' \quad \text{and} \quad \cos \angle AC'C = -\cos \angle BC'C,$$

$$(AC)^2 + (BC)^2 = 2(CC')^2 + 2(AC')^2.$$

Theorem 11.8. The perpendicular bisectors of the sides of a triangle are concurrent. (Their intersection S is called the *circumcenter*.)

 Proof. See Exercise 14 in Exercises 9.8.

 Theorem 11.9. The bisectors of the angles of a triangle are concurrent. (Their intersection I is called the *incenter*.)

 Proof. See Exercise 15 in Exercises 11.8.

Exercises 11.4

1. Prove Theorem 11.1.

2. Prove Theorem 11.2.

3. Prove Theorem 11.4.

4. Prove Theorem 11.5.

5. Given that $\overline{SP}, \overline{PQ}, \overline{QR}, \overline{RS}$ bisect the exterior angles, with vertices at A, B, C, D, respectively, of convex quadrilateral $ABCD$. Prove that $PB \cdot QC \cdot RD \cdot SA = PA \cdot SD \cdot RC \cdot QB$. *Hint*: Let $\alpha = m\angle A$, etc. Use the laws of sines on $\triangle PBA$ to get $PB/PA = (\cos \alpha/2)/(\cos \beta/2)$, etc.

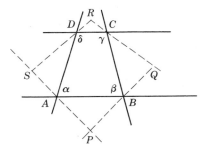

6. Given $\triangle ABC$ with $CA = CC'$ and $AC' = C'B$. Prove that $(BC)^2 = (CC')^2 + 2(AC')^2$.

7. Given two distinct points A, B in a plane p. A point C "moves" in p so that the sum of the squares of its distances from A and B is a constant. Prove using the Theorem of Apollonius (Theorem 11.7) that the locus of C is a circle.

8. Prove using coordinates that the locus of C in Exercise 6 is a circle.

9. Given parallelogram $ABCD$ with diagonals $\overline{AC}$ and $\overline{BD}$. Prove using the Theorem of Apollonius that $AB^2 + BC^2 + CD^2 + DA^2 = AC^2 + BD^2$.

10. Do Exercise 9 using coordinates.

11. Prove: For any convex quadrilateral the sum of the squares of the lengths of the four sides exceeds the sum of the squares of the lengths of the diagonals by (a) four times the square of the length of the segment joining the midpoints of the diagonals, if these midpoints are distinct, and (b) zero if the diagonals bisect each other. *Hint*: Use the Theorem of Apollonius several times.

12. Prove: The sum of the squares of the lengths of the diagonals of a convex quadrilateral is equal to twice the sum of the squares of the lengths of the segments joining the midpoints of opposite sides. *Hint*: Use the parallelogram whose vertices are the midpoints of the sides of the given quadrilateral.

13. Prove: Three times the sum of the squares of the lengths of the sides of a triangle equals four times the sum of the squares of the lengths of its medians. *Hint*: Use the Theorem 11.7 three times on the given triangle.

14. Through each vertex of a triangle a pair of segments is drawn parallel to the segments joining the circumcenter to the other two vertices, forming a hexagon. Show that this hexagon is equilateral and that its opposite angles are congruent.

15. Given $\triangle ABC$. Prove: $K = rs$. *Hint:* Express the areas of triangle ABI, BCI, and CAI in terms of r, a, b, c.

16. Construct a circle tangent to a given circle and two of its tangents. *Hint:*

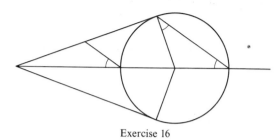

Exercise 16

17. Prove: Every circle with center I and radius x, $x > r$, "cuts off" congruent segments on $\overleftrightarrow{AB}$, $\overleftrightarrow{BC}$, $\overleftrightarrow{CA}$.

18. Given $\triangle ABC$. Prove: If the intersection of $\overline{AI}$ and the incircle is the point P (P is the midpoint of $\overline{AH}$), then $AB = AC$ and $\overline{AY} \parallel \overline{BE}$. (For notation, see Section 11.2.)

19. Given $\triangle ABC$. Prove: If the intersection of $\overline{AI}$ and the incircle is the point P, then P is the incenter of $\triangle AZY$.

20. Given that U and U' are points on the circumcircle of $\triangle ABC$, that $\overrightarrow{AU'}$ bisects the exterior angle at A, and that $\overrightarrow{AU}$ bisects angle A. Prove that $\overleftrightarrow{UU'}$ is the perpendicular bisector of $\overline{BC}$.

21. Given that $\overrightarrow{AI}$ intersects the circumcircle of $\triangle ABC$ at distinct points A and U. Prove that $\overline{SU} \perp \overline{BC}$.

11.5   *Excircles*

   Definitions. Given $\triangle ABC$. A circle which is tangent to the three lines $\overleftrightarrow{AB}$, $\overleftrightarrow{BC}$, $\overleftrightarrow{CA}$, and which intersects $\triangle ABC$ at one and only one point, is called an *excircle* of the triangle. Its center is called an *excenter* and its radius an *exradius*.

   Theorem 11.10. Let $\angle B_1$ be the exterior angle of $\triangle ABC$ with vertex at B and with $\overrightarrow{BC}$ as one side. Let $\angle C_1$ be the exterior angle with vertex at C and with $\overrightarrow{CB}$ as one side. The rays which bisect angles A, B_1, C_1 are concurrent. The point I_1 in which they intersect is an excenter.

   Proof. Since the sum of the measures of angles B_1 and C_1 is less than 360, it follows that the rays which bisect these angles intersect. Call their intersection I_1. Let M be the foot of the perpendicular from I_1 to $\overleftrightarrow{AC}$, N the foot of the perpendicular from I_1 to $\overleftrightarrow{AB}$. Then $I_1M = I_1N$, $MA =$

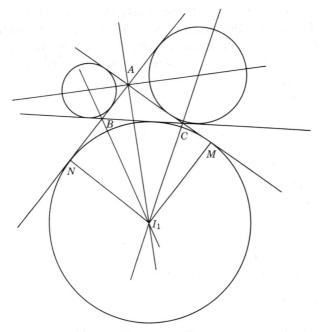

Theorem 11.10

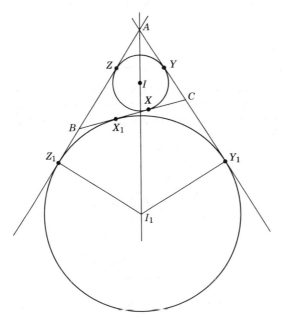

Theorem 11.11

NA (Why?), $AI_1 = AI_1$. Therefore $\triangle I_1 AM \cong \triangle I_1 AN$ and $\overrightarrow{AI_1}$ bisects angle A. Therefore the bisectors of angles A, B_1, C_1 are concurrent, and I_1 is the point of concurrence. Using basic congruence theorems it is easy to show that the perpendiculars from I_1 to $\overleftrightarrow{AB}$, $\overleftrightarrow{AC}$, and $\overleftrightarrow{BC}$ are congruent, and hence that I_1 is an excenter.

Theorem 11.11. $r_1(s - a) = r_2(s - b) = r_3(s - c) = K$.

Proof.

Area $\triangle I_1 CA$ + Area $\triangle I_1 AB$ = Area $\triangle I_1 BC$ + Area $\triangle ABC$.

Area $\triangle I_1 CA = \frac{1}{2} r_1 b$.

Area $\triangle I_1 AB = \frac{1}{2} r_1 c$.

Area $\triangle I_1 BC = \frac{1}{2} r_1 a$.

Therefore

$$K = \frac{r_1}{2}(b + c - a) = r_1\left(\frac{a + b + c}{2} - a\right) = r_1(s - a).$$

Similarly the other parts of the theorem may be proved.

Exercises 11.5

Given $\triangle ABC$, its incircle, and its excircles. See figure in the proof of Theorem 11.11. Draw an expanded figure to show all three excircles.

1. Prove: A, I, I_1 are collinear.

2. Prove: I_2, A, I_3 are collinear.

3. Prove: $\overline{AI_1} \perp \overline{I_2 I_3}$ and I is the orthocenter of $\triangle I_1 I_2 I_3$.

4. Given that the incircle and the excircle with center at I_1 are not tangent. These two circles have two distinct interior common tangents, one of them being the line $\overleftrightarrow{BC}$. If the other interior common tangent intersects $\overleftrightarrow{BC}$ in V, prove that V lies on $\overleftrightarrow{II_1}$.

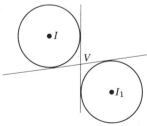

Exercise 4

5. Prove that if $\triangle ABC$ is equilateral, then $r = \frac{1}{2}R, r_1 = r_2 = r_3 = 3R/2$.

6. Prove: $\triangle I_1 I_2 I_3 \sim \triangle XYZ$.

7. Given the circle in the plane of $\triangle ABC$ which has II_1 as a diameter. Prove that this circle contains B and C.

8. Prove: $AZ_1 + AY_1 = a + b + c$; $AZ_1 = AY_1 = s$.

9. Prove: $AZ + AY = c + b - a$; $AY = AZ = s - a$.

10. Prove: $ZZ_1 = YY_1 = a$.

11. Prove: $BX_1 = CX = s - c$.

12. Prove: $BX = CX_1 = s - b$.

13. Prove: $XX_1 = |b - c|$ and $XA' = \frac{1}{2} \cdot |b - c|$.

14. Find the lengths of the segments into which the point of contact of the incircle divides the hypotenuse of a right triangle whose legs are of length 6 and 8.

15. Given right triangle ABC with right angle at C. Prove that $r = \frac{1}{2}(a + b - c)$.

16. Given a convex quadrilateral $ABCD$ whose diagonals are perpendicular. Prove that the sum of the inradii of the triangles AOB, BOC, COD, DOA is equal to the difference between the sum of the lengths of the diagonals and the semi-perimeter of the quadrilateral.

17. Given noncollinear rays $\overrightarrow{AU}$ and $\overrightarrow{AV}$ and a number $2s$. If B is a variable point on $\overrightarrow{AU}$ and C is a variable point on $\overrightarrow{AV}$ subject to the restriction that $\triangle ABC$ has perimeter $2s$, prove that there is a (fixed) circle which is tangent to all of the possible segments $\overline{BC}$.

18. Find the lengths of the inradius and the exradii of a right triangle whose sides are of length 3, 4, and 5.

19. Prove: $1/r_1 + 1/r_2 + 1/r_3 = 1/r$.

20. Complete the following proof that $K = \sqrt{s(s - a)(s - b)(s - c)}$.
    Proof.

$$K = \tfrac{1}{2}bc \sin A,$$

$$K^2 = \frac{b^2c^2}{4}\left[1 - \left(\frac{b^2 + c^2 - a^2}{2bc}\right)^2\right].$$

21. Prove: $K = \sqrt{rr_1r_2r_3}$.

22. Given $a = 5, b = 6, c = 7$. Compute r, r_1, r_2, r_3.

23. Given $a = 3, b = 4$. Prove that $K \leqslant 6$.

24. Prove:

$$r = \sqrt{\frac{(s - a)(s - b)(s - c)}{s}}.$$

25. Express r in terms of a, if $a = b = c$.

26. Given a sequence of triangles $A_n B_n C_n$ with $a_n = 3$, $b_n = 4$, $c_n = 7 - 2/n$. Prove that the limit of r_n (the inradius of $A_n B_n C_n$) approaches 0 as $n \to \infty$.

27. Same as Exercise 26 except that $c_n = 1 + 2/n$.

28. Given a triangle ABC with $a = 3$, $b = 4$, $c = 5 + 2p$, where $0 < p < 1$. Prove that $r < 1$.

11.6   *The Nine-Point Circle and the Simson Line*

Theorem 11.12. If $\overline{AM}$ is the chord of the circumcircle of $\triangle ABC$ which contains $\overline{AD}$, then $HD = DM$.

Proof. (HDA), or $H = D$, or (DHA), or $H = A$, or (DAH), where (HDA) means that D is between H and A, etc.

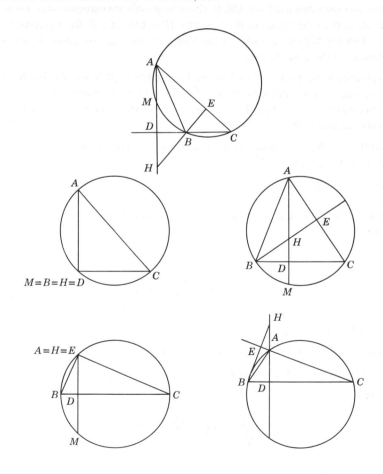

Case 1. (HDA). In this case H and A lie on opposite sides of $\overline{BC}$ and H is outside $\triangle ABC$.

$$m\angle HBD = m\angle CBE = 90 - m\angle BCE = 90 - m\angle DCA = m\angle DAC$$

$$= m\angle MAC$$

$$= \tfrac{1}{2}m\widehat{MBC} = 180 - \tfrac{1}{2}m\widehat{MAC} = 180 - m\angle MBC$$

$$= m\angle MBD.$$

$\triangle DBM \cong \triangle DBH$, and $MD = DH$.

Case 2. $H = D$. In this case $\angle B$ is a right angle, $H = D = M = B$ and $MD = 0 = DH$.

Case 3. (DHA). In this case A is an acute angle and H lies within $\triangle ABC$. Since $\angle BDA$ and $\angle BEA$ are right angles, it follows that A, E, B, D are concyclic. $\angle MBD \cong \angle MAC$. (Why?) $\angle DBH \cong \angle DAE$. (Why?) $\angle DAE \cong \angle MAC$. (Why?) $\angle MBD \cong \angle DBM$. (Why?) Then $\triangle DBM \cong \triangle DBH$ and $MD = DH$.

Case 4. $H = A$. In this case A is a right angle, $\overline{BC}$ is a diameter of the circumcircle, $\overline{BC}$ is the perpendicular bisector of the chord $\overline{AM}$ at D, and $AD = DM$.

Case 5. (DAH). The proof in this case is assigned as an exercise.

Theorem 11.13. $AH = 2 \cdot SA'$.

Proof. Let $\overline{QC}$ be the diameter of the circumcircle of $\triangle ABC$ which contains C. If $Q = B$ then $A = H$, $S = A'$, and $AH = 0 = SA'$. Suppose

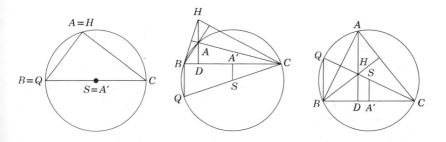

$Q \neq B$. Since A' and S are the midpoints of $\overline{BC}$ and $\overline{QC}$, respectively, it follows that $QB = 2 \cdot SA'$. Since $\overline{QB}$ and $\overline{HD}$ are each perpendicular to $\overline{BC}$, it follows that $\overline{QB} \parallel \overline{HD}$. Since $\overline{QA}$ and $\overline{BH}$ are each perpendicular to $\overline{AC}$, it follows that $\overline{QA} \parallel \overline{BH}$. Therefore $BHAQ$ is a parallelogram, $AH = QB$, and $AH = 2 \cdot SA'$.

Theorem 11.14. H, G, S are collinear and $HG = 2 \cdot GS$.

Proof. If $D = A'$, then $AB = AC$ and S, G, H all lie on $\overrightarrow{AA'}$. Then, since $\overline{SB'}$ and $\overline{BE}$ are both perpendicular to $\overline{AC}$, it follows that $\overline{SB'} \parallel \overline{BE}$. Then $\triangle BHG \sim \triangle B'SG$. Since $BG = 2 \cdot GB'$ (see Exercise 11 in Exercises 9.8), it follows that $HG = 2 \cdot GS$.

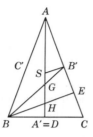
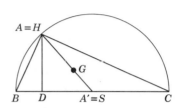

Suppose next that $D \neq A'$. If $A = H$, then $A' = S$ and, since $AG = 2 \cdot GA'$, it follows that $HG = 2 \cdot GS$. Suppose, next, that $A \neq H$ and $D \neq A'$. Then $AH = 2 \cdot SA'$, $\overline{AH} \parallel \overline{SA'}$, (AGA'), $AG = 2 \cdot GA'$, $\angle HAG \cong$

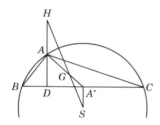
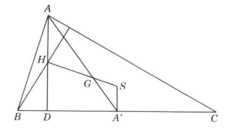

$\angle SA'G$, and $\triangle HAG \sim \triangle SA'G$. Therefore $HG = 2 \cdot GS$, $\angle AGH \cong \angle A'GS$, and H, G, S are collinear.

Theorem 11.15 (*Nine-Point Circle Theorem*). The circle whose center N is the midpoint of $\overline{HS}$, and whose radius is $\frac{1}{2}R$, contains D, E, F (the feet of the altitudes), A', B', C' (the midpoints of the sides), and P, Q, T (the midpoints of $\overline{HA}$, $\overline{HB}$, $\overline{HC}$).

Proof. If $H = S$, then $N = H = G = S$ (Theorem 11.14), $A' = D$, $B' = E$, and $C' = F$. If $H = S$, then it follows from Theorem 11.13 that $PN = NA'$, $QN = NB'$ and $TN = NC'$. But $\frac{1}{2}R = \frac{1}{2}AS = \frac{1}{2}AN = PN$, etc. Also $\frac{1}{2}R = \frac{1}{2} \cdot AS = SA' = NA'$, etc. In this special case there are six points and they are all at a distance of $\frac{1}{2}R$ from N.

Suppose then that $H \neq S$. Let N be the point of intersection of $\overline{PA'}$ and $\overline{HS}$. (If $\overleftrightarrow{PA'} = \overleftrightarrow{HS}$, let N be the intersection of $\overleftrightarrow{QB'}$ and $\overleftrightarrow{HS}$, and adjust the following argument accordingly.) Now $PH = \frac{1}{2}AH = SA'$, $\overline{PH} \parallel \overline{SA'}$. Since $\overline{HS}$ and $\overline{PA'}$ are the diagonals of a parallelogram, it follows that N is the midpoint of $\overline{HS}$ and of $\overline{PA'}$. Let C^* be the circle which contains P, D, A'. Since $\angle PDA'$ is a right angle, it follows that $\overline{PA'}$ is a diameter of C^*. Since N is the midpoint of $\overline{PA'}$, it follows that N is the center of C^*.

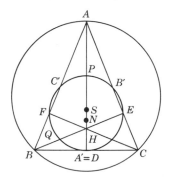 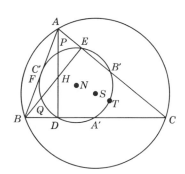

Now $APA'S$ is a parallelogram. Therefore $A'P = SA$ and $A'N = \frac{1}{2}R$. Therefore the circle of radius $\frac{1}{2}R$, whose center is the midpoint of $\overline{HS}$, contains the points P, D, and A'. Similarly, this same circle contains Q, E, B', and T, F, C'.

Theorem 11.16 (*Simson Line Theorem*). If from a point W on the circumcircle of $\triangle ABC$, perpendiculars $\overline{WL}, \overline{WM}, \overline{WN}$ are dropped to $\overleftrightarrow{BC}, \overleftrightarrow{CA}, \overleftrightarrow{AB}$, respectively, then L, M, N are collinear. (The line which contains them is called the Simson line.)

Proof. If W is one of the vertices of the triangle, the assertion is trivial. Suppose, then, that W is not one of the vertices. If $L = C$, then $\angle WCB$ is a right angle, $\overline{WB}$ is a diameter of the circumcircle, $\angle BAW$ is a right angle, and $N = A$. In this case $\overleftrightarrow{AC}$ is the Simson line. Similarly, if any one of the points L, M, N is a vertex of $\triangle ABC$, then L, M, and N all lie on one of the lines which contains a side of the triangle.

Suppose, then, that none of the four points W, L, M, N is a vertex. Since $\angle WNB$ and $\angle WLB$ are right angles, it follows that B, N, W, L lie on the circle C^* with diameter $\overline{BW}$. Similarly, W, N, A, M lie on circle C^{**} with diameter $\overline{AW}$.

Suppose W and C lie on opposite sides of $\overleftrightarrow{AB}$. Then $m\angle WAC + m\angle WBC = 180$. Then M and L are on opposite sides of $\overleftrightarrow{AB}$. (This follows from the exterior angle theorem.) If M and L are both on the W-side of $\overleftrightarrow{AB}$, then $180 = m\angle WMC + m\angle WLC < m\angle WAC + m\angle WBC = 180$. (Contradiction.) If M and L are both on the C-side of

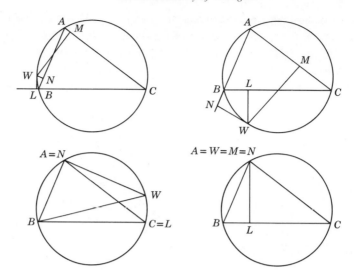

$\overleftrightarrow{AB}$, then $180 = m\angle WMC + m\angle WLC > m\angle WAC + m\angle WBC = 180$. (Contradiction.)

Then:

1. $m\angle WBC + m\angle WNL = 180$, $\quad m\angle WBC + m\angle WAC = 180$,
   $\angle WNL \cong \angle WAC$, $\quad \angle WNM \cong \angle WAM$,
   $m\angle WNL + m\angle WNM = m\angle WAC + m\angle WAM = 180$.

or

2. $m\angle WAC + m\angle WNM = 180$, $\quad m\angle WAC + m\angle WBC = 180$,
   $m\angle WNM \cong \angle WBC$, $\quad \angle WNL \cong \angle WBL$,
   $m\angle WNL + m\angle WNM = m\angle WBL + m\angle WBC = 180$.

In either case $\angle WNL$ and $\angle WNM$ are a linear pair of angles and L, M, N are collinear.

If W and C lie on the same side of $\overleftrightarrow{AB}$, then W and A lie on opposite sides of $\overleftrightarrow{BC}$, or W and B lie on opposite sides of $\overleftrightarrow{AC}$. The proof of the collinearity of L, M, N in these cases is similar to that for the case in which W and C lie on opposite sides of $\overleftrightarrow{AB}$.

Exercises 11.6

Prove the following:

1. Theorem 11.12, Case 5.

2. A is the orthocenter of $\triangle BCH$, B of $\triangle CAH$, C of $\triangle ABH$.

3. $\angle BHC$ and $\angle A$ are supplementary angles.

4. $\cos \angle 2A = \cos \angle BSC$. ($2A$ is an angle whose measure is twice the measure of angle A.)

5. $2R^2(1 - \cos 2A) = a^2$.

6. $\triangle ABC$ and $\triangle BHC$ have equal circumradii.

7. $(BD, DA) \underset{p}{=} (HD, HC)$.

8. $\angle A$ is acute if and only if (DHA).

9. (DHA) if and only if S and A lie on the same side of $\overleftrightarrow{BC}$.

10. If A is not a right angle, then $PSA'H$ is a parallelogram. (What is it if A is a right angle?)

11. $A'P = R$.

12. The perpendicular bisectors of $\overline{DA'}, \overline{EB'}, \overline{FC'}$ are concurrent.

13. The perpendicular bisectors of $\overline{DP}, \overline{EQ}, \overline{FT}$ are concurrent.

14. $\triangle A'B'C' \sim \triangle ABC$.

15. $\triangle PQH \sim \triangle ABH$.

16. $\triangle PQT \sim \triangle ABC$.

17. $\triangle PQT \cong \triangle A'B'C'$.

18. The circumradius of $\triangle A'B'C'$ is $\frac{1}{2}R$.

19. The minor arcs $\overarc{C'D}$ and $\overarc{B'A'}$ have the same measure.

20. If $D \neq A'$, then A', B', C', D are the vertices of an isosceles trapezoid.

21. The circumcircle of $\triangle ABC$ is the nine-point circle of $\triangle I_1 I_2 I_3$.

22. The circumcircle of $\triangle ABC$ bisects $\overline{II_1}, \overline{II_2}, \overline{II_3}$.

23. The midpoints of $\overline{I_1 I_2}, \overline{I_2 I_3}, \overline{I_3 I_1}$ lie on the circumcircle of $\triangle ABC$.

24. The circumcenter of $\triangle I_1 I_2 I_3$ is the midpoint of the segment joining I and S.

25. S is the midpoint of the segment joining I and the circumcenter of $\triangle I_1 I_2 I_3$.

26. Triangles ABC and HBC have the same nine-point circle. *Hints:*
    ———— is the orthocenter of $\triangle HBC$.
    ————, ————, ———— are the feet of the altitudes of $\triangle HBC$.
    ————, ————, ———— are the midpoints of $\overline{HA}, \overline{BA}, \overline{CA}$.
    ————, ————, ———— are the midpoints of $\overline{HB}, \overline{BC}, \overline{CH}$.

27. $\angle BAD \cong \angle CAS$.

28. If $\overleftrightarrow{AD}$ intersects the circumcircle in U, $U \neq A$, then the Simson line of U is parallel to the tangent at A.

29. If $\overleftrightarrow{AI}$ intersects the circumcircle in U, $U \neq A$, then the Simson line of U bisects $\overline{BC}$.

11.7   *The Theorems of Ceva and Menelaus*

The Simson line was named after Robert Simson (1687–1768), professor of mathematics at Glasgow. The theorems of this section were first published by Ceva, an Italian, in 1678, and by Menelaus of Alexandria, in about 98 A.D.

Theorem 11.17 (*The Theorem of Ceva*). Given $\triangle ABC$ and a point P not on $\overleftrightarrow{AB}$, $\overleftrightarrow{BC}$, $\overleftrightarrow{CA}$. If the lines $\overleftrightarrow{PA}$, $\overleftrightarrow{PB}$, $\overleftrightarrow{PC}$ intersect $\overleftrightarrow{BC}$, $\overleftrightarrow{CA}$, $\overleftrightarrow{AB}$ in X, Y, Z, respectively, then

$$\frac{BX}{XC} \cdot \frac{CY}{YA} \cdot \frac{AZ}{ZB} = 1,$$

and either one or three of the following statements is true : $(BXC), (CYA), (AZB)$.

Proof. If P is within $\triangle ABC$, then $(BXC), (CYA)$, and (AZB). If P is in region 1 (see figure), then $(BXC), (YAC), (ZAB)$. If P is in region 2, then

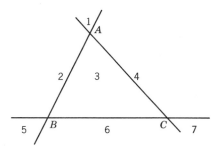

$(XBC), (YAC), (AZB)$. Similarly if P is in any region except 3, one and only one of the three statements $(BXC), (CYA), (AZB)$ is true, that is, one and only one of the three points X, Y, Z lies on the triangle. If P is in region 3, then all three of the points X, Y, Z lie on the triangle.

The remainder of the proof follows from the fact that two triangles which have the same height have areas whose ratio is equal to the ratio

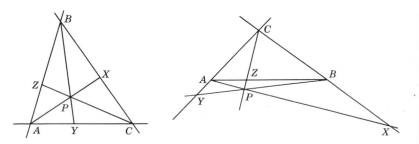

of the lengths of their bases, and from some of the basic properties of ratios. We use $|\triangle ABC|$ to denote the area of $\triangle ABC$.

$$\frac{BX}{XC} = \frac{|\triangle BXA|}{|\triangle CXA|} = \frac{|\triangle BXP|}{|\triangle CXP|} = \frac{|\triangle BPA|}{|\triangle CPA|},$$

$$\frac{CY}{YA} = \frac{|\triangle CYB|}{|\triangle AYB|} = \frac{|\triangle CYP|}{|\triangle AYP|} = \frac{|\triangle CPB|}{|\triangle APB|},$$

$$\frac{AZ}{ZB} = \frac{|\triangle AZC|}{|\triangle BZC|} = \frac{|\triangle AZP|}{|\triangle BZP|} = \frac{|\triangle APC|}{|\triangle BPC|},$$

$$\frac{BX}{XC} \cdot \frac{CY}{YA} \cdot \frac{AZ}{ZB} = \frac{|\triangle BPA|}{|\triangle CPA|} \cdot \frac{|\triangle CPB|}{|\triangle APB|} \cdot \frac{|\triangle APC|}{|\triangle PBC|} = 1.$$

Theorem 11.18 (*Converse of Ceva's Theorem*). Given $\triangle ABC$ and three points X, Y, Z on $\overleftrightarrow{BC}, \overleftrightarrow{CA}, \overleftrightarrow{AB}$, respectively. If exactly one or three of the following statements is true: (BXC), (CYA), (AZB), and if $(BX/XC) \cdot (CY/YA) \cdot (AZ/ZB) = 1$, then the lines $\overleftrightarrow{AX}, \overleftrightarrow{BY}, \overleftrightarrow{XZ}$ are concurrent.

Proof. Suppose first that (BXC), (CYA), and (AZB). Let P be the intersection of $\overrightarrow{AX}$ and $\overrightarrow{BY}$, and suppose that $\overrightarrow{CP}$ intersects $\overrightarrow{AB}$ in Z', $Z' \neq Z$. Then it follows from Ceva's Theorem that

$$\frac{BX}{XC} \cdot \frac{CY}{YA} \cdot \frac{AZ'}{Z'B} = 1,$$

$$\frac{BX}{XC} \cdot \frac{CY}{YA} \cdot \frac{AZ}{ZB} = 1,$$

$$\frac{AZ'}{Z'B} = \frac{AZ}{ZB}, \quad \frac{AZ'}{AB} = \frac{AZ}{AB}, \quad AZ' = AZ, \quad Z' = Z.$$

(Contradiction.) Therefore $\overrightarrow{CP}$ intersects $\overrightarrow{AB}$ at the point Z, and $\overrightarrow{AX}$, $\overrightarrow{BY}, \overrightarrow{CZ}$ are concurrent.

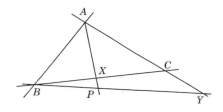

Suppose next that (BXC) and (ACY). Then (ZBA) or (BAZ). Let P be the intersection of $\overrightarrow{AX}$ and $\overrightarrow{BY}$, and suppose $\overleftrightarrow{CP}$ intersects $\overleftrightarrow{AB}$ in Z',

$Z' \neq Z$. Then (ABZ') and it follows from Ceva's Theorem that

$$\frac{BX}{XC} \cdot \frac{CY}{YA} \cdot \frac{AZ'}{Z'B} = 1.$$

$$\frac{BX}{XC} \cdot \frac{CY}{YA} \cdot \frac{AZ}{ZB} = 1, \quad \text{and} \quad \frac{AZ'}{Z'B} = \frac{AZ}{ZB}.$$

Since $AZ'/Z'B > 1$ it follows that $AZ/ZB > 1$, and that (ZBA). Then $Z' = Z$. (Contradiction.) Therefore $\overrightarrow{CP}$ intersects $\overrightarrow{AB}$ in Z, and $\overleftrightarrow{AX}$, $\overleftrightarrow{BY}$, $\overleftrightarrow{CZ}$ are concurrent.

The remainder of the proof follows in a similar manner.

Theorem 11.19 (*The Theorem of Menelaus*). Given $\triangle ABC$ and a line m which intersects $\overleftrightarrow{BC}$, $\overleftrightarrow{CA}$, $\overleftrightarrow{AB}$ in the points L, M, N, respectively. If none of these three points is a vertex of $\triangle ABC$, then exactly zero or two of the statements (BLC), (CMA), (ANB), are true, and

$$\frac{BL}{LC} \cdot \frac{CM}{MA} \cdot \frac{AN}{NB} = 1.$$

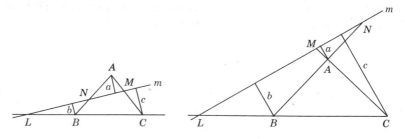

Proof.

Let a, b, c be the lengths of the perpendiculars from A, B, C, to m. Then

$$\frac{BL}{LC} = \frac{b}{c}, \quad \frac{CM}{MA} = \frac{c}{a}, \quad \frac{AN}{NB} = \frac{a}{b}, \quad \frac{BL}{LC} \cdot \frac{CM}{MA} \cdot \frac{AN}{NB} = \frac{b}{c} \cdot \frac{c}{a} \cdot \frac{a}{b} = 1.$$

The fact that exactly zero or two of the statements (BLC), (CMA), (ANB) are true follows from the earlier work on foundations.

Theorem 11.20 (*Converse of Menelaus's Theorem*). If L, M, N are points on $\overleftrightarrow{BC}$, $\overleftrightarrow{CA}$, $\overleftrightarrow{AB}$, respectively, with exactly zero or two of the following statements true : (BLC), (CMA), (ANB), and such that $(BL/LC) \cdot (CM/MA) \cdot (AN/NB) = 1$, then L, M, N are collinear.

Proof. Suppose (BLC), (AMC), and (NBA). Suppose, contrary to the assertion of the theorem, that N, L, M are noncollinear. Then $\overleftrightarrow{NL}$

intersects $\overline{AC}$ in some point M', $M' \neq M$, such that $(AM'C)$ and

$$\frac{BL}{LC} \cdot \frac{CM'}{M'A} \cdot \frac{AN}{NB} = 1.$$

But

$$\frac{BL}{LC} \cdot \frac{CM}{MA} \cdot \frac{AN}{NB} = 1.$$

Therefore $(CM'/M'A) = (CM/MA)$, and $M' = M$. (Contradiction.) Therefore L, M, N are collinear.

The remainder of the proof follows in a similar manner.

Exercises 11.7

1. Use the converse of Ceva's Theorem to prove that the medians of a triangle are concurrent.

2. Use the converse of Ceva's Theorem to prove that the altitudes of a triangle are concurrent. (Express the lengths BL, LC, etc., in terms of a, b, c, $\cos A$, $\cos B$, $\cos C$.)

3. Use the converse of Ceva's Theorem to prove that the bisectors of the angles of a triangle are concurrent.

4. Use the converse of Ceva's Theorem to prove that the bisector of an interior angle and the bisectors of the exterior angles at the other vertices are concurrent.

5. Given $\triangle ABC$ and X, Y, Z, the points of contact of the incircle with the triangle. Prove that $\overline{AX}$, $\overline{BY}$, $\overline{CZ}$ are concurrent. (The point of concurrence is called the Gergonne point of $\triangle ABC$.)

6. Given $\triangle ABC$ and X_1, X_2, X_3, the points of contact of the opposite sides with the excircles. Prove that $\overline{AX_1}$, $\overline{BX_2}$, $\overline{CX_3}$ are concurrent. (The point of concurrence is called Nagel's point of $\triangle ABC$.)

7. Prove: The bisectors of two interior angles of a triangle and the bisector of the exterior angle at the third vertex intersect the lines which contain the sides of the triangle in collinear points.

CHAPTER 12

Cross Ratio

12.1 Cross Ratio of a Range of Points

The concept of cross ratio is basic in projective geometry.

Definition. A set of collinear points is a *range*.

Definition. If A, B, C, D, with $C \neq D$, are collinear points, then $\dfrac{AB}{CD} = \dfrac{AB}{CD}$ if $\overrightarrow{AB}$ and $\overrightarrow{CD}$ are parallel rays, and $\dfrac{AB}{CD} = -\dfrac{AB}{CD}$ if $\overrightarrow{AB}$ and $\overrightarrow{CD}$ are antiparallel rays.

Note that $\dfrac{AB}{CD}$ is the ratio of the "signed" distances.

Definition. If $\{A, B, C, D\}$ is a range of four distinct points, then $\dfrac{AC}{CB} \bigg/ \dfrac{AD}{DB}$ is a *cross ratio* of the range. We denote it by $[AB, CD]$. We call $\{A, B\}$ and $\{C, D\}$ the two pairs of the cross ratio.

Since four letters may be permuted in 24 different ways, there are 24 cross ratios for four points. Although the 24 symbols which express these cross ratios are all different, the numbers which they denote are not.

Theorem 12.1. The cross ratio of four points is unchanged when two of the letters denoting points are interchanged if the letters denoting the other two points are also interchanged, that is,

$$[AB, CD] = [BA, DC] = [CD, AB] = [DC, BA].$$

218

Proof.

$$[AB, CD] = \frac{AC}{CB} \Big/ \frac{AD}{DB} = \frac{AC}{CB} \cdot \frac{DB}{AD},$$

$$[BA, DC] = \frac{BD}{DA} \Big/ \frac{BC}{CA} = \frac{DB}{AD} \Big/ \frac{CB}{AC} = \frac{AC}{CB} \cdot \frac{DB}{AD},$$

$$[CD, AB] = \frac{CA}{AD} \Big/ \frac{CB}{BD} = \frac{CA}{AD} \cdot \frac{BD}{CB} = \frac{AC}{CB} \cdot \frac{DB}{AD},$$

$$[DC, BA] = \frac{DB}{BC} \Big/ \frac{DA}{AC} = \frac{DB}{BC} \cdot \frac{AC}{DA} = \frac{AC}{CB} \cdot \frac{DB}{AD}.$$

Theorem 12.2. If the letters denoting two points of one pair of a cross ratio are interchanged but the letters for the other points are unchanged, the resulting cross ratio is the reciprocal of the given one, that is, if $[AB, CD] = r,$ then $[BA, CD] = [AB, DC] = [DC, AB] = [CD, BA] = 1/r.$

Proof. We shall show that $[BA, CD] = 1/r.$ The fact that the other three cross ratios in the conclusion of the theorem are equal to $[BA, CD]$ follows by applying Theorem 12.1 to the cross ratio $[BA, CD].$

$$[BA, CD] = \frac{BC}{CA} \Big/ \frac{BD}{DA} = \frac{CB}{AC} \cdot \frac{AD}{DB} = \frac{1}{r}.$$

Theorem 12.3. If $[AB, CD]$ remains unchanged when two letters in one pair are interchanged the other letters remaining unchanged, then $[AB, CD] = -1.$

Proof. Suppose $[AB, CD] = r.$ Since $C \neq D, r \neq 1,$ and it follows from Theorem 12.2 that $r = 1/r.$ Therefore $r = -1.$

Theorem 12.4. If $[AB, CD] = r,$ then

$$[AC, BD] = [CA, DB] = [BD, AC] = [DB, CA] = 1 - r.$$

Proof.

$$[AC, BD] = \frac{AB}{BC} \Big/ \frac{AD}{DC} = \frac{AB}{BC} \cdot \frac{DC}{AD} = \left(\frac{AC}{BC} + \frac{CB}{BC} \right)\left(\frac{DB}{AD} + \frac{BC}{AD} \right)$$

$$= \frac{AC}{BC} \cdot \frac{DB}{AD} + \frac{CB}{BC} \cdot \frac{DB}{AD} + \frac{CB}{BC} \cdot \frac{BC}{AD} + \frac{AC}{BC} \cdot \frac{BC}{AD}$$

$$= -\frac{AC}{CB} \cdot \frac{DB}{AD} + \frac{BC}{BC}\left(\frac{BD}{AD} + \frac{CB}{AD} + \frac{AC}{AD} \right)$$

$$= -r + 1 \cdot \left(\frac{CD}{AD} + \frac{AC}{AD} \right) = -r + \frac{AD}{AD} = 1 - r.$$

Now apply Theorem 12.1 to $[AC, BD]$.

Theorem 12.5. If $[AB, CD] = r$, then

$$[BC, AD] = [CB, DA] = [AD, BC] = [DA, CB] = \frac{r-1}{r}.$$

Proof. Use Theorems 12.1, 12.2, 12.4.

$$[BC, AD] = 1 - [BA, CD] = 1 - \frac{1}{r} = \frac{r-1}{r}.$$

Theorem 12.6. If $[AB, CD] = r$, then

$$[CA, BD] = [AC, DB] = [BD, CA] = [DB, AC] = \frac{1}{1-r}$$

and

$$[CB, AD] = [BC, AD] = [AD, CB] = [DA, BC] = \frac{r}{r-1}.$$

Proof. Assigned as an exercise.

Exercises 12.1

1. Given a range of points A, B, C, D whose coordinates are 0, 1, 3, 5, respectively. Compute the values of the following:

$$\frac{AC}{CB}, \quad \frac{AD}{DB}, \quad \frac{BD}{DA}, \quad \frac{BC}{CA}, \quad \frac{CA}{AD}, \quad \frac{CB}{BD}, \quad \frac{DB}{BC}, \quad \frac{DA}{AC},$$

$$[AB, CD], \quad [BA, DC], \quad [CD, AB], \quad [DC, BA].$$

2. Given a range of points A, B, C, D whose coordinates are 2, -3, 4, -7, respectively. Compute the values of:

$$[AB, CD], \quad [AB, DC], \quad [AC, BD], \quad [AC, DB], \quad [AD, BC], \quad [AD, CB].$$

Let $[AB, CD] = r$ and express the other five cross ratios in terms of r. Let $[AD, CB] = s$ and express each of the other five cross ratios in terms of s.
Answer: $[AB, CD] = \frac{8}{63}$, etc.
If $[AB, CD] = r$, then $[AB, DC] = 1/r$, etc.
If $[AD, CB] = s$, then $[AB, CD] = s/(s-1)$, etc.

3. If $r = -1$, compute:

$$\frac{1}{r}, \quad 1 - r, \quad \frac{r-1}{r}, \quad \frac{1}{1-r}, \quad \frac{r}{r-1}.$$

4. If $r = \frac{1}{2}$, compute:

$$\frac{1}{r}, \quad 1 - r, \quad \frac{r-1}{r}, \quad \frac{1}{1-r}, \quad \frac{r}{r-1}.$$

5. Prove Theorem 12.6.

12.2 *Cross Ratio of a Pencil of Lines*

Definition. A set of distinct, coplanar, concurrent lines is a *pencil* of lines.

Definition. A cross ratio of a pencil of lines $\overleftrightarrow{OA}, \overleftrightarrow{OB}, \overleftrightarrow{OC}, \overleftrightarrow{OD}$ is denoted and defined as follows:

$$O[AB, CD] = \frac{\sin AOC}{\sin COB} \Big/ \frac{\sin AOD}{\sin DOB}.$$

In this definition AOC is a sensed angle and, as in trigonometry, angles sensed clockwise have a positive measure and angles sensed counterclockwise have a negative measure. The number $\sin AOC$ is the sine of any angle whose initial side is $\overrightarrow{OA}$ and whose terminal side is $\overrightarrow{OC}$.

Let A' be a point on $\overleftrightarrow{OA}$ such that $(A'OA)$. Since in all cases $\sin AOC = \sin A'OC$ and $\sin AOD = \sin A'OD$, and since similar statements hold for B', C', D' related to B, C, D, respectively, as A' is to A, it follows that $O[AB, CD]$ does not depend upon which side of O the points A, B, C, D are chosen.

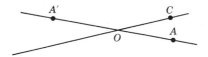

Definition. If $\overleftrightarrow{OA}, \overleftrightarrow{OB}, \overleftrightarrow{OC}, \overleftrightarrow{OD}$ is a pencil of four lines and if A, B, C, D are collinear, then we say that cross ratios $[AB, CD]$ and $O[AB, CD]$ are *corresponding cross ratios*. If A', B', C', D' are points on $\overleftrightarrow{OA}, \overleftrightarrow{OB}, \overleftrightarrow{OC}, \overleftrightarrow{OD}$, respectively, and if A', B', C', D' are collinear points, then $[AB, CD]$ and $[A'B', C'D']$ are called *corresponding cross ratios* formed by the two transversals.

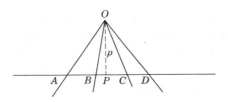

Theorem 12.7. Corresponding cross ratios are equal.

Proof. Let $O[AB, CD]$ and $[AB, CD]$ be corresponding cross ratios. Let P be the foot of the perpendicular from O to $\overleftrightarrow{AB}$, and let $p = OP$. Note that for all possible arrangements of the points A, B, C, D on the line that $\dfrac{AC}{CB}$ and sin AOC/sin COB are both positive or both negative, and that $\dfrac{AD}{DB}$ and sin AOD/sin DOB are both positive or both negative. Therefore the given corresponding cross ratios are both positive or both negative. To complete the proof we show that their absolute values are equal. Recall that $|\triangle ABC|$ denotes the area of $\triangle ABC$.

$$|\triangle AOC| = \tfrac{1}{2} \cdot AO \cdot OC \cdot |\sin AOC|$$

$$|\triangle AOD| = \tfrac{1}{2} \cdot AO \cdot OD \cdot |\sin AOD|$$

$$|\triangle COB| = \tfrac{1}{2} \cdot CO \cdot OB \cdot |\sin COB|$$

$$|\triangle DOB| = \tfrac{1}{2} \cdot DO \cdot OB \cdot |\sin DOB|$$

$$|[AB, CD]| = \frac{AC}{CB} \bigg/ \frac{AD}{DB} = \frac{|\triangle AOC|}{|\triangle COB|} \bigg/ \frac{|\triangle AOD|}{|\triangle DOB|} = \left| \frac{\sin AOC}{\sin COB} \bigg/ \frac{\sin AOD}{\sin DOB} \right|.$$

$$|[AB, CD]| = |O[AB, CD]|,$$

and therefore $[AB, CD] = O[AB, CD]$.

Theorem 12.8. Given a pencil of four lines and two intersecting transversals. The corresponding cross ratios formed by those transversals are equal.

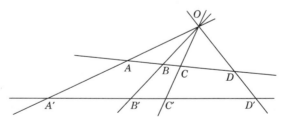

Proof. $[AB, CD] = O[AB, CD] = O[A'B', C'D'] = [A'B', C'D']$.

Theorem 12.8 proves that a cross ratio of a range of points is invariant under a central projection.

Theorem 12.9. Cross ratios of pencils which correspond to the same cross ratio of a range are equal.

Proof. $O[AB, CD] = [AB, CD] = O'[AB, CD]$.

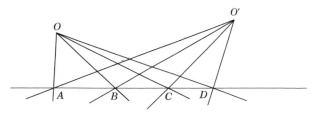

Theorem 12.10. If $[AB, CD] = [A'B', C'D']$, $A \neq A'$, $B \neq B'$, $C \neq C'$, $D \neq D'$, and if $\overleftrightarrow{AA'}, \overleftrightarrow{BB'}, \overleftrightarrow{CC'}$ are concurrent, then $\overleftrightarrow{DD'}$ passes through the point of concurrence.

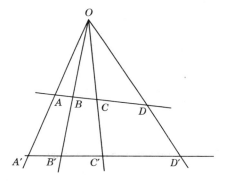

Proof. Let O be the intersection of $\overleftrightarrow{AA'}$ and $\overleftrightarrow{BB'}$. Let E be the intersection of $\overleftrightarrow{AB}$ and $\overleftrightarrow{OD'}$. Then

$$[AB, CE] = [A'B', C'D'] = [AB, CD],$$

$$\frac{AC}{CB} \bigg/ \frac{AE}{EB} = \frac{AC}{CB} \bigg/ \frac{AD}{DB}, \quad \frac{AE}{EB} = \frac{AD}{DB}.$$

Then E bears the same betweenness relation to A and B as does D, and $AE/EB = AD/DB$. From basic properties of ratios it follows that $D = E$. Therefore $\overleftrightarrow{DD'}$ passes through O.

Theorem 12.11. If $[AB, CD] = [AB', C'D']$, $B \neq B'$, $C \neq C'$, $D \neq D'$, and if $\overleftrightarrow{BB'}, \overleftrightarrow{CC'}$ intersect at O, then $\overleftrightarrow{DD'}$ passes through O.

Proof. Let E be the point in which $\overleftrightarrow{OD'}$ intersects $\overleftrightarrow{AC}$. Then

$$[AB, CD] = [AB', C'D'] = [AB, CE] \quad \text{and} \quad D = E.$$

Therefore $\overleftrightarrow{DD'}$ passes through O.

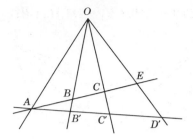

Theorem 12.12. If $O[AB, CD] = O'[AB, CD]$ and if A, B, C are collinear, then D lies in $\overleftrightarrow{AB}$.

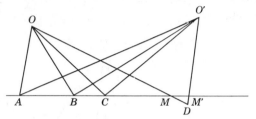

Proof. Let M and M' denote the points in which $\overrightarrow{OD}$ and $\overrightarrow{O'D'}$ intersect $\overleftrightarrow{AB}$, respectively. Then

$$[AB, CM] = O[AB, CM] = O[AB, CD] = O'[AB, CD]$$

$$= O'[AB, CM'] = [AB, CM'].$$

Therefore

$$[AB, CM] = [AB, CM'], \quad M = M' = D,$$

and D lies in $\overleftrightarrow{AB}$.

Theorem 12.13. If $O[AB, CD] = O'[AB, CD]$ and if O' lies on $\overleftrightarrow{OD}$, then A, B, C are collinear.

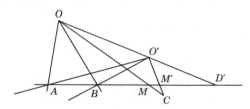

Proof. Let D' be the point in which $\overleftrightarrow{AB}$ and $\overrightarrow{OO'}$ intersect. Then A, B, D' are collinear. But $O[AB, D'C] = O'[AB, D'C]$. It follows from Theorem 12.12 that A, B, C are collinear.

Exercises 12.2

1. Is it true that if $[AB, CD] = [A'B', C'D']$ then every cross ratio of the range A, B, C, D is equal to the corresponding range of A', B', C', D'? Explain.

2. Is it true that if $O[AB, CD] = O'[A'B', C'D']$, then every cross ratio of one of the pencils is equal to the corresponding cross ratio of the other pencil? Explain.

3. Given an xy-coordinate system with points $O = (0,0)$, $A = (1,0)$, $B = (1,1)$, $C = (2,4)$, $D = (3,9)$. Compute $O[AB, CD]$. Use the fact that $O[AB, CD] = O[AB, C'D'] = [AB, C'D']$ where C' is the intersection of $\overleftrightarrow{AB}$ with $\overleftrightarrow{OC}$ and D' is the intersection of $\overleftrightarrow{AB}$ with $\overleftrightarrow{OD}$.

4. Given an xy-coordinate system with points $O = (0,0)$, $A = (-1, -1)$, $B = (0, 1)$, $C = (1, -1)$, $D = (1, 0)$. Compute $O[AB, CD]$. Investigate the possibility of taking B' and D' as the intersections of $\overleftrightarrow{BO}$ and $\overleftrightarrow{DO}$ with $\overleftrightarrow{AC}$. If D'' approaches D on $\overleftrightarrow{AD}$, and if D''' is the projection of D'' onto $\overleftrightarrow{AC}$ (using O as the center of projection), what does $[AB, CD''']$ approach?

5. Given a range A, B, C, D. If C divides $\overline{AB}$ internally in the ratio $2/3$ and D divides $\overline{AB}$ externally in the ratio $2/3$, finish the following computation for $[AB, CD]$.

$$\frac{AC}{CB} = \frac{2}{3}, \quad \frac{AD}{DB} = -\frac{2}{3}, \quad [AB, CD] = \underline{\hspace{1.5cm}}.$$

6. The coordinates of points A, B, P_n, Q_n on a line L are $0, 1, \frac{1}{2} + 1/2n, n$, respectively. Compute $[AB, P_nQ_n]$. As n is assigned values 2, 3, 4, 5, and so on, what number does $[AB, P_nQ_n]$ approach? What point does P_n approach? Describe the behavior of Q_n.

7. The coordinates of A, B, P_n, Q_n on a line L are $0, 1, \frac{1}{2} + 1/2n, -n$, respectively. Compute $[AB, P_nQ_n]$. As n is assigned values 2, 3, 4, 5, and so on, what number does $[AB, P_nQ_n]$ approach? What point does P_n approach? Describe the behavior of Q_n.

12.3 Harmonic Ranges and Pencils

Definition. If $[AB, CD] = -1$, then $\overline{AB}$ is said to be *divided harmonically* by C and D, and C and D are called *harmonic conjugates* with respect to A and B.

Theorem 12.14. Let E be the midpoint of $\overline{AB}$. Then $\overline{AB}$ is divided harmonically by C and D if and only if $\overrightarrow{EC}$ and $\overrightarrow{ED}$ are parallel rays and C and D divide $\overline{AB}$ in the same ratio, one internally and one externally.

Proof. Suppose $\overrightarrow{EC}$ and $\overrightarrow{ED}$ are parallel and that C and D divide $\overline{AB}$ in the same ratio, one internally and one externally. Then $AC/CB = AD/DB$, and one of the numbers $\dfrac{AC}{CB}$ and $\dfrac{AD}{DB}$ is positive and the other is negative. Therefore $\dfrac{AC}{CB} = -\dfrac{AD}{DB}$ and $[AB, CD] = -1$.

Suppose, next, that $[AB, CD] = -1$. Then $\dfrac{AC}{CB} = -\dfrac{AD}{DB}$.

Case 1. A, E, C, B are collinear in the order named.

In this case $\dfrac{AC}{CB} > 1$ and $\dfrac{AD}{BD} > 1$. Then A, E, B, D are collinear in the order named and $\overrightarrow{EC}$ and $\overrightarrow{ED}$ are parallel rays. Also $AC/CB = AD/DB$, (ACB), and (ABD). Therefore C and D divide $\overline{AB}$ in the same ratio, C internally and D externally.

Case 2. A, E, B, C are collinear in the order named.

In this case $\dfrac{AC}{BC} > 1$ and $\dfrac{AD}{DB} > 1$. Then A, E, D, C are collinear in the order named and $\overrightarrow{ED}$ and $\overrightarrow{EC}$ are parallel rays. Also $AC/CB = AD/DB$, (ADC), and (ABC). Therefore C and D divide $\overline{AB}$ in the same ratio, C externally and D internally.

Case 3. A, C, E, B are collinear in the order named.

Interchange A and B in Case 1.

Case 4. C, A, E, B are collinear in the order named.

Interchange A and B in Case 2.

Theorem 12.15. If $\overline{AB}$ is divided harmonically by C and D, then $\overline{CD}$ is divided harmonically by A and B.

Proof. $[AB, CD] = [CD, AB]$. See Theorem 12.1.

Definition. Given positive numbers a, b, and c, b is the *harmonic mean* between a and c if $1/b$ is the arithmetic mean between $1/a$ and $1/b$.

Theorem 12.16. If $[AB, CD] = -1$, then 1 is the harmonic mean between $\dfrac{AC}{AB}$ and $\dfrac{AD}{AB}$.

Proof. Let $[AB, CD] = -1$. Then

$$\frac{AC}{CB} = -\frac{AD}{DB}, \quad \frac{CB}{AC} = \frac{BD}{AD},$$

$$\frac{AB}{AC} - \frac{AC}{AC} = \frac{AD}{AD} - \frac{AB}{AD}, \quad \frac{AB}{AC} - 1 = 1 - \frac{AB}{AD},$$

$$\frac{AB}{AC} + \frac{AB}{AD} = 2, \quad \frac{\dfrac{AB}{AC} + \dfrac{AB}{AD}}{2} = 1.$$

Since 1 is the arithmetic mean between $\dfrac{AB}{AC}$ and $\dfrac{AB}{AD}$, it follows (taking reciprocals) that 1 is the harmonic mean between $\dfrac{AC}{AB}$ and $\dfrac{AD}{AB}$. Using the traditional terminology of *directed* distances this amounts to saying that $(AB)^*$ is the harmonic mean between $(AC)^*$ and $(AD)^*$, where $*$ indicates a directed distance.

Sometimes coordinates are useful in studying cross ratios.

Theorem 12.17. If A, B, C, D is a range of points with coordinates a, b, c, d, respectively, then

$$\frac{\overline{\overline{AB}}}{\overline{\overline{CD}}} = \frac{b - a}{d - c}.$$

Proof. If $\overrightarrow{AB}$ and $\overrightarrow{CD}$ are parallel rays, then $b - a$ and $d - c$ are both positive or both negative, and

$$\frac{\overline{\overline{AB}}}{\overline{\overline{CD}}} = \frac{AB}{CD} = \frac{b - a}{d - c}.$$

If $\overrightarrow{AB}$ and $\overrightarrow{CD}$ are antiparallel rays, then one of the differences $b - a$ and $d - c$ is positive and the other is negative, and

$$\frac{\overline{\overline{AB}}}{\overline{\overline{CD}}} = -\frac{AB}{CD} = \frac{b - a}{d - c}.$$

Using Theorem 12.17 we write an alternate proof of Theorem 12.16.

Proof. Let $[AB, CD] = -1$ and let a, b, c, d be the coordinates of A, B, C, D, respectively, in some coordinate system. Then

$$\frac{\overline{\overline{AC}}}{\overline{\overline{CB}}} = -\frac{\overline{\overline{AD}}}{\overline{\overline{DB}}}, \quad \frac{c - a}{b - c} = -\frac{d - a}{b - d}, \quad \frac{b - c}{c - a} = \frac{b - d}{a - d},$$

$$\frac{b - a}{c - a} - 1 = 1 - \frac{b - a}{d - a}, \quad \frac{b - a}{c - a} + \frac{b - a}{d - a} = 2, \quad \frac{\overline{\overline{AB}}}{\overline{\overline{AC}}} + \frac{\overline{\overline{AB}}}{\overline{\overline{AD}}} = 2.$$

Theorem 12.18. If E is the midpoint of $\overline{AB}$, then $[AB, CD] = -1$ if and only if $EC \cdot ED = (EB)^2$ and $\overrightarrow{EC}$ and $\overrightarrow{ED}$ are parallel rays.

Proof. Let a, b, c, d be the coordinates of A, B, C, D, respectively. Then the coordinate of E is $e = (a + b)/2$.

Let $[AB, CD] = -1$. Then by Theorem 12.14 we know that $\overrightarrow{EC}$ and $\overrightarrow{ED}$ are parallel rays, and that the differences $c - e$ and $d - e$ are both positive or both negative. Therefore $|c - e| \cdot |d - e| = (c - e)(d - e)$.

Then

$$\frac{\overline{AC}}{\overline{CB}} = -\frac{\overline{AD}}{\overline{DB}},$$

$$\frac{c-a}{b-c} = -\frac{d-a}{b-d},$$

$$(c-a)(d-b) = (d-a)(b-c),$$

$$cd - ad - bc + ab = db - ab - cd + ac,$$

$$2cd + 2ab - ad - bd - ac - bc = 0,$$

$$2cd - d(a+b) - c(a+b) - 2b^2 + 2b(a+b) = 0,$$

$$2cd - 2de - 2ce - 2b^2 + 4be = 0,$$

$$2(c-e)(d-e) - 2(b-e)^2 = 0,$$

$$(c-e)(d-e) = (b-e)^2,$$

$$|c-e| \cdot |d-e| = (b-e)^2,$$

$$EC \cdot ED = (EB)^2.$$

Next, let $EC \cdot ED = (EB)^2$ and $\overrightarrow{EC}$ and $\overrightarrow{ED}$ be parallel rays. Then we may reverse the steps in the preceding paragraph to prove that $[AB, CD] = -1$.

Consider a segment $\overline{AB}$ with its midpoint E. If C is a point on $\overline{AB}$ close to E, and if $[AB, CD] = -1$, then D is far removed from E. In other words if $[AB, CD] = -1$ and if CE approaches O, then DE becomes infinite. There is no point D on $\overleftrightarrow{AB}$, not on $\overline{AB}$, such that $AD = DB$. Hence there is no point D on $\overleftrightarrow{AB}$ such that $[AB, ED] = -1$. In projective geometry the line $\overleftrightarrow{AB}$ determined by A and B contains all of the points of the Euclidean line $\overleftrightarrow{AB}$ as well as a (only one) "point at infinity." Using the language of projective geometry we say that the harmonic conjugate of E with respect to A and B is D_∞, where D_∞ is the point at infinity on $\overleftrightarrow{AB}$. Also, we define

$$\frac{D_\infty A}{D_\infty B} = \frac{AD_\infty}{BD_\infty} = 1, \quad \frac{AD_\infty}{D_\infty B} = \frac{D_\infty A}{BD_\infty} = -1,$$

$$\frac{AD_\infty}{BD_\infty} = \frac{AD_\infty}{D_\infty B} = \frac{D_\infty A}{D_\infty B} = \frac{D_\infty A}{BD_\infty} = 1.$$

Similarly, if B, C, D is a range of points and A_∞ is the point at infinity on

$\overleftrightarrow{BC}$, then

$$\frac{A_\infty B}{BC} \bigg/ \frac{A_\infty D}{DC} = \frac{A_\infty B}{A_\infty D} \cdot \frac{DC}{BC} = \frac{DC}{BC}.$$

Theorem 12.19. Given a pencil of four lines $\overleftrightarrow{OA}, \overleftrightarrow{OB}, \overleftrightarrow{OC}, \overleftrightarrow{OD}$ with two transversals, one cutting these lines at A, B, C, D, respectively, the other parallel to and distinct from $\overleftrightarrow{OA}$, and cutting $\overleftrightarrow{OB}, \overleftrightarrow{OC}, \overleftrightarrow{OD}$, at B, C', D', respectively. Then $[A_\infty B, C'D'] = [AB, CD]$.

Proof. It is easy to verify that both of these cross ratios are positive or that both of them are negative. It is sufficient, then, to show that their

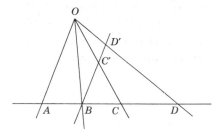

absolute values are equal. In the following equations all angle measures are considered as positive and between 0 and π.

$$|[AB, CD]| = \frac{AC}{BC} \bigg/ \frac{AD}{BD} = \frac{\sin AOC}{\sin BOC} \bigg/ \frac{\sin AOD}{\sin BOD} = \frac{\sin AOC}{\sin AOD} \cdot \frac{\sin BOD}{\sin BOC},$$

$$|[A_\infty B, C'D']| = \left|\frac{A_\infty C'}{C'B} \bigg/ \frac{A_\infty D'}{D'B}\right| = \frac{BD'}{BC'} = \frac{\text{area} \triangle BOD'}{\text{area} \triangle BOC'}$$

$$= \frac{BO \cdot OD' \sin BOD'}{BO \cdot OC' \sin BOC'} = \frac{OD' \cdot \sin BOD'}{OC' \cdot \sin BOC'}$$

$$= \frac{\sin OC'D'}{\sin OD'C'} \cdot \frac{\sin BOD}{\sin BOC} = \frac{\sin AOC}{\sin AOD} \cdot \frac{\sin BOD}{\sin BOC}.$$

Therefore $[AB, CD] = [A_\infty B, CD]$, and the proof is complete.

Exercises 12.3

1. Let $[AB, CD] = -1$. Consider A and B as "fixed" and C as a "moving" point. Describe the motion of D as C moves from A to B.

2. Given $\triangle ABC$. Prove that the bisector of $\angle A$ and the bisector of an exterior angle at A divide $\overline{BC}$ harmonically.

3. Where does the bisector of an exterior angle at the vertex of an isosceles triangle meet the line which contains the base of the triangle?

4. Given a range A, B, C, D, with coordinates 0, 10, 6, x, respectively. If $[AB, CD] = -1$, find x.

5. Given a range A, B, C, D, with coordinates 0, 10, 4, x, respectively. If $[AB, CD] = -1$, find x.

6. Given a range A, B, C, D, with coordinates -10, 10, 5, x, respectively. If $[AB, CD] = -1$, find x.

7. Given a range A, B, C, D, with coordinates -10, 10, -5, x, respectively. If $[AB, CD] = -1$, find x.

8. Given $\triangle ABC$ with X on $\overline{AB}$ such that $\overrightarrow{AX}$ bisects $\angle A$. Prove that $\overline{AX}$ is divided harmonically by the perpendiculars from B and C to $\overleftrightarrow{AX}$.

9. Given coplanar points A, B, C, D, E, F, G with collinearity and betweenness properties as suggested in the figure. Prove that if $FB = BG$ and $\overleftrightarrow{AE} \parallel \overleftrightarrow{FG}$, then $[AB, CD] = -1$.

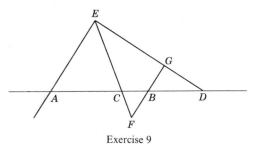

Exercise 9

10. Given the figure of Exercise 9. Prove that if $\overleftrightarrow{AE} \parallel \overleftrightarrow{FG}$ and $[AB, CD] = -1$, then $FB = BG$.

11. Is Theorem 12.8 true for all transversals not through O in the plane of the given pencil? One or both transversals might be parallel to one of the lines in the pencils. Are corresponding cross ratios formed by such transversals equal?

12. What is the harmonic conjugate of the line that contains the median to one side of a triangle with respect to the lines that contain the other two sides?

CHAPTER 13

Further Geometry of Circles

13.1 Introduction

This is another chapter in plane geometry. All sets of points under consideration lie in a given plane.

There is voluminous material in the literature related to the geometry of the circle. Topics discussed in this chapter are pole and polar, orthogonal circles, and radical axis.

13.2 Pole and Polar

Definition. If s and t are distinct tangents from an external point T to a circle, the segment $\overline{PQ}$ joining their points of contact with the circle is called their *chord of contact* (see figure with Theorem 13.2).

Theorem 13.1. If s and t are distinct tangents from an external point T to a circle with center C, then their chord of contact is perpendicular to $\overleftrightarrow{CT}$.

Proof. Assigned as an exercise.

Theorem 13.2. Given a circle with center C, an external point T, and two distinct tangents from T to the circle. If $\overleftrightarrow{CT}$ intersects the chord of contact at N and the circle at A, then $CN \cdot CT = (CA)^2$.

Proof. Let P and Q denote the points of contact. It follows from the A.A. similarity theorem that $\triangle CNP \sim \triangle CPT$. Then $(CN, CP) \underset{p}{=} (CP, CT)$ and $CN \cdot CT = (CP)^2 = (CA)^2$. (See figure on page 232.)

231

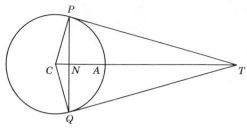

Theorem 13.2

Definition. Given a circle of radius r and with center C, interior points P and N of a ray m with endpoint C, and the line p perpendicular to m at N. If $CP \cdot CN = r^2$, then p is the *polar* of P, and P is the *pole* of p, each with respect to the given circle.

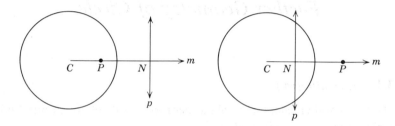

Theorem 13.3. Given a circle with center C, a point P distinct from C, a line m through P intersecting the circle in S and R, p the polar of P with respect to the given circle, H the intersection of p and m, and K the midpoint of $\overline{SR}$. Then $KH \cdot KP = (KR)^2$.

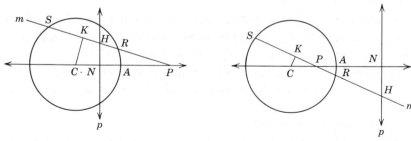

Proof.

$\overline{CK} \perp \overline{SR}$

$$KH \cdot KP = KP(KP - PH) \qquad \text{or} \qquad KH \cdot KP = KP(KP + PH)$$

$$= (KP)^2 - KP \cdot HP \qquad\qquad\qquad = (KP)^2 + KP \cdot HP$$

C, N, H, K are concyclic points since $\angle CNH$ and $\angle CKH$ are right angles. Considering $\overleftrightarrow{PK}$ and $\overleftrightarrow{PC}$ as secant lines of the circle containing C, N, H, K, we see [using what theorem(s)?] that $KP \cdot HP = CP \cdot NP$. Then

$$KH \cdot KP = (KP)^2 - CP \cdot NP \qquad\qquad KH \cdot KP = (KP)^2 + CP \cdot NP$$
$$= (KP)^2 \qquad\qquad\qquad\qquad\qquad = (KP)^2$$
$$\quad - CP(CP - CN) \qquad\qquad\qquad\quad + CP(CN - CP)$$
$$= (KP)^2 - (CP)^2 \qquad\qquad\qquad\quad = (KP)^2 - (CP)^2$$
$$\quad + CP \cdot CN \qquad\qquad\qquad\qquad\quad + CP \cdot CN$$
$$= (KP)^2 - (CP)^2 \qquad\qquad\qquad\quad = (KP)^2 - (CP)^2$$
$$\quad + (CA)^2 \qquad\qquad\qquad\qquad\qquad + (CA)^2$$
$$= -(KC)^2 + (CA)^2 \qquad\qquad\qquad = -(KC)^2 + (CA)^2$$
$$= -(KC)^2 + (CR)^2 \qquad\qquad\qquad = -(KC)^2 + (CR)^2$$
$$= (KR)^2 \qquad\qquad\qquad\qquad\qquad\quad = (KR)^2$$

Theorem 13.4. Given a circle and two points P and Q. If the polar of P passes through Q, then the polar of Q passes through P.

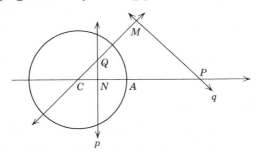

Proof. Let C be the center of the circle and $\overleftrightarrow{QN}$ the polar of P. Let A be the point in which $\overrightarrow{CP}$ meets the circle, and let M be the foot of the perpendicular from P to $\overleftrightarrow{CQ}$. Then P, M, Q, N are concyclic points, and $CM \cdot CQ = CN \cdot CP = (CA)^2$. Therefore $\overleftrightarrow{PM}$ is the polar of Q, that is, the polar of Q passes through P.

Exercises 13.2

1. Given a circle C, a point P, and p the polar of P with respect to C. Keep C fixed and imagine that P moves about. Describe the resulting motion of p.

2. Given a circle C and a tangent line p. What is the pole of p with respect to C.

3. Where are the poles of the lines which contain the sides of a triangle, if the poles are taken with respect to its incircle?

4. Where are the polars of the vertices of a triangle, if the polars are taken with respect to its circumcircle?

5. Given $\triangle ABC$ and D, E, F, the feet of the altitudes from A, B, C, to the lines containing the opposite sides, and a circle with center A and radius r, where $r^2 = AB \cdot AF$. Identify the polars of B and C and the pole of $\overleftrightarrow{BC}$.

6. Given the figures in the proof of Theorem 13.3. Prove that if $\overline{SR}$ is not a diameter of the given circle, then the tangents to the circle at S and R intersect at a point of p. *Hint:* Use Theorem 13.4.

7. Given the situation of Exercise 6 except that $\overline{SR}$ is a diameter. Discuss the relationship of the tangents at S and R to the line p. In what sense is the assertion of Exercise 6 true?

8. Given the situation of Theorem 13.3. Prove that (SR, HP) is a harmonic range and that $N(SR, HP)$ is a harmonic pencil.

9. Given the situation of Theorem 13.3 with P outside the circle. Prove that $\angle SNH \cong \angle RNH$.

10. Given the situation of Theorem 13.3 with P inside the circle. Prove that $\angle SNP \cong \angle RNP$.

11. In the situation of Theorem 13.3 suppose that S and C remain fixed while R moves: (1) toward R_0, where $\overline{SR_0}$ is a diameter, and (2) toward R_1, where $\overline{SR_1} \parallel \overline{CP}$. Discuss in each case the corresponding movements of P, H, and N, and whether or not the angle congruences of Exercises 9 and 10 hold in these limiting situations.

13.3   *Orthogonal Circles*

Definition. If C_1 and C_2 are distinct curves which intersect at a point P, and if the tangent lines to C_1 and C_2 at P are distinct, then the angles formed by these tangents are called the *angles of intersection* at that point. If the tangents are perpendicular, the curves C_1 and C_2 are called *orthogonal* curves, and each is said to be orthogonal, or perpendicular, to the other.

Theorem 13.5. If two distinct circles intersect in two distinct points, then one of the angles of intersection at one point of intersection is congruent to one of the angles of intersection at the other point.

Proof. Let two circles with centers at A and A' intersect at P and P'. Let the tangents at P and P' intersect at R and R'. Since $AP = AP'$ and

$A'P = A'P'$, it follows that $\overleftrightarrow{AA'}$ is the perpendicular bisector of $\overleftrightarrow{PP'}$. Also $RP = RP'$ and $R'P = R'P'$. Why? Therefore A, R, R', A' are collinear

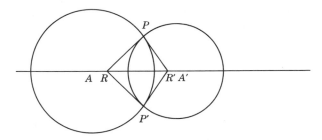

as suggested in the figure. From the S.S.S. congruence theorem it follows that $\triangle RPR' \cong \triangle RP'R'$, and hence that $\angle RPR' \cong \angle RP'R'$.

Theorem 13.6. If circles C and C' with centers A and A', respectively, are orthogonal at P, then the tangent to C at P contains A', and the tangent to C' at P contains A'.

Proof. Assigned as an exercise.

Theorem 13.7. Given circles C and C' with centers A and A', respectively, and intersecting at P. If the tangent to C at P contains A' and the tangent to C' at P contains A, then the circles are orthogonal.

Proof. Assigned as an exercise.

Theorem 13.8. The sum of the squares of the radii of two orthogonal circles is equal to the square of the distance between their centers.

Proof. Assigned as an exercise.

Theorem 13.9. If the sum of the squares of the radii of two intersecting circles is equal to the square of the distance between their centers, then the circles are orthogonal.

Proof. Assigned as an exercise.

Theorem 13.10. Given orthogonal circles C and C' with centers at A and A', respectively. If a line through A intersects C in P and Q and C' in R and S, then (PQ, RS) is a harmonic range.

Proof. Let B be a point of intersection of the given circles. Then $\overleftrightarrow{AB}$ is a tangent to C' and $(AB)^2 = AR \cdot AS$. Then $(AQ)^2 = AR \cdot AS$ and since A is the midpoint of $\overline{PQ}$, it follows from Theorem 12.18 that (PQ, RS) is a harmonic range.

Exercises 13.3

1. Prove Theorem 13.6.

2. Prove Theorem 13.7.

3. Prove Theorem 13.8.

4. Prove Theorem 13.9.

5. Given a quadrilateral $ABCD$. Prove that if A and C are the centers of two orthogonal circles and if B and D are their points of intersection, then $ABCD$ is a cyclic quadrilateral.

6. Given two orthogonal circles with centers at A and A'. If $AA' = k$, express the sum of the areas of the two circles in terms of k.

7. If r and s are the radii of two orthogonal circles, and if d is the distance between their centers, prove that $d > r$ and $d > s$.

8. Given a harmonic range $\{AB, CD\}$. If $\overline{AB}$ is a diameter of a circle R and $\overline{CD}$ is a chord of a circle S, prove that R and S are orthogonal circles.

9. Given a line L and circles C and D. If L is tangent to C at A and to D at B, prove that the circle with diameter $\overline{AB}$ is orthogonal to C and to D.

10. Given $\triangle ABC$ with orthocenter H. Prove that the circle with diameter $\overline{AB}$ is orthogonal to the circle with diameter $\overline{CH}$.

11. Given two circles with centers C and D and with radii r and s, respectively, intersecting at distinct points A and B. Prove that $\overleftrightarrow{CD}$ is the perpendicular bisector of $\overleftrightarrow{AB}$.

12. Given two circles with centers C and D and with radii r and s, respectively, intersecting at distinct points A and B. Prove that if P is a point of $\overleftrightarrow{AB}$, then $(CP)^2 - r^2 = (DP)^2 - s^2$. *Hint:* Let Q be the intersection of $\overline{AB}$ and $\overline{CD}$. Why is $(CQ)^2 - r^2 = (BQ)^2 - s^2$? Let P, $P \neq Q$, be any other point of $\overleftrightarrow{AB}$. Then $(CP)^2 - r^2 = (CQ)^2 + (QP)^2 - r^2 = (QP)^2 - [r^2 - (CQ)^2] = (QP)^2 - (AQ)^2$, and $(DP)^2 - s^2 = \dots$.

13. Given two circles with centers C and D and with radii r and s, respectively, intersecting at distinct points A and B, respectively. Prove that if P is a point of $\overleftrightarrow{AB}$, but not of $\overline{AB}$, and if R and S are points of the two circles such that $\overleftrightarrow{PR}$ and $\overleftrightarrow{PS}$ are tangents to the circles with centers C and D, respectively, then $PR = PS$.

14. Given two circles with centers C and D and with radii r and s, respectively, which do not intersect and such that neither circle is inside the other; R and S are points on the circles with centers C and D, respectively, and P is a point such that $\overleftrightarrow{PR}$ and $\overleftrightarrow{PS}$ are tangents to the given circles. Prove that if $(PC)^2 - r^2 = (PD)^2 - s^2$, then $PR = PS$.

13.4   Radical Axis

Definition. Given circles C and D with distinct centers A and B, respectively, and with radii r and s, respectively. The set of all points P

such that $(AP)^2 - r^2 = (BP)^2 - s^2$ is called the *radical axis* of the circles.

Note that if two circles intersect in two distinct points, their radical axis is the line through their points of intersection. See Exercises 13 and 14 in Exercises 13.3. If a point of the radical axis of two circles is outside both circles, then tangent segments from that point to the circles are congruent. The concept of the radical axis for any two circles with distinct centers is, in a sense, a generalization of the line determined by the points of intersection of the two circles which intersect.

Theorem 13.11. The radical axis of two circles is a line perpendicular to their line of centers.

Proof. Let A and B, with $A \neq B$, be the centers and r and s the radii, respectively, of the given circles. Set up an xy-coordinate system in which $A = (0, 0)$ and $B = (a, 0)$, with $a > 0$. Then $P(x, y)$ is a point of the radical axis if and only if

$$(AP)^2 - r^2 = (BP)^2 - s^2,$$

$$x^2 + y^2 - r^2 = (a - x)^2 + y^2 - s^2,$$

$$2ax = a^2 + r^2 - s^2,$$

that is, if and only if P is on the line given by the equation

$$x = \frac{a^2 + r^2 - s^2}{2a}$$

Exercises 13.4

1. Given two circles which are tangent to each other at a point P and the line L which is tangent to them at P. Prove that L is the radical axis of the given circles.

2. Given two concentric circles C and D, center at A, with radii r and s, $r \neq s$, respectively. Describe the set S of points P given as follows:

$$S = \{P : (PA)^2 - r^2 = (PA)^2 - s^2\}.$$

3. See the proof of Theorem 13.11. Prove that if $a > r + s$, then the radical axis of the given circles intersects neither circle.

4. See the proof of Theorem 13.11. Prove that if $r > s$ and $0 < a < a + s < r$, then the radical axis of the given circles intersects neither circle.

5. Prove that if a line intersects one of two circles but not the other, then it is not the radical axis of the two circles.

6. Given three circles whose centers are noncollinear. Prove that the radical axes of these circles taken in pairs are concurrent. (The point of concurrence is called the *radical center* of the three circles.)

7. If each of three circles is tangent to the other two, prove that the three common tangents at the points of contact are concurrent.

8. Given a $\triangle ABC$ and the circles which have $\overline{AB}, \overline{BC}, \overline{CA}$ as diameters. Prove that the radical center of these circles is the orthocenter of $\triangle ABC$.

9. Given a $\triangle ABC$, its incircle, and its excircle opposite A. Prove that the radical axis of these circles bisects $\overline{BC}$ and intersects $\overleftrightarrow{AB}$ and $\overleftrightarrow{AC}$ in points P and Q such that $AP = AQ = \frac{1}{2}(AC + AB)$.

10. If the centers of two circles are the points A and B, if their radii are 5 and 10, if $AB = 25$, if the radical axis of these circles intersects $\overleftrightarrow{AB}$ at P, find AP/PB.

11. Same as Exercise 10 except that $AB = 75$.

12. Given an xy-coordinate system and circles

$$C = \{x, y): x^2 + y^2 = 1\}$$

and

$$D = \{(x, y): (x - 2n)^2 + y^2 = n^2\}.$$

If $P(a, 0)$ is on the radical axis of C and D, express a in terms of n. Consider n a variable, and evaluate the limit of $a/2n$ as $n \to \infty$.

13. Given an xy-coordinate system and

$$C = \{x, y): x^2 + y^2 = 1\},$$
$$C' = \{(x, y): (x - a)^2 + y^2 = b^2\},$$

where $a > 0, b > 0$. For every real number $k \neq 1$ let

$$C_k = \{(x, y): (x - a)^2 + y^2 - b^2 = k(x^2 + y^2 - 1)\}.$$

Prove that if L is the radical axis of C and C', it is also the radical axis of C and C_k.

CHAPTER 14

Construction with Euclidean Ruler
and Compasses

14.1 *Introduction*

This is another chapter in plane geometry. All sets of points under consideration lie in a given plane. The ruler, or straightedge, and compass are the traditional tools of Euclidean geometry for drawing pictures of plane geometric figures. The Euclidean ruler has no marks on it. It can be used to draw a line through two distinct points, and that is all it can be used for. It cannot be used to measure distances or even to determine if two segments are congruent.

The Euclidean compass is a collapsible one. Given two distinct points P and Q, the compass may be used to draw a circle with center P and passing through Q. Given a third point R, the compass cannot be moved to draw a circle with center R and radius PQ. When the point of the compass is lifted from P, it collapses and apparently the compass is an inadequate tool for drawing a circle with center R and radius PQ. The next section contains a sequence of basic constructions which show that the collapsible feature of the Euclidean compass is not a real restriction. We shall see that the Euclidean compass and ruler can be used in a sequence of steps to draw a circle with center R and with radius PQ.

14.2   Basic Constructions

1. To construct the perpendicular bisector of a given segment, or to construct the point which bisects a given segment.

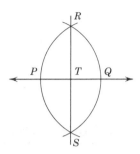

Given a segment $\overline{PQ}$. Draw the circle with center P and passing through Q. Draw the circle with center Q and passing through P. Using coordinates it is easy to prove that these two circles intersect in two distinct points R and S which are separated by the line $\overleftrightarrow{PQ}$. Draw $\overleftrightarrow{RS}$. Let T be the point in which $\overleftrightarrow{RS}$ intersects $\overleftrightarrow{PQ}$. It is easy to prove that $\triangle PRS \cong \triangle QRS$, $\triangle PRT \cong \triangle QRT$, and hence that (1) $\overleftrightarrow{RS}$ is the perpendicular bisector of $\overline{PQ}$, and (2) T bisects $\overline{PQ}$.

2. To construct the perpendicular to a line, through a given point on the line.

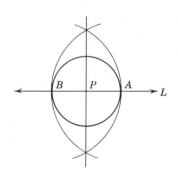

Given a line L and a point P on it. Let A be any point of L other than P. Draw the circle with center P and passing through A. This circle intersects L at A and at a second point B such that $BP = AP$, and such that P is between A and B. Next construct the perpendicular bisector of $\overline{AB}$.

3. Given three distinct points A, B, C. To construct a rectangle $BCDE$ such that $BE = CD = AB$.

Draw $\overleftrightarrow{AB}$ and $\overleftrightarrow{BC}$. Draw $\overleftrightarrow{BE'}$ perpendicular to $\overleftrightarrow{BC}$ at B, and $\overleftrightarrow{CD'}$ perpendicular to $\overleftrightarrow{BC}$ at C. Draw the circle with center B and passing

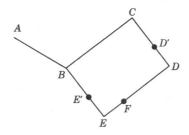

through A. Let E be one of the points in which this circle intersects $\overleftrightarrow{BE'}$. Draw $\overleftrightarrow{EF}$ perpendicular to $\overleftrightarrow{BE}$ at E. Then $\overleftrightarrow{EF}$ and $\overleftrightarrow{CD'}$ intersect in some point D. Why? Then $BCDE$ is a rectangle with $BE = CD = AB$.

4. Given a segment $\overline{AB}$ and a ray $\overrightarrow{CE}$. To construct the point D on $\overrightarrow{CE}$ such that $AB = CD$.

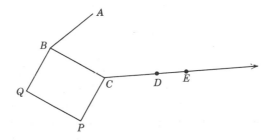

Construct a rectangle $BCPQ$ such that $BA = BQ = CP$. Then draw the circle with center C and passing through P. Let D be the point in which this circle intersects $\overrightarrow{CE}$.

Using these basic constructions it is possible to do with a collapsible compass whatever could be done with a noncollapsible one. To simplify matters we shall omit from now on the steps in showing how to do basic construction No. 4, for we know that if the construction is possible with a noncollapsible compass it is also possible with a collapsible one.

5. Given an angle, $\angle ABC$, a ray $\overrightarrow{ED}$, and a side H of the line $\overleftrightarrow{DE}$. To construct a ray $\overrightarrow{EF}$ with F in H so that $\angle ABC \cong \angle DEF$.

Draw circle K with center B and passing through A. Draw the point A' on $\overrightarrow{ED}$ such that $EA' = BA$. Draw the circle K' with center E and radius EA'. Let F' be the point in which K intersects $\overrightarrow{BC}$. Draw the circle K'' with center A' and radius AF'. Let F be the point in H which is in the intersection of K' and K''. Draw $\overrightarrow{EF}$. Then $\triangle BAF' \cong \triangle EA'F$ by S.S.S.; and therefore $\angle ABC = \angle DEF$.

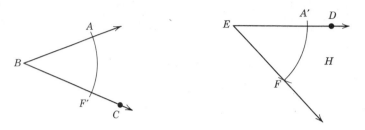

6. Given three segments of length 1, a, and b. Construct a segment of length ab.

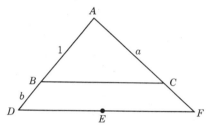

Let $\overline{AB}$ be a segment of length 1. On the ray opposite to $\overrightarrow{BA}$ take D so that $BD = b$. On a ray with endpoint A, but not collinear with $\overrightarrow{AB}$, take C so that $AC = a$. On the C-side of $\overleftrightarrow{AB}$ construct a point E so that $\angle BDE \cong \angle ABC$. Then $\overrightarrow{DE}$ intersects $\overrightarrow{AC}$ in some point F. Since $\overline{BC} \parallel \overline{BF}$, it follows that $(1, b) \overset{}{\underset{p}{=}} (a, CF)$, and hence that $CF = ab$.

Exercises 14.2

1. Given segments of length a and b. Construct a segment of length $a + b$.

2. Given segments of length a and b with $a > b$. Construct a segment of length $a - b$.

3. Given segments of length a and b. Construct a segment of length $a \div b$. *Hint:* $(b, a) \overset{}{\underset{p}{=}} (1, a/b)$.

4. Given segments of length a and b. Construct a segment of length $\sqrt{ab}$. *Hint:* $(a, \sqrt{ab}) \overset{}{\underset{p}{=}} (\sqrt{ab}, b)$.

5. Given a line l and a point P not on l. Construct the line containing P which is parallel to l.

6. Given three segments of length a, b, c, where $a \geqslant b \geqslant c$. Construct a triangle whose sides are congruent to the three given segments. What condition (in addition to what is given) is necessary and sufficient to insure that the construction is possible?

7. Given two segments, $\overline{AB}$ and $\overline{CD}$, and an angle $\angle R$. Construct a triangle $\triangle XYZ$ such that $\overline{XY} \cong \overline{AB}$, $\overline{XZ} \cong \overline{CD}$, $\angle X \cong \angle R$.

8. Given a segment $\overline{AB}$ and two angles $\angle C$ and $\angle D$. Construct a triangle $\triangle XYZ$ such that $\overline{XY} \cong \overline{AB}$, $\angle X \cong \angle C$, and $\angle Y \cong \angle D$. What condition on $m\angle C$ and $m\angle D$ is necessary and sufficient to insure that the construction is possible?

9. Given a segment $\overline{AB}$ and a point D not on $\overleftrightarrow{AB}$. Construct the triangle $\triangle ABC$ in which D is the midpoint of $\overline{BC}$.

10. Given a segment $\overline{AB}$ and a point G not on $\overleftrightarrow{AB}$. Construct the triangle $\triangle ABC$ which has G as its centroid.

11. Given segment $\overline{AB}$ and $\overline{CD}$. Construct a triangle $\triangle ABE$ such that the distance from E to $\overleftrightarrow{AB}$ is CD.

12. Given three noncollinear points A, B, G. Construct the triangle $\triangle ABC$ such that G is its centroid.

13. Given segments of length 1, a, b. Construct segments whose lengths are the roots of the equation $x^2 - ax + b = 0$. *Hint:* Set up a coordinate system and construct the points A $(0, 1)$ and B (a, b). Draw the circle with diameter $\overline{AB}$. Let O be the origin of the coordinate system and C and D the points in which the circle intersects the x-axis. Show that OC and OD are roots of the equation $x^2 - ax + b = 0$. What condition on a and b will insure that the circle intersects the x-axis in two distinct points whose abscissas are positive or is tangent to the x-axis at a point whose abscissa is positive?

14. Same as Exercise 13 except that $a < 0$ and $b > 0$ and segments of length 1, $-a$, b are given.

15. Same as Exercise 13 except that $a < 0$ and $b < 0$ and segments of length 1, $-a$, $-b$ are given.

16. Given $\angle BAT$, construct a circle tangent to $\overleftrightarrow{AT}$ at A and passing through B.

17. Given two distinct points A and B and an angle $\angle CDE$. Construct a circle through A and B, this circle being the union of two distinct arcs APB and AQB such that an angle inscribed in $\overparen{APB}$ is congruent to $\angle CDE$. *Hint:* Use Exercise 16.

18. Given two segments $\overline{AB}$ and $\overline{DE}$, with $AB < DE$. Construct a right triangle with a right angle at C and such that $AC + CB = DE$. *Hint:* Construct $\angle DEG$ such that $m\angle DEG = 45$. Draw circle with center D and radius AB cutting $\overrightarrow{EG}$ in F. Drop a perpendicular from F to $\overline{DE}$. Etc.

19. Given three collinear points A, C', B, collinear in that order. Construct a right triangle ABC with right angle at C and such that $\overline{CC'} \perp \overline{AB}$.

20. Given a segment $\overline{AB}$. Construct points $A_1, A_2, \ldots, A_6$ collinear in the order named on $\overrightarrow{AD}$ such that $AA_1 = A_1A_2 = A_2A_3 = \ldots = A_6B$.

21. Given three noncollinear points, construct the center of the circle which passes through the three points.

22. Given a circle C (including its center) and an external point P. Construct the tangents from P to C.

23. Given two circles with centers at C and D ($C \neq D$) and radii r and s (such that $s > r$), respectively. Construct the point A on the ray opposite to $\overrightarrow{CD}$ such that $(AC, AD) \underset{\overline{P}}{=} (r, s)$. *Hint:* Construct points E and F on the same side of $\overleftrightarrow{CD}$ such that $\overline{CE} \parallel \overline{CF}$, $CE = r$ and $CF = s$. Draw $\overleftrightarrow{EF}$.

24. Same as Exercise 23 except that A is required to be a point of $\overline{CD}$.

25. Given two nonintersecting circles with centers at C and D, neither inside the other, and with radii r and s, respectively. Construct two points E and F, one on each of the given circles and on the same side of $\overleftrightarrow{CD}$, such that $\overleftrightarrow{EF}$ is tangent to each of the given circles. *Hint:* Exercises 22 and 23.

26. Same as Exercise 25 except E and F are required to be on opposite sides of $\overleftrightarrow{CD}$.

27. Given three points A, C, B, collinear in that order on a line L and such that $AC \neq CB$. Construct the point D on L such that $D \neq C$ and $AC/CB = AD/DB$ (that is, A, C, B, D is a harmonic range). *Hint:* The following figure in which $\overleftrightarrow{FG} \parallel \overleftrightarrow{AE}$ and $FB = BG$.

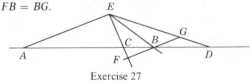

Exercise 27

28. Given two nonintersecting circles C and D with distinct centers. Construct their radical axis. *Hint:* The following figure.

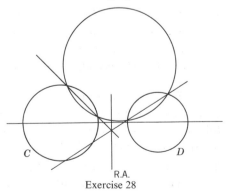

R.A.
Exercise 28

29. Given three noncollinear points D, E, F. Construct the triangle ABC such that D, E, F are the feet of altitudes from A, B, C to the lines which contain the opposite sides. *Hint:* The following figure. $CEHD$ and $BDHF$ are cyclic quadrilaterals. Why? $\angle 1 \cong \angle 2$. Why? $\angle 3 \cong \angle 4$. Why? $\angle 1 \cong \angle 4$. Why? $\overrightarrow{DH}$ is the bisector of $\angle EDF$. Etc.

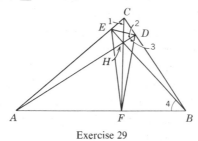

Exercise 29

30. Given three segments of length x, y, z. Construct a triangle ABC whose medians are of length x, y, z.

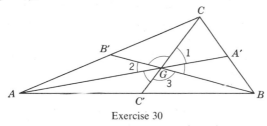

Exercise 30

Hint: Prove that B and C are equidistant from $\overleftrightarrow{AG}$. Etc.
 Prove that $GC \sin \angle 1 = GB \sin \angle 2$. Etc.
 Prove that $(GA, GB, GC) \doteqdot (\sin \angle BGC, \sin \angle CGA, \sin \angle AGB)$,
 $(AA', BB', CC') \doteqdot (\sin \angle 3, \sin \angle 1, \sin \angle 2)$,
 $m\angle 1 + m\angle 2 + m\angle 3 = 180$.
 Construct a triangle T with side lengths AA', BB', CC'. Construct $\triangle ABC$.

14.3   Angle Trisection

To "bisect an angle" is an easy Euclidean construction closely related to the S.S.S. congruence theorem. To bisect angle ABC means to

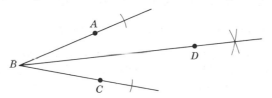

construct the midray $\overrightarrow{BD}$ of the angle, or what is good enough, to construct an angle E such that $m\angle E = \frac{1}{2}m\angle ABC$.

To "trisect an angle," say $\angle ABC$, is to construct an angle F such that $m\angle F = \frac{1}{3}m\angle ABC$. How to bisect an angle appears in every elementary geometry book. How to trisect an angle is not found in elementary geometry books. Why not? The answer is that it is impossible to trisect all angles with Euclidean ruler and compass.

Why do elementary textbooks omit a proof that angle trisection is an impossible Euclidean construction? It is omitted because it is not an elementary proof. For centuries amateurs have been attempting to trisect the angle with Euclidean tools. Why don't they stop? Perhaps they do not know that there are proofs of the impossibility of the construction. Perhaps they know of such proofs but prefer to ignore them. Perhaps they prefer not to accept the postulates on which such proofs rest. Some of them do not understand the meaning of impossible. Some think it means that no one has succeeded in finding a way to do it, but that they might be more lucky. An analogy in elementary algebra might be helpful.

To solve an equation such as $3x + 6 = 0$ means to find every number which can be put in place of x to yield a true statement. Since $3 \cdot (-2) + 6 = 0$ is a true statement, and since $3x + 6 = 0$ becomes a false statement if x is replaced by any number except -2, we say that the $x = -2$ is the solution. Another way to express the answer is to say that the solution set of the equation is the set whose only element is -2. Consider now the problem of solving, that is, of finding the solution set, of the equation $x + 1 = x$. An amateur might say, "I can't do it," or "It is impossible." A modern professional would say, "The solution set of this equation (if the set of replacement values for x is the set of all real numbers) is the null set." There is no admission here that the lack of roots has anything to do with the professional's lack of ingenuity.

The angle trisection problem might be more clearly stated as follows: *Find a Euclidean construction for trisecting an arbitrary angle and prove that it works or prove that no such construction is possible.* The professional mathematicians have solved this problem completely. They have proved that there is no Euclidean construction for trisecting an arbitrary angle.

14.4   *A Trisection and a Cubic Equation*

We shall outline a proof that the trisection of an angle of measure $60°$ is an impossible Euclidean construction. We shall suppose it is possible and show that this leads to a contradiction. Suppose, then, that it is possible to start with an angle of measure 60° and a segment of unit length and construct an angle of measure 20°. Then, as suggested in the figure, we could construct a segment $\overline{AC}$ of length $x = 2 \cos 20°$.

Then

$$1 = 2 \cos 60°$$

$$= 2 \cos(40° + 20°)$$

$$= 2 \cos 40° \cos 20° - 2 \sin 40° \sin 20°$$

$$= 2 \cos 20°(2 \cos^2 20° - 1 - 2 + 2 \cos^2 20°)$$

$$= 8 \cos^3 20° - 6 \cos 20°$$

$$= x^3 - 3x$$

Thus we could construct a segment of length x such that $x^3 - 3x - 1 = 0$. Using elementary algebra we can determine that this equation has no rational roots. Using calculus we can show that two of its roots are negative and that one is positive. Therefore our supposition implies that we can construct with Euclidean ruler and compass a segment of length x where x is the positive irrational root of the equation $x^3 - 3x - 1 = 0$.

14.5   *Algebraic Criterion for Constructibility*

In a Euclidean construction, points are constructed as intersections of lines, or of circles, or of lines and circles. A Euclidean construction consists of a finite number of lines and circles. Consider any Euclidean construction. For every pair of intersecting circles in the construction, draw the radical axis of these circles if they have not already been drawn. (Recall that if two circles intersect in two distinct points, P and Q, then their radical axis is the line $\overleftrightarrow{PQ}$, and that if two circles intersect in one and only one point R, then their radical axis is their common tangent at R.) Since there is a finite number (maybe zero) of lines in the construction, there is an xy-coordinate system S such that the y-axis is not parallel to any of the lines in the construction. Suppose S has been established subject to this restriction and based on a given segment of unit length. Let

$y = ax + b$ and $y = cx + d$ be the equations of any two distinct intersecting lines in the construction. Then $a \neq c$ and their point of intersection is the point $P(x, y)$ where $x = (d - b)/(a - c)$, $y = (ad - bc)/(a - c)$. Thus the coordinates of P are given by rational expressions involving the coefficients of the equations of the lines.

Let $y = ax + b$ and $(x - c)^2 + (y - d)^2 = e^2$ be the equations of an intersecting line and circle in the construction. Then $Q(x, y)$ is a point in their intersection if and only if $(x - c)^2 + (y - d)^2 = e^2$ *and* $y = ax + b$. Solving for x and y in terms of the parameters a, b, c, d, e we see that x and y are given by expressions which are either rational expressions involving the parameters, or expressions which involve the rational operations (addition, subtraction, multiplication, division—except by zero) and extractions of real square roots. Our supposition that angle trisection is a Euclidean construction leads to the conclusion, then, that *the positive irrational root of the equation* $x^3 - 3x - 1 = 0$ *can be obtained by a finite number of rational operations and extractions of real square roots, performed on rational numbers and on numbers derived from such numbers by such operations.*

14.6   *A Contradiction*

Suppose that $x_1^3 - 3x_1 - 1 = 0$ and that x_1 is a positive irrational number expressed in terms of rational numbers as described in the italicized statement above. We may, and do, restrict radicals, if any, in this expression to be square root radicals. Since x_1 is irrational, there is at least one radical present in the expression. There may be multiple-story radicals present, such as $\sqrt{12 - \sqrt{3}}$. Some 2-story radicals can be simplified, such as $\sqrt{4 - 2\sqrt{3}} = \sqrt{3} - 1$. Some radicals can be combined with others, for example, $\sqrt{2} \cdot \sqrt{2} = 2$. A 2-story radical is of order 2 if it is *not* expressible as a rational expression with rational coefficients and involving no radicals of order higher than 1. In general, an n-story radical is said to be of order n if it is not expressible as a rational expression with rational coefficients and involving no radicals of order higher than $n - 1$.

We suppose now that all simplifications have been made in the expression for x, so that the resulting expression has the following property: No one of the radicals of highest order n in the expression can be expressed as a rational expression, with rational coefficients, of the remaining radicals of order n and radicals of lower order which may be present.

Let $\sqrt{A}$ be a radical of highest order n in the expression for x_1. Then

$$x_1 = \frac{a + b\sqrt{A}}{c + d\sqrt{A}}$$

where a, b, c, d do not involve $\sqrt{A}$ but may involve other radicals. If $d = 0$, then $c \neq 0$ and we write e for a/c, f for b/c, and get $x_1 = e + f\sqrt{A}$, $f \neq 0$, where neither e nor f involves $\sqrt{A}$. If $d \neq 0$, we have

$$x_1 = \frac{a + b\sqrt{A}}{c + d\sqrt{A}} \cdot \frac{c - d\sqrt{A}}{c - d\sqrt{A}}$$

which can be simplified to get an expression

$$x_1 = e + f\sqrt{A}, \qquad f \neq 0$$

where neither e nor f involves $\sqrt{A}$. (Note that $c - d\sqrt{A} \neq 0$. For if $c - d\sqrt{A} = 0$, then $\sqrt{A} = c/d$, which contradicts the fact that in our expression for x_1 it is impossible to express $\sqrt{A}$ in terms of the other radicals present or to simplify it by eliminating the $\sqrt{A}$.)

Since $x_1^3 - 3x_1 - 1 = 0$, we get by substitution that $(e + f\sqrt{A})^3 - 3(e + f\sqrt{A}) - 1 = 0$. Then $g + h\sqrt{A} = 0$ where $g = e^3 + 3ef^2 A - 3e - 1$ and $h = 3e^2 f + f^3 A - 3f$. If $h \neq 0$, then $\sqrt{A} = -g/h$ and $\sqrt{A}$ can be expressed in terms of e, f, A, and rational numbers. This contradicts the fact that $\sqrt{A}$ cannot be expressed in terms of other radicals of order n or of radicals of lower order. Therefore $h = 0$ and since $g + h\sqrt{A} = 0$, it follows that $g = 0$.

Let $x_2 = e - f\sqrt{A}$. Substitute x_2 for x in $x^3 - 3x - 1 = 0$ to get $(e - f\sqrt{A})^3 - 3(e - f\sqrt{A}) - 1 = 0$. Simplify to get $g - h\sqrt{A} = 0$, where $g = e^3 + 3ef^2 A - 3e - 1$ and $h = 3e^2 f + f^3 A - 3f$, as above in the expression for x_1. But g and h are both zero. Therefore x_1 and x_2 are both roots of the equation $x^3 - 3x - 1 = 0$.

We know from elementary algebra that the sum of the three roots of a cubic equation $x^3 + px^2 + qx + r = 0$ is $-p$. It follows that the sum of the three roots of $x^3 - 3x - 1 = 0$ is 0, and that its roots are given by $x_1 = e + f\sqrt{A}$, $x_2 = e - f\sqrt{A}$; $x_3 = -2e$, where neither e nor f involves $\sqrt{A}$, but may involve other radicals of order n or lower order. Now we know that $x^3 - 3x - 1 = 0$ has no rational roots. Therefore $-2e$ is irrational and e is irrational. But the reasoning we applied to the expression for x_1 can also be applied to the expression for e. Suppose e is expressed with rational operations and real square roots extractions in terms of rational numbers and numbers which can be obtained from them by rational operations and real square root extractions. Suppose $\sqrt{B}$ is a radical of highest order in the expression for e. Then it follows that $e = i + j\sqrt{B}$, $j \neq 0$, and hence that $x_3 = -2e = k + m\sqrt{B}$, where neither k nor m involves $\sqrt{B}$ and $m \neq 0$. Just as $x_1^3 - 3x_1 - 1 = 0$ (with $x_1 = e + f\sqrt{A}$) implied that $x_2^3 - 3x_2 - 1 = 0$ (with $x_2 = e - f\sqrt{A}$), so also $x_3^3 - 3x_3 - 1 = 0$ (with $x_3 = k + m\sqrt{B}$) implies that $x_4^3 - 3x_4 - 1 = 0$ (with $x_4 = k - m\sqrt{B}$). Now $x_1 \neq x_2$ and $x_3 \neq x_4$, and x_1, x_2, x_3 are distinct numbers. Since a cubic equation has at most three distinct roots it follows that $x_4 = x_1$ or $x_4 = x_2$. Therefore $k - m\sqrt{B} = e + f\sqrt{A}$ or $k - m\sqrt{B} = e - f\sqrt{A}$. Now $\sqrt{B}$ is a radical of highest order in the expression for e. Also, every radical which appears in the expressions for k and m also appears in the expression for x_3 ($x_3 = k + m\sqrt{B}$), hence also in the expression for e since $e = -\frac{1}{2}x_3$. But

$$\sqrt{A} = \frac{k - m\sqrt{B} - e}{f} \quad \text{or} \quad \sqrt{A} = \frac{k - m\sqrt{B} - e}{-f}.$$

Therefore $\sqrt{A}$ is expressible rationally in terms of the remaining radicals appearing in e and f, hence rationally in terms of the other radicals which appear in the expression for x_1 ($x_1 = e + f\sqrt{A}$). This contradicts the fact that $\sqrt{A}$ is a radical of highest order in the expression for x_1.

It follows that x_1 cannot be obtained by a finite number of rational operations and extractions of real square roots performed on rational numbers and on numbers derived from such numbers by rational operations. Applying the contrapositive rule of inference to the last sentence of Section 14.5 we deduce that a 20° angle cannot be constructed using Euclidean tools. This proves that a 60° angle cannot be trisected using a Euclidean construction, and hence that *it is impossible to trisect all angles with a Euclidean ruler and compass*. It is true that some angles can be trisected with Euclidean ruler and compass. But *the trisection of an arbitrary angle is an impossible Euclidean construction.*

14.7 *Other Impossible Euclidean Constructions*

Since the construction of a 20° angle is not a Euclidean construction it is easy to see that the construction of a 40° angle is also not a Euclidean construction. In a regular polygon of nine sides the angle subtended at the center by one side is a 40° angle. Therefore *a regular polygon of nine sides cannot be constructed with Euclidean ruler and compass*. Here we understand, as we always do unless otherwise stated, that the only given element is a segment of unit length.

Since none of the numbers 2, −2, 1, −1 (the integral divisors of 2) is a root of $x^3 = 2$, it follows that $x^3 = 2$ has no rational root. Using a reasoning similar to that in Section 14.6, it can be shown that $x^3 = 2$ does not have a Euclidean constructible root. One of the famous problems of antiquity is the problem of duplicating a cube, actually to construct an altar in the shape of a cube with twice the volume of a given cube. This amounts to constructing a segment of length $\sqrt[3]{2}$, starting with a segment of length 1. Since $\sqrt[3]{2}$ is a root of $x^3 = 2$ and since $x^3 = 2$ has no constructible root, it follows that *the duplication of a cube is impossible* as a Euclidean construction.

Exercises 14.7

1. Prove that it is impossible to construct with Euclidean ruler and compass a segment of length $\sqrt[3]{3}$, starting with a segment of length 1.

2. Given a circle with radius of length 1. Construct with Euclidean ruler and compass a regular hexagon inscribed in the circle.

3. Construct a segment of length $\sqrt{2 + \sqrt{3}}$, using Euclidean ruler and compass, and starting with a segment of length 1.

4. Construct a segment of length 2 cos 15°, using Euclidean ruler and compass, and starting with a segment of length 1.

 5.

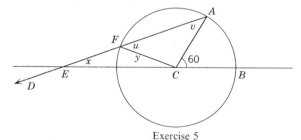

Exercise 5

In the figure a circle with center C and radius $CB = CA = 1$ is given. A ruler with one end at A is rotated until $EF = FC$, where $E \in \overrightarrow{BC}$ and F is on the circle. Let x, y, u, v denote the degree measures of the angles indicated in the figure. Show that $x = 20$ and hence that this construction trisects the 60° angle. Why is this not a Euclidean construction?

Informal Solid Geometry

A1.1 *Surfaces and Solids*

A dictionary says that a surface is the exterior of an object that has length and width, and that in geometry a surface is a continuous magnitude that has length and breadth. If a person knows the meaning of every word in these definitions, then he will read them and acquire some idea of what a surface is. Suppose, however, that a person's vocabulary does not include exterior, length, width, breadth, continuous, and magnitude. The dictionary definitions will do him little good. The dictionary helps a person to increase his vocabulary after he has acquired a vocabulary.

It seems reasonable that a textbook in solid geometry should tell us what a surface really is. But most of them do not. They contain pictures and examples, and perhaps that is the most effective way to tell students about surfaces.

Perhaps the simplest surface is a plane. Some geometry books define a plane as a surface which has the property that a line joining any two of its points lies entirely in the surface. This makes sense if we know what a surface is. If we think of all of space as being a surface and A and B as any two points of this surface, then according to the definition, the line $\overleftrightarrow{AB}$ would be a subset of the surface, and hence the surface would be a plane. As you can see, if we do violence to the concept of surface, then we may do violence to the concept of a plane.

Many mathematicians have spent years attempting to clarify the concept of a surface. To be useful the concept must include the surfaces of elementary geometry, which we shall discuss presently. But to state precisely what a surface is, either through properties of a set of points or by means of equations and inequalities which place the desired restrictions on the coordinates of a point, is a difficult task. Indeed, some modern day mathematicians treat surfaces in a manner which would make little or no sense to most people. The surface concept is a sophisticated one and there may be no satisfactory way to define surface in elementary mathematics. Our purpose here, then, is not to define a surface but to present the idea in an elementary way through examples.

An inflated rubber balloon divides all of physical space into three parts: the part inside, the part outside, and the space occupied by the balloon itself. Suppose that A is a point outside the balloon and that B is a point within the balloon. Then the segment $\overline{AB}$ contains a subset of points which lie outside the balloon, a subset of points which lie inside the balloon, and a subset consisting of the "rubber points." If we imagine that the balloon is so thin that among the infinity of points which make up the set $\overline{AB}$ there is exactly one "rubber point," and if we imagine that the same thing is true of every segment joining a point inside the balloon to a point outside the balloon, then the balloon is a good example of a surface. Note that this idealized balloon does not have an "exterior" which we think of as its surface; rather the entire balloon is the surface.

Just as an inflated balloon may be used to explain the idea of a surface, so any one of a variety of physical objects may be used to explain the idea of a solid. We may talk about ice cubes, ice cream cones, or oxygen cylinders. Of course geometrical solids are not composed of ice, or ice cream, or oxygen; they are sets of points. When we think of the points of space occupied by a billiard ball, when we think of the properties of the set of all these points, when we conceive of this set as one object of thought, then we have a good intuitive notion of the geometric solid which is called a sphere. Other geometric solids are suggested by the following figures.

Each of these solids has a surface and an interior. It is natural to think of some of these surfaces as consisting of several pieces. Thus the surface of a triangular prism consists of five flat pieces, each of which is a portion of a plane. The surface of a cone consists of two pieces, one curved and one flat. However, in studying geometry we usually talk about the surface of a solid; we lump all the pieces together to make one surface.

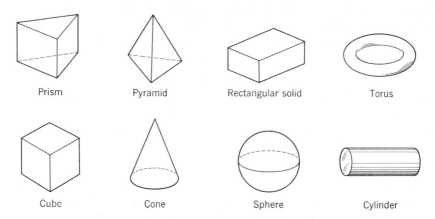

Prism   Pyramid   Rectangular solid   Torus

Cube   Cone   Sphere   Cylinder

Perhaps the most elementary geometric solids are the polyhedrons, such as the tetrahedron, the hexahedron, and the octahedron. The surface of a polyhedron consists of several parts called its *faces*. Each face is a polygon (strictly speaking, the union of a polygon and its interior, which

Tetrahedron   Hexahedron   Octahedron

we call a polygonal region). If two faces are adjacent, their intersection is a segment which is called an *edge* of the polyhedron. If two edges intersect, their intersection is a point called a *vertex* of the polyhedron. A segment joining two vertices of a polyhedron not lying in the same face is called a *diagonal* of the polyhedron.

Exercises A1.1

1. Try to describe the surfaces of the solids pictured without referring to physical objects. Imagine you are talking by telephone to someone who knows plane geometry.

2. Compute the surface area of a triangular prism if three of its five faces are squares 1 inch on a side.

3. Compute the surface area of a right circular cylinder if its ends are circles 1 inch in diameter and its length is 6 inches.

4. How many faces does a rectangular solid have? How many edges? How many vertices? How many diagonals?

5. How many faces does a tetrahedron have? How many edges? How many vertices? How many diagonals?

A1.2 *Determining a Plane*

The individual faces of a polyhedron can be described completely using the language of plane geometry. But the relationships which exist among the faces transcend the scope of plane geometry since they do not all lie in one plane. These relations are relations involving the faces and the edges. A large segment of solid geometry is concerned with lines and planes and relations between them.

In Euclidean geometry two points determine a line. Given two points A and B, there is one and only one line which contains A and B. What is the analogous situation for a plane? A plane is a set of points; and if it contains any two points, it contains the entire line determined by those two points. Let A and B be any two points. Do these points determine a plane? In other words, is there one and only one plane containing these two points? Do three points determine a plane? It is true that, given any three points, there is always a plane containing those points. But in some cases this plane is not unique. Consider two planes P_1 and P_2 which intersect in a line m. If A, B, and C are three points on m, then these three points do not determine a plane. For there is more than one plane containing these three points.

There are many ways to determine a plane, the most familiar ones being the following:

1. A line and a point outside the line determine a plane.
2. Three noncollinear points determine a plane.
3. Two parallel lines determine a plane.
4. Two intersecting lines determine a plane.

Exercises A1.2

1. Why are tripods used for the support of a surveyor's transit?

2. Is it always possible to eliminate the wobble in a four-legged stool by adjusting the length of just one leg?

3. If two straight two-by-fours are used as the side forms in building a concrete sidewalk and if the surface is formed by pushing the excess off with another straight two-by-four laid across the side forms, is the surface of the sidewalk a portion of a plane?

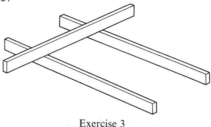

Exercise 3

4. If *A*, *B*, *C*, *D* are four points which do not all lie in the same plane and if no three of them lie in the same line, how many different planes are there with each containing three of these points?

5. If *p*, *q*, *r* are three parallel lines which are not coplanar, how many planes are there with each containing two of these lines?

6. If *p* is a line and *A*, *B* are points not on *p*, how many planes are there which contain the points *A*, *B* and at least one point on the line *p*? Discuss the various possible cases.

7. If *p* and *q* are skew lines (nonintersecting and not parallel), how many planes are there which contain the entire line *p* and at least one point of *q*? How many planes are there which contain the entire line *p* and at least two points of *q*?

8. Two distinct planes *p* and *q* intersect having two distinct points *A* and *B* in common. Does the line $\overleftrightarrow{AB}$ lie entirely in *p*? Does the line $\overleftrightarrow{AB}$ lie entirely in *q*?

9. Plane *p* and plane *q* have points *A*, *B*, and *C* in common. Suppose *A*, *B*, and *C* are noncollinear. Then they determine a plane. What conclusion can you draw in regard to *p* and *q*? If *r* and *s* are distinct planes having distinct points *D*, *E*, *F* in common, then what conclusion can you draw in regard to points *D*, *E*, *F*?

10. Write a general statement which includes the facts of Exercise 9.

A1.3 *Parallelism and Perpendicularity*

Two planes are *parallel* if there is no point which lies in both planes. The floor and ceiling of a room suggest portions of parallel planes. If two planes are not parallel, then they have at least one point in common. If two planes have one point in common, their intersection is a line. So if "*p*" and "*q*" are names of planes, there are three possibilities. Either *p* and *q* have no point in common, in which case they are parallel; or they have a line (and no point not on this line) in common, in which case they are called intersecting planes; or "*p*" and "*q*" are names for the same plane.

Similarly, if "*a*" and "*b*" are symbols for lines, there are four possibilities. Either *a* and *b* lie in the same plane and have no common point, in which case they are parallel; or there is no plane which contains both *a* and *b*, in which case they are called *skew* lines; or *a* and *b* have exactly one (one and only one) point in common, in which case they are called intersecting lines; or "*a*" and "*b*" are names for the same line.

A line and a plane are parallel if they do not intersect, that is, if there is no point which lies in both the line and the plane. If *a* is a line and *p* is a plane, there are three possibilities. Either *a* and *p* have no point in common, in which case they are parallel; or *a* and *p* have exactly one point in common, in which case *a* is said to intersect *p*; or *a* lies entirely in *p*. For if *p* contains two distinct points *A* and *B* of line *a*, then it contains the entire line $\overleftrightarrow{AB}$.

A line and a plane are perpendicular if the line intersects the plane in a point and is perpendicular to every line in the plane through the point of intersection.

Horizontal and vertical are adjectives applied to certain lines and planes. As normally used they do not have precise meanings. It is convenient to use them in informal communication. Horizontal means having the property of the horizon. Most floors in newly constructed buildings are horizontal. Any line lying in a horizontal plane is a horizontal line. A line perpendicular to a horizontal plane is a vertical line. Any plane containing a vertical line is a vertical plane.

If *p* and *q* are distinct planes which intersect in a line *m*, and if a plane *r* perpendicular to *m* intersects *p* and *q* in lines which are perpendicular, then *the planes p and q are perpendicular*.

Exercises A1.3

In Exercises 1 through 6 use a labeled cube or the accompanying figure to suggest one.

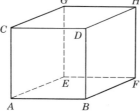

1. Name three quadruples of parallel lines.

2. Name three pairs of skew lines.

3. How many different combinations of an edge and a face perpendicular to that edge are there?

4. How many different combinations of an edge and a face parallel to that edge are there?

5. How many different pairs of parallel faces are there?

6. How many different pairs of perpendicular faces are there?

7. Line $\overleftrightarrow{AB}$ is perpendicular to $\overleftrightarrow{BC}$ and to $\overleftrightarrow{BD}$. Is line $\overleftrightarrow{AB}$ perpendicular to the plane m which is determined by B, C, D? Use two carpenter's squares (or rectangular pieces of cardboard) to represent the right angles ABC and ABD. Now measure angle ABE for various positions of E in plane m. State your conclusion in the form of a theorem.

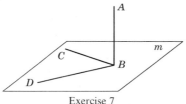

Exercise 7

8. Planes m and n are parallel. Plane p intersects m in line $\overleftrightarrow{AB}$ and n in line $\overleftrightarrow{CD}$. Is it possible that $\overleftrightarrow{AB}$ and $\overleftrightarrow{CD}$ are skew lines? Is it possible that $\overleftrightarrow{AB}$ and $\overleftrightarrow{CD}$ are intersecting lines? What conclusion seems reasonable in regard to $\overleftrightarrow{AB}$ and $\overleftrightarrow{CD}$? State your conclusion in the form of a theorem.

9. Planes m and n are parallel. Point A lies in m and point B lies in n. Line $\overleftrightarrow{AB}$ is perpendicular to plane m. Is line $\overleftrightarrow{AB}$ necessarily also perpendicular to plane n?

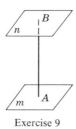

Exercise 9

Arrive at a conclusion by intuition, by experimentation with models, or perhaps by an indirect proof which might start as follows: Suppose $\overleftrightarrow{AB}$ is not perpendicular to n. Then $\overrightarrow{AB}$ is not perpendicular to some line $\overleftrightarrow{BC}$ lying in n. The plane determined by A, B, C intersects m in a line $\overleftrightarrow{AD}$. Then $\overleftrightarrow{AD}$ is perpendicular to $\overleftrightarrow{AB}$ while $\overleftrightarrow{BC}$ is not perpendicular to $\overleftrightarrow{AB}$. So from our knowledge of plane geometry we know that $\overleftrightarrow{BC}$ and $\overrightarrow{AD}$ intersect and hence *m* and *n* intersect. State your conclusion as a theorem.

10. Two distinct lines are perpendicular to the same plane. Are they necessarily parallel? Give an answer based on intuition.

11. *A* and *B* are points in plane *m*. *C* and *D* are points in plane *n*. Planes *m* and *n* are parallel. Lines $\overleftrightarrow{AC}$ and $\overleftrightarrow{BD}$ are parallel. Are the segments $\overline{AC}$, $\overline{BD}$ congruent? Give an answer based on intuition.

12. Line $\overleftrightarrow{AB}$ is perpendicular to plane *m*. Point *B* lies in plane *m*. Points *C* and *D* lie in *m*. It is given that segments $\overline{AC}$, $\overline{AD}$ are congruent. Are the segments $\overline{BC}$, $\overline{BD}$ congruent? Give an answer based on a proof that two triangles are congruent.

13. Line $\overleftrightarrow{AB}$ is perpendicular to line $\overleftrightarrow{BC}$ which lies in plane *m*. Is $\overleftrightarrow{AB}$ necessarily perpendicular to plane *m*?

A1.4 *Theorems on Lines and Planes*

Some of the following statements have appeared in the preceding pages. Others are essentially new. All of them seem plausible on the basis of our experiences with physical objects. For reference purposes it is convenient to have these basic facts of solid geometry tabulated in one list.

1. If two planes intersect, their intersection is a line.
2. If two parallel planes are cut by a third plane, the lines of intersection are parallel.

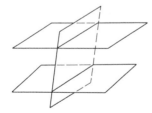 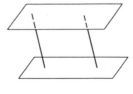

3. Parallel segments included between parallel planes are congruent.
4. If a plane contains one and only one of two parallel lines, it is parallel to the other line.

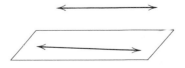

5. If a line is perpendicular to each of two intersecting lines at their point of intersection, it is perpendicular to their plane.

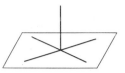

6. There is exactly one plane perpendicular to a given line and passing through a given point.

7. All the lines perpendicular to a given line at a given point on it lie in the plane perpendicular to the line at that point.

8. There is exactly one line perpendicular to a given plane and passing through a given point.

9. Two lines perpendicular to the same plane are parallel.

10. If one of two parallel lines is perpendicular to a plane, then so is the other.

11. If two lines are parallel to a third line, they are parallel to each other.

12. The perpendicular is the shortest segment from a point to a plane.

13. Two planes perpendicular to the same line are parallel.

14. Congruent oblique (not perpendicular) segments from a point to a plane meet the plane at points equidistant from the foot of the perpendicular drawn from the external point to the plane.

15. If oblique segments from a point to a plane meet the plane in points which are equidistant from the foot of the perpendicular from the point to the plane, then the oblique segments are congruent.

16. If a line is perpendicular to one of two parallel planes, then it is perpendicular to the other also.

17. Through a point not in a given plane there is exactly one plane parallel to the given plane.

18. If two intersecting lines are each parallel to a plane, then the plane of these lines is parallel to that plane.

19. If a side of one angle and a side of another angle lie on parallel lines, and if the other sides of these angles lie on parallel lines, then the angles are either congruent or supplementary, and the angles lie either in the same plane or in parallel planes.

20. If two lines are cut by three parallel planes, the lengths of corresponding segments are proportional.

A1.5   *Dihedral and Polyhedral Angles*

An angle is the union of two noncollinear, concurrent rays. Sometimes we say plane angle in order to differentiate such an angle from dihedral and polyhedral angles. Plane angles are formed by intersecting lines. Dihedral and polyhedral angles are formed by intersecting planes. Thus if two planes intersect, they form four dihedral angles much like two intersecting lines form four plane angles.

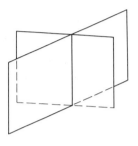

Every line in a plane *separates* the plane. It separates the points of the plane which are not on the line into two parts called the *sides of the line.* The segment joining any two points on the same side of a line lies entirely on that side, and the segment joining a point on one side of the line to a point on the other side of the line intersects the line. If *m* is any line in a plane *p*, and *A* is any point of *p* not on *m*, then the set of all points of *p* which lie on the same side of *m* as does *A* is a *halfplane.* The line *m* is called the *edge* of the halfplane. The union of a halfplane and its edge is a *closed halfplane.*

Dihedral Angle. A dihedral angle is the union of two noncoplanar closed halfplanes which have the same edge. Thus if two noncoplanar halfplanes have a common edge, then the union of these halfplanes and their common edge is called a dihedral angle. The two halfplanes are called the *faces* of the dihedral angle and their common edge is called

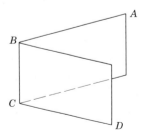

the *edge* of the dihedral angle. Note that a dihedral angle is a set and that its elements are points. It is a set of points since it is the union of two sets of points. A dihedral angle may be designated by naming four of its points, two on its edge and one in each of its faces. This is so because two points determine the line which is the edge; and each of the two other points together with the edge determines a face. Thus *A-BC-D* is a suitable symbol for a dihedral angle. In this symbol $\overleftrightarrow{BC}$ is the edge; *A-BC* is the halfplane with edge $\overleftrightarrow{BC}$ and containing the point *A*; *BC-D* is the halfplane with edge $\overleftrightarrow{BC}$ and containing the point *D*; and *A-BC-D* is the dihedral angle formed by the two halfplanes and their common edge.

Plane Angle of a Dihedral Angle. A plane angle formed by two rays, one in each face of a dihedral angle, each ray having its endpoint on the edge of the dihedral angle and each ray being perpendicular to the edge, is called a *plane angle of the dihedral angle.*

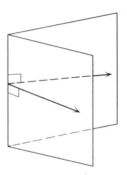

Measure of a Dihedral Angle. If $\angle EFG$ and $\angle HIJ$ are two plane angles of a dihedral angle, then their corresponding sides are parallel and the measures of the plane angles are equal. So the measures of all the plane angles of a dihedral angle are equal. The *measure* of a dihedral angle is the measure of a plane angle of the dihedral angle. Dihedral angles with equal measures are called *congruent* dihedral angles.

Polyhedral Angle. Let $A_1 A_2 \ldots A_n$ be a polygon, and let *A* be a point not in the plane of the polygon. The polyhedral angle $A\text{-}A_1 A_2 \ldots A_n$ is the union of all rays $\overrightarrow{AP}$ where *P* is a point of the polygon $A_1 A_2 \ldots A_n$. The point *A* is called the *vertex* of the polyhedral angle; the rays from *A* through the vertices of the polygon are called the *edges* of the polyhedral angle. That part of a polyhedral angle which lies in one plane determined by two adjacent edges of the polyhedral angle is called a *face* of the polyhedral angle. For example, the union of $\angle A_1AA_2$ and its interior is a face of the polyhedral angle $A\text{-}A_1A_2\ldots A_n$. An angle formed by two

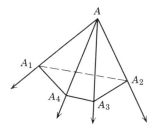

adjacent edges of a polyhedral angle is called a *face angle of the polyhedral angle*. A dihedral angle whose edge contains an edge of a polyhedral angle and each of whose faces contains a face of the polyhedral angle is called a *dihedral angle of the polyhedral angle*. A polyhedral angle $A\text{-}A_1A_2\ldots A_n$ is *convex* if the polygon $A_1A_2\ldots A_n$ is convex. Polyhedral angles of three, four, five, six, and eight faces are called respectively *trihedral, tetrahedral, pentahedral, hexahedral,* and *octahedral* angles. Two polyhedral angles are *congruent* if the face angles and the dihedral angles of one are congruent, each to each, to the face angles and the dihedral angles of the other and are arranged in the same order. A trihedral angle is *rectangular, bi-rectangular,* or *trirectangular* according to whether it has one, two, or three right dihedral angles.

Exercises A1.5

1. Draw a cube and label each of its vertices with a letter. List letter designations, as $A\text{-}BC\text{-}D$, for each of the dihedral angles formed by halfplanes parts of which form the surface of the cube.

2. List letter designations, as $A\text{-}BCD$, for each of the trihedral angles formed by the surface of the cube in Exercise 1.

3. Select one of the trihedral angles in Exercise 2 and list letter designations for each of its face angles and for each of its dihedral angles.

4. Select one of the dihedral angles in Exercise 1 and list letter designations for two of its plane angles which appear in the drawing.

5. Describe several dihedral angles formed by portions of the surface of a building or room.

6. Open a book to form a dihedral angle which you estimate to be a 60° angle. Can you check your estimate with a protractor?

7. How does a cabinetmaker test a dihedral angle for accuracy?

8. Draw a line perpendicular to an edge of a sheet of paper. Fold the paper on the line that you drew. Is the plane angle formed by the folded edge a plane angle of the dihedral angle which has been formed? Explain.

9. Use a pencil or a ruler to represent a line perpendicular to a table top and a piece of cardboard to represent any plane through the line. Is the cardboard perpendicular to the table top? Point out a plane angle of one of the dihedral angles formed. Is it a right angle? Explain.

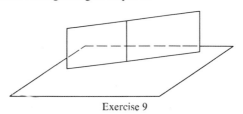

Exercise 9

10. Let *p* and *q* be two perpendicular planes which meet in line *m*. If line *n* in plane *q* is perpendicular to line *m*, explain why it must be perpendicular to *p*. *Hint:* Draw a ray *r* in *p* from the foot of *n* and perpendicular to *m*. Then *n* is perpendicular to *r*. Why? Then *n* is perpendicular to *p*. Why?

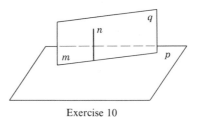

Exercise 10

11. Make a model (coat hanger wire might be used) of a plane figure consisting of three rays emanating from a point as suggested by the figure. Measure the angles *AOB, BOC,* and *COA.* Then hold *AOB* fixed on a table and rotate the segment $\overline{OC}$ about *O* so that *C* rises from the surface of the table a short distance. Now

Exercise 11

measure the angles *AOB* and *BOC* again. What was the sum of the three angle measures when the points *O, A, B, C* were coplanar? What is the sum of the measures of three face angles of the trihedral angle formed after $\overline{OC}$ was bent upward? State a theorem which this suggests. Do you think there is a similar theorem for all convex polyhedral angles?

12. Make a model of two adjacent (same vertex and a common side) angles which lie in the same plane and whose measure-sum is less than 180. See accompanying figure.

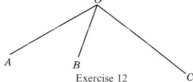

Exercise 12

Let p be the plane of O, A, B, C and q the plane perpendicular to p and containing the segment $\overline{OB}$. Rotate $\overline{OB}$ about O in plane q. What relationship exists among the measures of the angles AOB, BOC, and AOC initially? Describe the variation in $m\angle AOB + m\angle BOC$ as $\overrightarrow{OB}$ rotates through 180°. What is the least value of this sum? What is the greatest value of this sum? If $O\text{-}ABC$ is a trihedral angle, what relationships exist among the measures of its face angles:

$$m\angle AOB + m\angle BOC + m\angle AOC \qquad \text{in relation to} \quad 360,$$
$$m\angle AOB + m\angle BOC \qquad \text{in relation to} \quad m\angle AOC,$$
$$m\angle AOB + m\angle AOC \qquad \text{in relation to} \quad m\angle BOC,$$
$$m\angle AOC + m\angle COB \qquad \text{in relation to} \quad m\angle AOB?$$

13. Place a yardstick on a table and hold another yardstick so that the two represent a pair of skew lines. Try to find a position for a third yardstick so that it will be perpendicular to both of the skew lines.

14. Let $\overleftrightarrow{AB}$ and $\overleftrightarrow{CD}$ denote skew lines. Let m be the plane through $\overleftrightarrow{AB}$ and parallel to $\overleftrightarrow{CD}$, n the plane through $\overleftrightarrow{CD}$ perpendicular to m, and $\overleftrightarrow{EF}$ the line in which m and n intersect. Then $\overleftrightarrow{CD}$ is parallel to $\overleftrightarrow{EF}$. (If $\overleftrightarrow{CD}$ intersects $\overleftrightarrow{EF}$, then $\overleftrightarrow{CD}$ is not parallel to m.) Line $\overleftrightarrow{AB}$ intersects line $\overleftrightarrow{EF}$ in some point G. (If $\overleftrightarrow{AB}$ and $\overleftrightarrow{EF}$ do not intersect, then lying in the same plane, they must be parallel; and if $\overleftrightarrow{AB}$ is parallel to $\overleftrightarrow{EF}$ and $\overleftrightarrow{EF}$ is parallel to $\overleftrightarrow{CD}$, then $\overleftrightarrow{AB}$ is parallel to $\overleftrightarrow{CD}$. But this contradicts the fact that $\overleftrightarrow{AB}$ and $\overleftrightarrow{CD}$ are skew lines.) Draw $\overline{GH}$ in plane n and perpendicular to $\overline{EF}$. Then $\overline{GH}$ is also perpendicular to $\overline{CD}$. Why? And $\overline{GH}$ is perpendicular to plane m. Why? (Review Exercise 10.) And $\overline{GH}$ is perpendicular to $\overline{AB}$. Why?

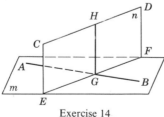

Exercise 14

15. Describe a procedure for "finding" the common perpendicular between two skew lines.

A1.6   *Theorems*

1. If a line is perpendicular to a given plane, every plane which contains this line is perpendicular to the given plane.

2. If two planes are perpendicular to each other, a line in one of them perpendicular to their line of intersection is perpendicular to the other.

3. If two planes are perpendicular, a line perpendicular to one of them through a point of their line of intersection lies in the other.

4. If a plane is perpendicular to the line in which two other planes intersect, then it is perpendicular to each of these other planes.

5. If each of two intersecting planes is perpendicular to another plane, their line of intersection is also perpendicular to that plane.

6. Between any two skew lines there is one common perpendicular.

7. Between any two skew lines there is only one common perpendicular.

8. The shortest distance between two skew lines is the length of their common perpendicular.

9. The sum of the measures of any two face angles of a trihedral angle is greater than the measure of the third face angle.

10. The sum of the measures of the face angles of any convex polyhedral angle is less than 360.

Exercises A1.6

1. Line $\overleftrightarrow{AB}$ intersects plane m in point B. Is there a plane n containing $\overleftrightarrow{AB}$ and perpendicular to m? Describe the "construction" of a point C in m such that A, B, and C determine n.

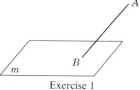

Exercise 1

2. In Exercise 1, could it happen that there are many planes n with the required properties? Explain and illustrate.

3. Three rays $\overrightarrow{OA}, \overrightarrow{OB}, \overrightarrow{OC}$ have a common endpoint O. If the measure of each of

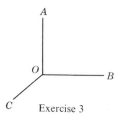

Exercise 3

the plane angles *AOB*, *AOC*, *BOC* is 90, is the measure of each of the dihedral angles *A-OC-B* and *B-OA-C* also 90? Why?

4. Given a dihedral angle *A-BC-D* and a plane *m* perpendicular to $\overline{BC}$, is plane *m* perpendicular to plane *ABC*? To plane *BCD*? Which theorem above could you quote as authority for your answer?

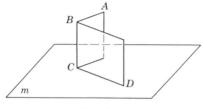

Exercise 4

5. Is the sum of the measures of the face angles of a trihedral angle the same for all trihedral angles?

6. Is the sum of the measures of the dihedral angles of a trihedral angle the same for all trihedral angles?

7. How large may the sum of the measures of the dihedral angles of a trihedral angle be?

8. How small may the sum of the measures of the dihedral angles of a trihedral angle be?

9. What is the sum of the measures of the face angles of a trihedral angle at the vertex of a cube?

10. What is the sum of the measures of the dihedral angles of a trihedral angle at the vertex of a cube?

11. In a trihedral angle *O-ABC*, $\overline{OA}$ is perpendicular to the plane of *ABC*, $\triangle ABC$ is an equilateral triangle, and the lengths *AB*, *BC*, *CA* are very small in comparison with *OA*. What is the sum of the measures of the face angles of the trihedral angle, approximately? What is the sum of the measures of the dihedral angles of the trihedral angle, approximately?

12. Given trihedral angle *O-ABC*, such that *AB* = *BC* = *CA*, *OA* = *OB* = *OC* and the distance from *O* to plane *ABC* is very small in comparison with the length *AB*. What is the sum of the measures of the face angles of the trihedral angle, approximately? What is the sum of the measures of the dihedral angles of the trihedral angle, approximately?

13. How small can the sum of the measures of the face angles of a polyhedral angle be? How large can the sum of the measures of the face angles of a polyhedral angle be?

14. How small can the sum of the measures of the dihedral angles of a polyhedral angle be?

15. Two face angles of a trihedral angle measure 45 and 50, respectively. How small can the measure of the third face angle be? How large can it be?

16. Five of the six face angles of a hexahedral angle measure 60 each. How small can the measure of the sixth face angle be? How large can it be?

17. The sum of the measures of the face angles of a trihedral angle is 100. What is the largest measure that one of the three face angles might have?

18. How many trihedral angles are formed when three planes intersect in a (one and only one) point?

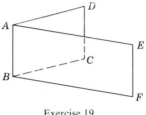

Exercise 19

19. Given dihedral angle *D-AB-F* with $\overleftrightarrow{DC}$ a line in one face and $\overleftrightarrow{FE}$ a line in the other face. If $\overleftrightarrow{DC}$ is parallel to $\overleftrightarrow{FE}$, is it true that $\overleftrightarrow{DC}$ is parallel to $\overleftrightarrow{AB}$? To help answer this, note that $\overleftrightarrow{DC}$ and $\overleftrightarrow{FE}$ are coplanar. So if $\overleftrightarrow{DC}$ cuts $\overleftrightarrow{AB}$, it must cut it in a point of the plane *CDEF*. Why? Call such a point *G*. Then *G-CD* is one of the faces of the dihedral angle and *G-EF* is the other face of the dihedral angle. Why? But this is a contradiction. Why? Therefore $\overleftrightarrow{DC}$ and $\overleftrightarrow{AB}$ are parallel.

A1.7 *Polyhedrons*

The set of points common to a solid and a plane (that is, the figure formed by their intersection) is called a *section* of the solid. If every section of a solid polyhedron is a convex polygonal region, then the polyhedron is called a *convex polyhedron*. Only convex polyhedrons are considered in this book, even though we usually omit the adjective convex. It is convenient to use the word polygon in two senses, in the sense of a plane curve which separates the remaining points of its plane into a set of exterior points and a set of interior points and in the sense of the union of such a curve and its interior, which is, strictly speaking, a polygonal region. Similarly, it is convenient to use the word polyhedron in two senses, in the sense of a surface bounding a portion of space and in the sense of such a surface together with its interior (the solid polyhedron). Thus the area of a triangle is the measure of that portion of a plane which is on and within the triangle; the volume of a tetrahedron is the measure of that portion of space which is on and within it.

Polyhedrons with four, six, eight, twelve, and twenty faces are called *tetrahedrons, hexahedrons, octahedrons, dodecahedrons,* and *icosahedrons,* respectively. A *regular polyhedron* is a polyhedron whose faces are congruent regular polygons.

Exercises A1.7

1. Count the vertices, edges, diagonals, and faces of a cube.

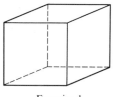 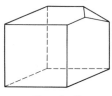

Exercise 1   Exercise 2

2. Count the vertices, edges, and faces of a solid obtained from a cube by cutting off one corner, as in the figure.

3. What is the smallest number of vertices for any polyhedron?

4. What is the smallest number of faces for any polyhedron?

5. What is the smallest number of edges for any polyhedron?

6. A regular tetrahedron has four triangular faces and four vertices. What is the sum of the measures of the face angles of the polyhedral angle formed by faces intersecting at one of the vertices of a regular tetrahedron?

7. A regular octahedron has eight triangular faces and six vertices. What is the sum of the measures of the face angles of the polyhedral angle at each vertex?

8. A regular icosahedron has twenty triangular faces and twelve vertices. What is the sum of the measures of the face angles of the polyhedral angle at each vertex?

9. A regular hexahedron has six square faces and eight vertices. What is the sum of the measures of the face angles of the polyhedral angle at each vertex?

10. A regular dodecahedron has twelve pentagonal faces. How many vertices does it have? How many edges does it have? *Hints:* The measure of each angle of a regular pentagon is 108. Therefore each polyhedral angle of a regular dodecahedron must have three face angles. But twelve pentagons furnish sixty face angles.

A1.8 *Euler's Formula*

Let V denote the number of vertices, E the number of edges, and F the number of faces of a polyhedron. Euler discovered an interesting formula which holds for all polyhedrons:

$$V - E + F = 2.$$

Consider, for example, a cube. It has 8 vertices, 12 edges, and 6 faces, and $V - E + F = 8 - 12 + 6 = 2$. For another example consider the solid obtained when one corner is chopped off a cube as in Exercise 2 of A1.7. It has 10 vertices, 15 edges, and 7 faces, and $V - E + F = 10 - 15 + 7 = 2$. When the corner is chopped off a trihedral angle, V increases by 2, E increases by 3, F increases by 1, and $V - E + F$ remains unchanged. When the corner is chopped off a tetrahedral angle, V increases by 3, E increases by 4, F increases by 1, and $V - E + F$ remains unchanged. This is the kind of reasoning which may be used to prove Euler's formula, but our purpose here is not to prove it but to use it to show that there are only five different kinds of regular polyhedrons. See Exercises 6, 7, 8, 9, 10 of A1.7.

Suppose, first, that the faces of a regular polyhedron are congruent triangles. Then each face angle is a 60° angle. Since there are at least three face angles at each vertex of a polyhedron, and since the sum of the measures of the face angles at each vertex must be less than 360, it follows that there are 3, 4, or 5 face angles at each vertex. Let V, E, and F denote the number of vertices, edges, and faces, respectively. If there are three face angles at each vertex, then there are $3V$ face angles, V faces, and $3V/2$ edges. (Each face is bounded by three edges, and each edge is an edge of two faces.) Therefore, using Euler's formula, we see that $V - 3V/2 + V = 2$. Then $V = 4$, $E = 6$, $F = 4$, and the polyhedron is a regular tetrahedron.

If a regular polyhedron has triangular faces and there are four face angles at each vertex, then there are $4V$ face angles, $4V/3$ faces, and $2V$ edges. Then $V - 2V + 4V/3 = 2$, $V = 6$, $E = 12$, $F = 8$, and the polyhedron is a regular octahedron.

If a regular polyhedron has triangular faces and there are five face angles at each vertex, then there are $5V$ face angles, $5V/3$ faces, and $5V/2$ edges. Then $V - 5V/2 + 5V/3 = 2$, $V = 12$, $E = 30$, $F = 20$, and the polyhedron is a regular icosahedron.

Suppose, next, that the faces of a regular polyhedron are congruent squares. Then each face angle is a right angle and the number of face angles at each vertex of the polyhedron must be three. (Every polyhedral angle has at least three face angles, and the sum of the measures of its face angles is less than 360.) It follows that there are $3V$ face angles, $3V/4$

faces, and $3V/2$ edges. Then $V - 3V/2 + 3V/4 = 2$, $V = 8$, $E = 12$, $F = 6$, and the polyhedron is a regular hexahedron, or cube.

Suppose, next, that the faces of a regular polyhedron are congruent pentagons. Then the measure of each face angle is 108 and the number of face angles at each vertex must be three. Then there are $3V$ face angles, $3V/5$ faces, and $3V/2$ edges. Then $V - 3V/2 + 3V/5 = 2$, $V = 20$, $E = 30$, $F = 12$, and the polyhedron is a regular dodecahedron.

Suppose that the faces of a regular polyhedron are n-gons with $n \geqslant 6$. Then the measure of each face angle is 120 or more, and the sum of the measures of the face angles at each vertex is 360 or more. But we know that this is impossible. Therefore there is no regular polyhedron with faces which are n-gons with $n \geqslant 6$. It follows that every regular polyhedron is one of the following types:

tetrahedron with triangular faces,	$V = 4$, $E = 6$, $F = 4$;
octahedron with triangular faces,	$V = 6$, $E = 12$, $F = 8$;
icosahedron with triangular faces,	$V = 12$, $E = 30$, $F = 20$;
hexahedron with square faces,	$V = 8$, $E = 12$, $F = 6$;
dodecahedron with pentagonal faces,	$V = 20$, $E = 30$, $F = 12$.

In this discussion we "discovered" all of the types of regular polyhedrons by classifying them first according to their faces (triangular, square, or pentagonal). As an alternate method we might classify them first according to the number of edges which meet at each vertex.

If three edges meet at each vertex, then since each edge connects two vertices it follows that $E = 3V/2$. Also each edge serves two faces. If the faces are triangles, then $F = 2E/3$. If the faces are squares, then $F = 2E/4$. If the faces are pentagons, then $F = 2E/5$.

Exercises A1.8

1. Using the equations of the preceding paragraph and Euler's formula, find V, E, F if three edges meet at each vertex and the faces are congruent triangles.

2. Same as Exercise 1, except that the faces are congruent squares.

3. Same as Exercise 1, except that the faces are congruent pentagons.

4. Explain in your own words why there is no regular polyhedron having congruent n-gons, with $n \geqslant 6$, for faces.

5. Explain why a regular polyhedron with congruent squares for faces, or congruent pentagons for faces, must have triple vertices. (A triple vertex is one in which exactly three edges intersect.)

6. Express V and F in terms of E for a regular polyhedron with congruent square faces. Then use Euler's formula to solve for V, E, and F.

7. Same as Exercise 6, except that the faces are congruent pentagons.

A1.9   *Cylinders*

If C is a curve lying in a plane p, and if L is a line not in p but intersecting p in a point of C, then the union of L and all lines parallel to L and passing through C is a *cylindrical surface*. The curve C may be unbounded, for example, a line or an angle, or it may be bounded, for example, a circle or a segment. The curve C is called a directrix of the surface and the line

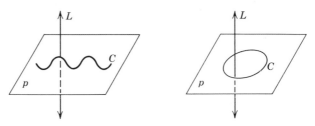

L (or one of its parallels through a point of C) is called the *generator* of the surface. The surface may be thought of as generated by a line which "moves" so that it is always parallel to a given line and so that it always contains a point of a given curve. Each of the lines parallel to L and through a point of C is called an *element* of the surface. If the curve C is a simple closed curve such as a circle or a square, the cylindrical surface is called a *closed cylindrical surface*.

Sometimes a portion of a cylindrical surface, such as that part of a cylindrical surface which lies between two parallel planes, also is called a cylindrical surface. Such a cylindrical surface can be thought of as generated by a segment which moves in a rather obvious way.

A *cylinder* is the set of all points which lie on or within a closed cylindrical surface and between two parallel planes which intersect all the elements of the cylindrical surface. That portion of an element which lies between the parallel planes is called an *element of the cylinder*. That

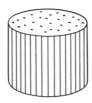

portion of the surface of a cylinder which lies in one of the parallel planes is called a *base* of the cylinder. That portion of the surface which lies in the closed cylindrical surface is called the *lateral surface* of the cylinder. A segment perpendicular to the planes of the bases and joining a point of one of these planes to a point of the other plane is called an *altitude* of the cylinder. Sometimes *altitude* means the distance between the planes which contain the bases.

A *right section* of a cylinder is a section made by a plane perpendicular to an element of the cylinder. A *right cylinder* is a cylinder whose bases are right sections of the cylinder. A *circular cylinder* is one whose bases are circles. A *right circular cylinder* is a cylinder which is a right cylinder and also a circular cylinder.

A *prism* is a cylinder whose directrix is a convex polygon. Prisms may be called triangular, quadrangular, pentagonal, etc., if their bases are triangles, quadrilaterals, pentagons, etc. The edges of a prism which lie within the lateral surface of the prism are called *lateral edges*.

A *parallelepiped* is a prism whose bases are parallelograms. A *rectangular solid* is a parallelepiped all of whose faces are rectangles.

Exercises A1.9

1. How many edges does a triangular prism have?

2. How many lateral edges does a triangular prism have?

3. How many vertices does a triangular prism have?

4. How many faces does a triangular prism have?

5. How many lateral faces does a triangular prism have?

6. Compute $V - E + F$ for a triangular prism, where V is the number of vertices, E is the number of edges, and F is the number of faces.

7. Is it possible for a cylindrical surface to have two skew lines as two of its elements?

8. Is it possible that two lateral edges of a prism are segments of skew lines?

9. Is it possible that two elements of a cylinder may have unequal lengths?

10. Is it possible that two lateral edges of a prism may have unequal lengths?

11. In what kind of a cylinder is an element of the cylinder also an altitude of the cylinder?

12. What is another name for a pentahedron which is also a prism?

13. Are the bases of a prism congruent?

14. Are the lateral faces of a prism parallelograms?

15. Explain why the lateral edges of a right prism are perpendicular to a base of the prism.

16. Explain why the lateral faces of a right prism are rectangles.

17. Are the bases of a cylinder congruent?

18. Is it necessary that a right prism with square lateral faces be a cube?

19. Is it necessary that a right prism with square lateral faces and square bases be a cube?

20. Is it necessary that every cylinder have a right section?

A1.10   *Theorems Regarding Prisms and Cylinders*

1. The lateral edges of a prism are parallel and congruent.
2. The lateral faces of a prism are parallelograms.
3. The lateral faces of a right prism are rectangles.
4. An altitude of a right prism is congruent to each of its lateral edges.
5. Sections of a cylinder made by parallel planes cutting all the elements are congruent.

A1.11   *Surface Area*

In Sections 1.5 and 1.6 we developed the concept of area for elementary planes figures. In this section the concept of area is extended to the surface area of several elementary solids.

The *surface area of a polyhedron* is the sum of the areas of its faces. The *lateral surface area of a prism* is the sum of the areas of the lateral faces of the prism. If p is the perimeter of a right section of a prism and e

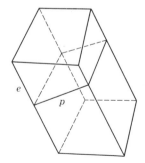
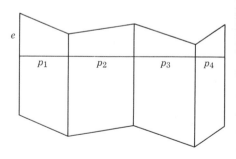

is the length of a lateral edge, then it is easy to prove on the basis of the additive property of length, the additive property of area, and the distributive property of multiplication over addition, that the lateral surface area is *ep*. For

$$ep_1 + ep_2 + \cdots + ep_n = e(p_1 + p_2 + \cdots + p_n) = ep.$$

If we think of a cylinder as approximated by an inscribed prism where n is very large, it seems plausible to define (and so we do) the *lateral surface area of a cylinder* as ep, where e is the length of an element and p is the perimeter of a right section.

A1.12 *Volume*

The volume of a solid is the number of times it "contains" the unit of volume which is a cube whose edge is the unit of length. If the edge of the unit cube is one inch, then the unit of volume is one cubic inch. A right cylinder with elements of length one and with base area B has volume B, because each square unit of area in the base "supports" one cubic unit of volume. Thus a right prism with a rectangular base a by b and with an altitude of 1 has a base area of ab square units and a volume of ab cubic units. Or again, if the floor of a room has an area of 150 square feet and if there is water to a depth of 1 foot in the room, then the volume of the water is 150 cubic feet.

Using postulates similar to those for area we can prove that the volume of a rectangular solid whose dimensions are a, b, c is abc. The case in which a, b, c are natural numbers is illustrated in the following figure.

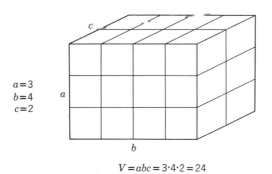

$a=3$
$b=4$
$c=2$

$$V = abc = 3 \cdot 4 \cdot 2 = 24$$

Formulas for computing volumes of other elementary solids are extensions of the formula $V = abc$. The postulates upon which these formulas rest include one called Cavalieri's Principle, which we discuss in the next section.

A1.13   *Cavalieri's Principle*

Imagine two solids with equal altitudes and such that sections of these solids formed by planes parallel to the bases and at equal distances from

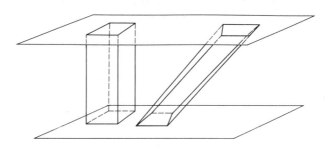

the bases have equal areas. Imagine these solids cut into thin slices of uniform thickness *d* by planes parallel to the bases. The volume of each slice is approximately equal to the product of its thickness and its base area. The percentage of error can be made as small as desired if *d* is taken sufficiently small. It seems reasonable that slices in the two solids at the same distance from their bases should have approximately the same volume, and that the total volumes should be equal.

We adopt this formally as a postulate.

Postulate (*Cavalieri's Principle*). If two solids have equal altitudes, and if sections of these solids formed by planes parallel to the bases and at equal distances from the bases have equal areas, then the solids have equal volumes.

An ordinary deck of playing cards may be used to illustrate this principle. Its volume when it stands erect is equal to its volume when it leans to one side. Obviously, sections at equal distances from the bases have equal areas.

The volume of a right cylinder is the product of the area *b* of its base and the length *h* of one of its elements or altitudes, all of which are congruent to each other, of course. For each unit of altitude contributes *b* units of volume. The volume of an arbitrary cylinder with base area *b*

and altitude length *h* is also *bh*. This is a simple instance of Cavalieri's Principle.

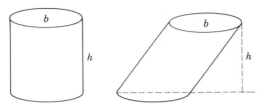

A1.14 *Theorems*

1. The lateral area of a cylinder is the product of the length of an element and the perimeter of a right section.

2. The lateral area of a prism is the product of the length of a lateral edge and the perimeter of a right section.

3. The lateral area of a right cylinder is the product of the length of an element and the perimeter of the base.

4. The lateral area of a right prism is the product of the length of a lateral edge and the perimeter of the base.

5. The opposite faces of a parallelepiped are congruent and parallel.

6. The volume of a rectangular solid is equal to the product of the length of its base, the width of its base, and its altitude.

7. The volume of a parallelepiped is equal to the product of the area of one of its faces and the perpendicular distance between this face and the face parallel to it.

8. The volume of a cylinder is the product of the area of the base and the length of an altitude.

Exercises A1.14

What does each letter in the formulas of Exercises 1 through 14 denote?

1. The lateral area of a cylinder.

$$\text{L.A.} = ep.$$

2. The total surface area of a cylinder.

$$\text{T.S.A.} = ep + 2B.$$

3. The lateral area of a regular prism with *n* lateral faces.

$$\text{L.A.} = nae.$$

4. The lateral area of a right circular cylinder.

$$\text{L.A.} = 2\pi rh.$$

5. The total surface area of a right circular cylinder.

$$\text{T.S.A.} = 2\pi rh + 2\pi r^2.$$

6. The volume of a cylinder.

$$V = Bh.$$

7. The volume of a right cylinder.

$$V = Be = Bh.$$

8. The volume of a prism.

$$V = Bh.$$

9. The volume of a right prism.

$$V = Be.$$

10. The volume of a right circular cylinder.

$$V = \pi r^2 h.$$

11. The volume of a rectangular solid.

$$V = abc.$$

12. The surface area of a rectangular solid.

$$S = 2ab + 2ac + 2bc.$$

13. The volume of a cube.

$$V = e^3.$$

14. The surface area of a cube.

$$S = 6e^2.$$

15. A room is 20 feet long, 16 feet wide, and 9 feet high. Find its volume in cubic yards.

16. Find the surface area of the room of Exercise 15 in square yards.

17. The volume of a room 10 feet high is 9000 cubic feet. Find the area of the floor in square feet.

18. Find the volume of a cylinder if the area of its base is 10 square inches and perpendicular distance between its bases is 10 inches.

19. Find the volume of a right circular cylinder if its base has a radius of 3 inches and its height is 5 inches.

20. Find the lateral area of the cylinder in Exercise 19.

21. Find the total surface area of the cylinder in Exercise 19.

22. Find the lateral area of a triangular right prism whose edge has a length of 10 inches and whose base is an isosceles right triangle with its hypotenuse of length 10 inches.

23. Find the total surface area of the prism in Exercise 22.

24. Find the volume of the prism in Exercise 22.

25. Find the "cubic footage" of a building 80 feet long, 40 feet wide, with a simple inverted-V roof, if it is 12 feet high at the eaves and 16 feet high at the peak of the roof.

A1.15 *Pyramids and Cones*

If C is a curve lying in a plane P and V is a point not in P, then C and V determine the *conical surface* CV which is the union of all lines each of which passes through V and a point of C. The conical surface is the set of all the points which lie on all these lines. The conical surface CV may be considered as generated by a moving line which in each of its positions passes through V and a point of C. The moving line is called the *generator*; each position of the generator is called an *element* of the conical surface; the curve C is called a *directrix*, and the point V is called the *vertex*. If

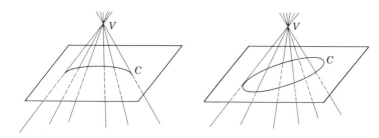

C is a closed curve, the surface is called a *closed conical surface*. The vertex separates the conical surface into two parts called the *nappes* of the conical surface; all the points which lie on the same side of V as the points of C comprise one nappe; all the points which lie on the opposite side of V from the points of C comprise the other nappe. If the curve C is a plane polygonal line, the conical surface is called a *pyramidal surface*.

If the curve C is a simple closed polygon, the conical surface is called a *closed pyramidal surface*.

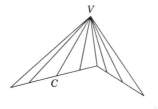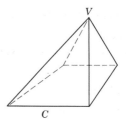

A *cone* is a solid bounded by one nappe of a closed conical surface and a plane which cuts all of the elements of the surface. If the conical surface is a pyramidal surface, then the cone is a *pyramid*. The surface of a cone consists of two parts, the lateral surface and the base. The *lateral surface* consists of those points of the surface which lie in the elements of the conical surface; the base consists of the remaining points of the surface. The lateral surface of a pyramid consists of triangles, one triangle for each side of the base. These lateral surface triangles are called the *lateral faces* of the pyramid. The *elements of a cone* are the segments of the elements of the conical surface that contains the lateral surface of the cone. The *vertex of a cone* is the vertex of the conical surface. The *lateral edges* of a pyramid are the elements of the pyramid which join the vertex of the pyramid to the vertices of the polygon which is its base. A pyramid is *triangular*, *quadrangular*, etc., according to whether its base is a triangle, quadrilateral, etc. A cone is called a *circular cone* if its base is a circle. The *altitude* of a cone is the perpendicular distance from the vertex to the base of the cone (or the segment from the vertex to the plane of the base and perpendicular to the base). The *axis* of a circular cone is the line determined by its vertex and the center of its base. A *right circular cone* is a circular cone whose axis is perpendicular to its base. The *slant height* of a right circular cone is the length of any one of its elements. If the base of a pyramid is a regular polygon, the line through the vertex of the pyramid and the center of the base is the *axis* of the pyramid. If the base of a pyramid is a regular polygon and if its axis is perpendicular to its base, then the pyramid is called a *regular pyramid*. The *slant height* of a regular pyramid is the distance between its vertex and the midpoint of any side of its base, or, equivalently, the altitude of any one of its lateral faces.

Exercises A1.15

1. Are all of the elements of a right circular cone congruent? (Each element is the hypotenuse of a right triangle with vertex at the center of the base of the cone. Are all these triangles congruent?)

2. Are all the lateral edges of a regular pyramid congruent? (Is there a right circular cone with these lateral edges as some of its elements? In other words, is there a right circular cone which circumscribes the pyramid?)

3. Are the lateral faces of a regular pyramid congruent to each other?

4. Are the altitudes of the lateral faces of a regular pyramid congruent to each other?

5. Are some tetrahedrons also pyramids?

6. Are all tetrahedrons also pyramids?

7. Are some pentahedrons also pyramids?

8. Are all pentahedrons also pyramids?

9. Find the lateral area of a regular pentagonal pyramid if its slant height (altitude of lateral face) is 10 and the length of a side of its base is 2.

10. Find the total surface area of a pyramid if its base is a square of side 10 and its altitude is 10.

A1.16 *Theorems*

1. The lateral edges of a regular pyramid are congruent.

2. The elements of a right circular cone are congruent.

3. The lateral faces of a regular pyramid are congruent isosceles triangles.

4. The altitudes of the lateral faces of a regular pyramid are congruent.

5. The lateral area of a regular pyramid is equal to one-half the product of its slant height and the perimeter of its base.

6. The lateral area of a right circular cone is one-half the product of the length of an element and the circumference of the base.

7. A section of a circular cone made by a plane parallel to the base of the cone is a circle or a point.

8. A section of a cone made by a plane through the vertex is a triangle, or a segment, or a point.

9. A section of a pyramid made by a plane parallel to its base is a polygon similar to the base.

10. If two pyramids have congruent bases and congruent altitudes, then plane sections parallel to the bases and at equal heights above the

bases are congruent. (This can be proved using properties of similar figures; it can be verified experimentally using measurements from models.)

11. If two pyramids have congruent bases and congruent altitudes, then they have equal volumes. (This follows from Theorem 10 and Cavalieri's Principle.)

12. The volume of a triangular pyramid is one-third the product of the area of its base and the length of its altitude. (This can be verified experimentally using a triangular pyramid as a ladle to fill a triangular prism with beans or water. It can be proved as indicated.)

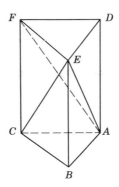

Proof. *ABC-DEF* is a triangular prism. *FEBC*, *EDAB*, *DFCA* are parallelograms. *FEC* and *BCE* are congruent triangles; *BEA* and *DAE* are congruent triangles. *A-BCE* and *A-CEF* are pyramids with congruent bases and altitudes; hence their volumes are equal. *C-ABE* and *F-DEA* are pyramids with congruent bases and altitudes; hence their volumes are equal. But *E-ABC*, *C-ABE*, and *A-BCE* are one and the same pyramid. So the volumes of *E-ABC*, *F-DEA*, *A-CEF* are equal. Since these three pyramids do not overlap, and since they form a partition of the prism, the volume of each of them is one-third the volume of the prism.

13. The volume of any pyramid is one-third the product of the area of its base and the length of its altitude. (If its base has more than three sides, it can be divided into triangular prisms all with the same altitude as the original pyramid.)

14. The volume of a cone is one-third the product of the area of its base and the length of its altitude. (The cone may be considered as approximated by an inscribed pyramid with an *n*-sided base. If *n* is large, the volume of the pyramid differs very little from the volume of the cone.)

15. The volume of a right circular cone of height h and base radius r is given by the formula $V = \frac{1}{3}\pi r^2 h$.

Exercises A1.16

1. The altitude of a regular pyramid is 5 inches long and its base is a square 10 inches on a side. Find its volume.

2. Find the lengths of the edges of the pyramid of Exercise 1.

3. Find the slant height of the pyramid of Exercise 1 (nearest 0.1 inch).

4. Find the lateral area of the pyramid of Exercise 1 (nearest square inch).

5. Find the total surface area of the pyramid of Exercise 1 (nearest square inch).

6. The slant height of a right circular cone is given as 10 inches. The circumference of its base is 5 inches. Find its lateral area.

7. Find the radius of the base of the cone of Exercise 6 (nearest 0.1 inch).

8. Find the total surface area of the cone of Exercise 6.

9. Find the altitude of the cone of Exercise 6.

10. Find the volume of the cone of Exercise 6.

11. The area of the base of a right circular cone is 25.4 square inches; its altitude is 12.7 inches. Compute its volume.

12. The area of the base of a pyramid is 25.4 square inches; its altitude is 12.7 inches. Find its volume.

13. The slant height of a regular pyramid is 10.3 inches; the perimeter of its base is 5.7 inches. Compute its lateral area.

14. The slant height of a right circular cone is 10.3 inches; the circumference of its base is 5.7 inches. Compute its lateral area.

15. A right triangle with sides 3, 4, 5 revolves about the side of length 3 to generate a right circular cone. Find the volume of the cone which is generated.

16. The triangle of Exercise 15 revolves about the side of length 4. Find the volume of the cone which is generated.

17. The triangle of Exercise 15 revolves about the side of length 5. Find the volume of the solid which is generated. *Hint:* Consider the solid as the union of two cones. Use similar triangles to find the dimensions of these cones.

18. A man whittles on a rectangular block of wood until all that remains is a quadrangular pyramid whose base is one of the faces of the original block and whose vertex is one of the vertices of the original block. What fractional part of the wood has been whittled away?

19. A paper drinking cup is in the form of a right circular cone with altitude two inches and diameter of "base" one and one-half inches. Find its capacity.

20. Find the surface area of the cup in Exercise 19.

A1.17   *Spheres*

If P is a point and p is a positive number, the set of all points Q in space which are at a distance p from P is called a *sphere*. The point P is the *center* of the sphere and the number p is the *radius* of the sphere. Any segment joining the center P and a point Q of the sphere also is called a *radius* of the sphere. Any segment through the center P and having endpoints Q and R on the sphere is a *diameter* of the sphere. Sometimes the length of one of these segments is called *the diameter* of the sphere. A *chord* of a sphere is any segment whose endpoints are points of the sphere.

The sphere as just defined is a surface. Sometimes we speak of the union of a sphere and its interior as a spherical region. The volume of a sphere means the volume of the spherical region.

A1.18   *Theorems*

1. The diameter of a sphere is twice its radius.

2. All radii of the same sphere are congruent.

3. All diameters of the same sphere are congruent.

4. A point is within a sphere if its distance from the center of the sphere is less than the radius of the sphere.

5. A point is outside a sphere if its distance from the center of the sphere is greater than the radius of the sphere.

6. Every section of a sphere made by a plane which intersects the sphere but is not tangent to it is a circle. (A plane is tangent to a sphere if it has exactly one point in common with the sphere. If the plane of a circular section of a sphere does not contain the center of the sphere, then the circle is called a *small circle* of the sphere. If the plane of a section contains the center of the sphere, then the circle is called a *great circle* of the sphere. The circumference of a great circle of a sphere is also the *circumference of the sphere*. Every great circle of a sphere separates the sphere into two *hemispheres*.)

7. Circles of a sphere made by planes at equal distances from the center of the sphere have equal radii.

8. The planes of circles with equal radii on a sphere are equally distant from the center.

9. Any three points of a sphere determine a plane.

10. A plane which is perpendicular to a radius of a sphere at its end-point on the sphere is tangent to the sphere.

Exercises A1.18

1. What is the relationship of the center and radius of a great circle of a sphere to the center and the radius of the sphere?

2. How could Theorem 6 of this section be verified experimentally?

3. One way to prove the "small circle part" of Theorem 6 is to drop a perpendicular from the center P of the sphere to the plane of the section. Join the foot of the perpendicular C to any two points A and B of the section. Then prove that $AC = BC$. ($m\angle ACP = m\angle BCP = 90$. Why? $AP = BP$. Why? Then $AC = BC$. Why?) Therefore the section is a circle. Why?

4. Is it possible for three distinct points of a sphere to be collinear?

5. What is the length of the longest chord of a sphere?

6. A given plane curve revolves about a line in its plane and generates a sphere. Describe such a plane curve.

A1.19   *Area and Volume of a Sphere*

The surface area of a sphere may be determined experimentally by wrapping cord on a hemispherical surface and covering a circular disk with cord. A comparison of the length of cord which covers a hemisphere

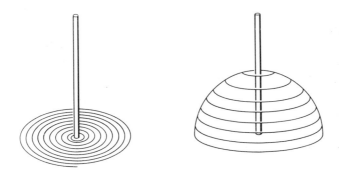

and the length which covers a circular disk of the same radius suggests that the hemisphere has twice as much area as the circle. This leads from the formula $A = \pi r^2$ for the area of a circle to the formula $A = 2\pi r^2$ for the surface area of a hemisphere, and the formula $A = 4\pi r^2$ for the surface area of a sphere.

A more sophisticated approach is to slice a spherical region into n thin slices of thickness $t_1, t_2, \ldots, t_n$, where the sum of the t's is the diameter

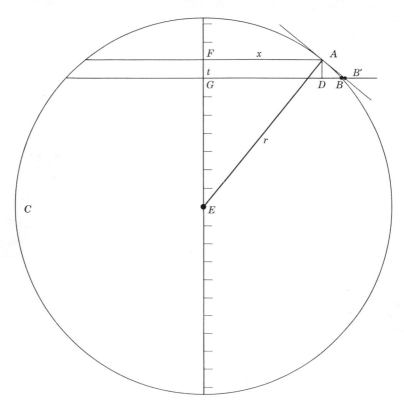

$2r$ of the sphere. This partitions the surface into n zones. The figure suggests a vertical cross section C of a sphere made by a plane which passes through the center E of the sphere. Imagine that the sphere related to this figure has been sliced into n zones of equal thickness by horizontal planes. One of these zones is the surface generated when the arc $\overset{\frown}{AB}$ rotates about the line $\overleftrightarrow{FG}$. Let B' be the point in which the tangent line to C at A intersects $\overleftrightarrow{GB}$. Then AB' is approximately equal to AB and the area of the surface generated when $\overline{AB'}$ rotates about $\overleftrightarrow{FE}$ is approximately equal to the area of the surface generated when $\overset{\frown}{AB}$ rotates about $\overleftrightarrow{FE}$.

Now $\overline{AB'} \perp \overline{AE}$, $\overline{B'D} \perp \overline{EF}$, $\overline{DA} \perp \overline{FA}$. Therefore $\triangle AB'D \sim \triangle AEF$. Let $s' = AB'$. Then $(s', t) \underset{p}{=} (r, x)$ and $s'x = rt$. Think of the zone as a narrow ribbon of width s; s is the length of the arc $\overset{\frown}{AB}$ and is approximately equal to s'. Then the area of the zone is approximately equal to the length of the ribbon, about $2\pi x$, times the width of the ribbon, s. Therefore the area of the zone is approximately $2\pi xs$, which equals approximately $2\pi xs' = 2\pi rt$. If we combine the areas of the n zones, we find that the area K of the sphere is the sum of n terms as follows:

$$K = 2\pi rt_1 + 2\pi rt_2 + \cdots + 2\pi rt_n$$

$$K = 2\pi r(t_1 + t_2 + \cdots + t_n)$$

$$K = 2\pi r(2r) = 4\pi r^2.$$

The total error introduced by using areas of ribbons to approximate areas of zones can be made as small as desired if the maximum thickness of the slices is made small enough. The formula $K = 4\pi r^2$ is an exact formula. Our approach has involved approximations. But our result is the correct one. In higher mathematics the *area of a sphere* is carefully defined, and the assertion that $K = 4\pi r^2$ is a theorem.

In the last development we showed that the area Z of a zone of a sphere is approximately equal to $2\pi rt$, where r is the radius of the sphere and t is the thickness of the zone. Actually, $Z = 2\pi rt$ is also an exact formula.

The formula for the volume of a sphere is obtained now without difficulty. Suppose that the surface of a sphere is divided into a finite number of small pieces. (Circles similar to latitude and longitude lines on the surface of the earth might be used to form the subdivision.) Suppose that the pieces are denoted by $S_1, S_2, \ldots, S_n$. For $i = 1, 2, \ldots, n$, let P_i be a point of S_i. Join P_i and each of the boundary points of S_i to the center of the sphere with a segment. The union of these segments and the piece S_i encloses a portion of the spherical region which is approximately a pyramid whose altitude is a radius of the sphere and whose base is the piece S_i. (We could "flatten" the base by using a portion of the plane which is tangent to the sphere at P_i. The error introduced by this flattening of the base, when accumulated for all n pieces, is as small as desired when n is sufficiently large and the pieces are sufficiently regular.) So the volume of this portion of the sphere is approximately $\frac{1}{3}rs_i$, where r is the radius of the sphere and s_i is the area of S_i. Summing the volumes of the portions of the sphere corresponding to all of the pieces S_i, we find that the volume of the sphere is $\frac{1}{3}r(s_1 + s_2 + \cdots + s_n) = \frac{1}{3}r(4\pi r^2) = \frac{4}{3}\pi r^3$. Therefore the volume of a sphere of radius r is given by the formula $V = \frac{4}{3}\pi r^3$.

Exercises A1.19

1. The radius of a sphere is 6 inches. Find its surface area. Find its volume.

2. The diameter of a sphere is 6 inches. Find its surface area. Find its volume.

3. Compute the ratio of the surface area of the larger sphere to the surface area of the smaller sphere in Exercises 1 and 2.

4. Compute the ratio of the volume of the larger sphere to the volume of the smaller sphere in Exercises 1 and 2.

5. When the radius of a spherical balloon doubles, what happens to its surface area? What happens to its volume?

6. A hemispherical tank has a radius of 6 feet. Find its capacity in gallons (nearest gallon). (231 cubic inches = 1 gallon.)

7. If a gallon of paint covers 300 square feet, how many spherical balls, 3 inches in diameter, can be painted with 1 gallon of paint?

8. If 1 cubic foot of rubber used in making solid rubber balls weighs 60 pounds, how much do 1000 balls, 3 inches in diameter, made from this rubber weigh (nearest pound)?

9. The interior of a box is a cube of edge 1 foot. What is the volume of the largest sphere it will hold?

10. Compute the surface areas of the cube and sphere in Exercise 9.

11. Find the edge of the largest cube which can be inscribed in the sphere of Exercise 9.

12. Compute the surface area of the earth in square miles. (Assume the earth is a sphere of diameter 8000 miles. Use $\pi = 3.14$ and compute the area to three significant figures.)

13. Find the radius of a sphere if its surface area is 1000 square inches.

14. Find the diameter of a sphere if its volume is $500\pi/4$ cubic inches.

15. Find the radius of a sphere if its volume is 113.4 cubic inches.

A1.20   *More Spherical Vocabulary*

As we have stated, every plane section of a sphere, other than the null set or a point, is a circle. If the plane passes through the center of the sphere, it is a *great circle*. Circles of a sphere which are not great circles are *small* circles of the sphere. The *spherical distance* between two points on a sphere which are diametrically opposite is one-half the circumference of the sphere. The spherical distance between two points of a sphere which are not diametrically opposite is measured along the great circle that passes through them and is the length of the shorter of the two arcs into which the two points divide the circle. One-fourth of a great circle is called a *quadrant*. The *axis of a circle of a sphere* is the diameter of the sphere which is perpendicular to the plane of the circle. The *poles of a circle of a sphere* are the endpoints of the axis of the circle. The spherical distance from the nearer pole of a circle to any point on the circle is called the *polar distance* of the circle. A *zone* of a sphere is the portion of a sphere between two parallel planes.

A1.21   *Theorems*

1. The axis of a circle of a sphere passes through the center of the sphere.

2. The diameter of a sphere which passes through the center of a circle of a sphere is the axis of that circle.

3. Every great circle of a sphere separates the sphere into two hemispheres of equal surface area.

4. Any two great circles of a sphere bisect each other.

5. Through the endpoints of a diameter of a sphere pass infinitely many great circles of the sphere.

6. Through two points of a sphere which are not the endpoints of a diameter of the sphere, there is exactly one great circle of the sphere.

7. A point on a sphere at a quadrant's distance from two other points, not the endpoints of a diameter, is a pole of the great circle passing through the two points.

8. A line tangent to a sphere lies in the plane which is tangent to the sphere at the point of contact.

9. A line perpendicular to a radius of a sphere at its endpoint on the sphere is tangent to the sphere.

10. Zones of a sphere which have equal thickness also have equal areas.

Exercises A1.21

1. A right circular cone is inscribed in a sphere, that is, its base is a circle of the sphere and its vertex is a point of the sphere. Is it necessary that the vertex be a pole of the circle?

2. A small circle on a sphere has a radius of 5 inches. The great circle lying in a plane parallel to the plane of the small circle has a radius of 10 inches. Find the distance between the plane of the small circle and the plane of the great circle.

3. Which points on the surface of the earth are at a quadrant's distance from the North Pole?

4. Describe the set of all points on the surface of the earth which are at a quadrant's distance from a certain point on the equator.

5. Is every diameter of a sphere the axis of some great circle of the sphere?

6. Is every diameter of a sphere the axis of some small circle of the sphere?

7. How many small circles of a sphere have the same axis as a given great circle of the sphere?

8. A sphere has a radius of 10 inches. Find the surface area of a zone 3 inches thick.

9. P and Q are fixed points on a sphere at a quadrant's distance from each other. How many small circles of the sphere pass through P and Q? How many great circles pass through P and Q?

10. Same as Exercise 9 except P and Q are at a distance of two quadrants from each other.

Computing with Measurement Data

How many students are in your class? How much do you weigh? Answers to these questions are numbers. Some numerical answers are found by counting, whereas others are found by measuring. The history of mathematics includes the development of the natural numbers to answer how many, and the rational numbers to answer how much.

Numbers obtained by measurement (measurement data) are approximate and results obtained by computing with such numbers are also approximate. We review in this section several rules for computing with approximate data.

Suppose that the length of a bar is reported as 1.486 meters. This may be interpreted to mean that the length is closer to 1.486 meters than it is to either 1.485 meters or 1.487 meters. The measurement might be reported more explicitly as (1.486 ± 0.0005) meters, meaning that the number of meters is between 1.486 − 0.0005 and 1.486 + 0.0005. In this example the *greatest possible error* is 0.0005, the measurement is *precise* to the nearest 0.001, and the measurement is *accurate* to four significant digits. Our rule for adding approximate data involves the precision of the data, and our rule for multiplying approximate data involves the accuracy of the data. Precision is expressed as to the nearest 10, to the nearest 1, to the nearest 0.1, etc. A datum which is precise to the nearest 0.01 has greater precision than one which is precise to the nearest 0.1. Accuracy is expressed as accurate to three significant figures (digits), to four significant figures, etc. A datum which is accurate to three significant figures is more accurate than one which is accurate to only two significant figures.

In interpreting measurement data given in decimal form all nonzero digits are considered to be significant, and some zeros are considered to be significant, whereas others are not. The zeros in 3.05003 are all significant, although the zeros in 0.053 are not significant. The zeros in 3.05003 would still be there if we divided the unit of measurement by 100, or by 1000, or by 10,000. Relative to these smaller units the measurements would be 305.003, 3050.03, and 30500.3, respectively. On the other hand, the zeros in 0.053 would not be necessary if we used a modified unit which is the original unit divided by 100. Thus 0.053 meter = 5.3 centimeters. Similarly, the weight of a sample of calcium chloride might be reported as 23.57 grams or as 0.02357 kilogram. The two zeros in 0.02357 are not significant figures.

If we are told that a projectile from a weapon traveled 15000 meters, it is not clear whether the zeros are significant or not. If they are all significant, this could be indicated by writing 15,000 meters, or 1.5000×10^4 meters in *scientific notation*. Lacking any information to the contrary we would be justified in concluding that only the 1 and 5 are significant in a reported distance of 15,000 meters. After all, the distance might just as well be reported as 15 kilometers.

We consider now the addition of measurement data. If we are adding several measures as in Column (1) we could add and round the answer to 26.8. We should not expect more precision in the computed result than we have in the least precise addend (6.1 in this example). Each number in Column (1) is an approximate measure and we understand that it lies between the corresponding numbers in Columns (2) and (3). Therefore the sum should be between 26.7555 and 26.8805. It is possible that the correct sum is 26.9 to the nearest 0.1, as well as 26.8. (In fact, the probability that it is 26.9 instead of 26.8, in this example, is about $\frac{1}{4}$.) In Column (4) we have rounded the measures so that no measure has more than two decimal places (one place more than the least precise measure). The rounded sum in Column (4) is the same as the rounded sum in (1), and this procedure of rounding down to one place more than the least precise measure seems to be a good working rule when adding several measures. If we round down to the nearest 0.1 as in Column (5), we note that the sum differs by 0.3 from the result in Column (1), and that it is about 0.22 larger than the sum could be as indicated by the sum in Column (3).

(1)	(2)	(3)	(4)	(5)
6.1	6.0500	6.1500	6.1	6.1
0.354	0.3535	0.3545	0.35	0.4
1.36	1.3550	1.3650	1.36	1.4
1.58	1.5750	1.5850	1.58	1.6
3.253	3.2525	3.2535	3.25	3.3
4.551	4.5505	4.5515	4.55	4.6
4.258	4.2575	4.2585	4.26	4.3
5.362	5.3615	5.3625	5.36	5.4
26.818, or 26.8	26.7555	26.8805	26.81, or 26.8	27.1

A good rule to follow when adding measures is to (a) round them down first so that the number of decimal places in no measure exceeds the number of decimal places in the least precise measure by more than one; (b) add; (c) round down to the precision of the least precise measure (that is round off one digit); and (d) cross your fingers to indicate that the answer may not be as precise as the form of the answer indicates.

When multiplying two measures, a good rule to use is the following one. Round off the answer so that it contains no more significant digits than the number of significant digits in the least accurate factor. Consider the product 10.573×1.14. If you multiply and then round off the answer you get 12.1, as in Column (1). If you round off the more accurate factor to four significant figures before multiplying, as in Column (4), you get 12.0. If you round the more accurate one to three significant figures before multiplying, as in Column (5), you get 12.1. As indicated by the products in Columns (2) and (3) the product could be 12.0 or 12.1, with about equal chances for each. Please note that it would be completely misleading to retain more than three significant figures in the result. The right-most digit in the rounded result [either (1) or (4) or (5)] may not be significant in the sense that the product is accurate to the nearest 0.1. The measurement reported as 10.573 may actually be as little as 10.5725 or as much as 10.5735. Similarly, the measurement reported as 1.14 may actually be as little as 1.135 or as much as 1.145. Hence, as reported in (2) and (3), the actual product might be as little as 11.9997875 or as much as 12.1066575. A general rule of thumb for multiplying approximate numbers is to round off the numbers first so that the number of significant figures in no number exceeds the number of significant figures in the least accurate number by more than one and then to round off the answer to the number of significant digits in the least accurate number. Thus (4) illustrates the recommended procedure.

(1)	(2)	(3)	(4)	(5)
10.573	10.5725	10.5735	10.57	10.6
1.14	1.135	1.145	1.14	1.14
42292	528625	528675	4228	424
10573	317175	422940	1057	106
10573	105725	105735	1057	106
12.05322, or 12.1	105725	105735	12.0498, or 12.0	12.084, or 12.1
	11.9997875	12.1066575		

Rules for computing with approximate data should be used with common sense. The rules discussed in this section are working rules for computations involving few data, say when multiplying two numbers or when adding less than ten numbers.

Exercises A.2

1. If the length of a segment is measured as (3.1 ± 0.0005) cm., which of the following reports the measurement best?

    3.1 cm.,   3.10 cm.,   3.100 cm.,   3.1000 cm.

2. Which of the following statements best indicates the accuracy of the measurement in Exercise 1?
    The measurement is accurate to 2 significant figures.
    The measurement is accurate to 3 significant figures.
    The measurement is accurate to 4 significant figures.
    The measurement is accurate to 5 significant figures.

3. Which of the following statements best indicates the precision of the measurement in Exercise 1?
    The measurement is precise to the nearest centimeter.
    The measurement is precise to the nearest 0.1 centimeter.
    The measurement is precise to the nearest 0.01 centimeter.
    The measurement is precise to the nearest 0.001 centimeter.
    The measurement is precise to the nearest 0.0001 centimeter.

4. Identify which zeros in the following measurement data are significant figures.

   1.500 cm.,   0.500 cm.,   0.0500 cm.,   0.005 cm.,   203.0 cm.,

   203.00 cm.,   2030 cm., 2.00×10^5 cm.

5. Express each of the measurements of Exercise 4 in terms of meters.

6. How many significant digits are there in each of the following measurement numbers?

   111000,   11100,   1110,   111,   111.0,   11.10,   11.001.

7. Round off each of the following measurement numbers to four significant figures.

   105.734,   1.03576,   34578.1,   9.0783219,   3.1416.

8. Round each of the following numbers to the nearest 0.01.

   78.537,   42.0051,   4.156789,   1.41421,   2.30103.

9. Add the following measurement numbers using the recommended procedure of this section.

$$245.68$$
$$39.936$$
$$333.3333$$
$$\underline{54.090}$$

10. Multiply the following measurement numbers following the recommended procedure of this section.

   235.76×400.0701.

11. Express $\sqrt{2} + \sqrt{3}$ in decimal notation correct to three decimal places.

12. Express $\sqrt{2} + \sqrt{3}$ in decimal notation correct to three significant figures.

13. Express $\sqrt{2}$ and $\sqrt{8}$ in decimal notation accurate to three significant figures. Multiply these decimal approximations and compare the result with 4.00.

14. Find the area of a rectangle whose sides measure 3.2 inches and 15.8 inches. (Assume that the angles are perfect right angles.) Compare the computed area, rounded to two significant figures, with the product of 3.2 and 16, rounded to two significant figures. Then compute the products 3.15×15.75 and 3.25×15.85. Which of the two-digit approximations to the area seems preferable.

The Language and Symbols of Sets

Sets and Elements of Sets. Ideas regarding sets of objects and relationships among sets are important in mathematics. We think of a set as a collection of objects or elements. The elements of a set are its members. To know the elements of a set is to know the set. To indicate that P is an element of a set Q, we write $P \in Q$. To indicate that R is not an element of Q, we write $R \notin Q$.

Braces. If A, B, C are points, then $\{A, B, C\}$ is a set of points. This symbol using braces for a set reveals the individual elements of the set by name. The order in which these names appear within the symbol is immaterial. Thus "$\{1, 2, 3, 4, 5\}$," and "$\{3, 4, 2, 1, 5\}$" are names for the same set. If $S = \{1, 2, 3, 4, 5\}$, then $1 \in S$, $2 \in S$, $3 \in S$, $4 \in S$, and $5 \in S$; if x is any number other than 1, 2, 3, 4, or 5, then $x \notin S$.

Set-Builder Symbol. If T is the set of all real numbers less than 10, then T is an infinite set; in other words, it has an infinite number of different elements. We cannot list all of its elements by name. In this case a set-builder symbol is convenient to use. Thus $T = \{x : x$ is a real number and $x < 10\}$. We read this as "T is the set of all x such that x is a real number and x is less than 10." If it is understood from the context that x is a real number, this could be shortened to $T = \{x : x < 10\}$.

Subsets and Supersets. If E and F are sets, and if every element of E

is also an element of F, then E is a *subset* of F and F is a *superset* of E; we also say that E is *contained* in F or that F *contains* E.

$E \subset F$ means that E is contained in F, hence also that E is a subset of F. $G \supset H$ means that G contains H, hence also that G is a superset of H. Therefore $E \subset F$ if and only if $F \supset E$.

$E \not\subset F$ means that E is not a subset of F. $G \not\supset H$ means that G is not a superset of H.

Example. If $A = \{1, 2, 3, 4\}$, $B = \{2, 4\}$, $C = \{2, 4, 5\}$, then $B \subset A$, $B \subset C$, $A \supset B$, $C \supset B$, $A \not\subset C$, $C \not\subset A$, $A \not\supset C$, $C \not\supset A$, and $B \not\supset A$.

Example. If $S = \{x : x < 10\}$, $T = \{x : 2 \leqslant x \leqslant 3\}$, then $T \subset S$.

Set Equality. $A = B$ means that "A" and "B" are names for the same thing. Thus $3 + 4 = 7$ since "$3 + 4$" and "7" are names for the same number. If A and B are sets, then $A = B$ if and only if "A" and "B" are names for the same set. Therefore $A = B$ if and only if A and B have the same elements; $A = B$ if and only if every element of A is also an element of B and every element of B is also an element of A. It follows that if $A = B$, then $A \subset B$ and $B \supset A$. Conversely, if $A \subset B$ and $B \subset A$, then $A = B$.

Examples. $\{1, 2, 3\} = \{1, 2, 3\}$, $\{1, 2, 2 + 1\} = \{1 + 2, 1, 2\}$, $\{x : x$ is a positive integer less than $5\} = \{1, 2, 3, 4\}$, and $\{1, 2, 2\} = \{1, 2\}$.

Unions and Intersections. If A and B are sets, then the *union* of A and B, denoted by $A \cup B$, is the set of all elements each of which is in A, or in B, or in both A and B, and the *intersection* of A and B, denoted by $A \cap B$, is the set of all elements each of which is in both A and B.

Thus $A \cup B = \{x : x \in A$ or $x \in B\}$, and $A \cap B = \{x : x \in A$ and $x \in B\}$. The connective "or" is used in the nonexclusive sense illustrated by the following true statements: $2 = 2$ or $2 = 3$; $2 = 4 - 2$ or $2 = 5 - 3$; $2 = 3$ or $2 = 1 + 1$.

Examples.

$$\{1, 2, 3\} \cup \{2, 3, 7\} = \{1, 2, 3, 7\},$$

$$\{1, 2, 3\} \cap \{2, 3, 7\} = \{2, 3\},$$

$$\{x : 0 < x < 5\} \cup \{x : 4 \leqslant x \leqslant 6\} = \{x : 0 < x \leqslant 6\},$$

$$\{x : 0 < x < 5\} \cap \{x : 4 \leqslant x \leqslant 6\} = \{x : 4 \leqslant x < 5\}.$$

If A is any set, then $A \cup A = A$ and $A \cap A = A$.

If $A \subset B$, then $A \cup B = B$ and $A \cap B = A$.

Null Set. It is convenient to think of a set which has no elements. This is an empty set. If E and F are empty sets, then $E = F$ since every element of E is also an element of F, and every element of F is also an element of E. So it is customary to speak of *the empty set*, or *the null set*. "$\varnothing$" is a symbol that denotes the empty set. Do you see that if x is any object whatsoever, then $x \notin \varnothing$? Do you see that if A is any set whatsoever, then $\varnothing \subset A$? It may be interesting to note that $\varnothing \notin \varnothing$, $\varnothing \in \{\varnothing\}$, $\varnothing \subset \varnothing$, and $\varnothing \subset \{\varnothing\}$. It should be clear that $\{\varnothing\}$ is the set whose only element is the empty set. (If it is difficult for you to think of the empty set as an object, try thinking of it as an *object of thought*.)

We think of union and intersection as set operations. These operations can be performed on any sets. If A and B are any sets, not necessarily distinct, then $A \cup B$ is a set, and $A \cap B$ is a set. It is recognized here that $A \cap B$ might be the null set. If $A \cap B = \varnothing$, we say that A and B do not intersect, even though they have an intersection, namely, the empty set.

If L and M are distinct lines intersecting at a point P, then $P \in L$, $P \in M$, and $L \cap M = \{P\}$. Here L and M are sets of points. Their intersection is a set of points, a set which has only one element.

Examples.

$$\{x : x > 5\} \cap \{x : x < 4\} = \varnothing.$$

$$\{x : x > 5\} \cup \{x : x < 4\} = \{x : x < 4 \text{ or } x > 5\}.$$

$$\{1, 2, 3\} \cup \varnothing = \{1, 2, 3\}.$$

$$\{1, 2, 3\} \cap \varnothing = \varnothing.$$

$$\{1, 2, 3\} \cap \{\varnothing\} = \varnothing.$$

$$\varnothing \cup \{\varnothing\} = \{\varnothing\}.$$

$$\varnothing \cap \{\varnothing\} = \varnothing.$$

Set Subtraction. If A and B are sets, not necessarily distinct, then $A - B$ is the set which results when all the elements which are both in A and B are removed from A. Thus $A - B = \{x : x \in A \text{ and } x \notin B\}$.

Examples.

If A is any set, then $A - A = \varnothing$.

If A is any set, then $A - \varnothing = A$.

If $A \cap B = \varnothing$, then $A - B = A$.

If $A = \{1, 2, 3, 6\}$, $B = \{7, 3, 2, 4\}$, then $A - B = \{1, 6\}$ and $B - A = \{7, 4\}$.

$$\{x : 3 \leqslant x \leqslant 4\} - \{3, 4\} = \{x : 3 < x < 4\}.$$

Ordered Pairs. If a and b are any objects, not necessarily distinct, then (a, b) is an *ordered pair*; a is called its first component, and b is called its second component. Thus $(3, 5)$ is an ordered pair whose components are different, whereas $(7, 7)$ is an ordered pair whose components are the same. We understand that $(x, y) = (u, v)$ if and only if $x = u$ and $y = v$. Thus $(3, 5) \neq (5, 3)$ and $(1 + 2, 1 + 4) = (3, 5)$.

This discussion of ordered pairs is adequate for most purposes in elementary mathematics. It is of interest, however, to note that the ordered pair concept can be defined in terms of sets as follows. Thus $(a, b) = \{a, \{a, b\}\}$. According to this definition $(3, 5) = \{3, \{3, 5\}\}$. Of course, also, in view of what set equality means, we have $(3, 5) = \{3, \{5, 3\}\} = \{\{3, 5\}, 3\} = \{\{5, 3\}, 3\}$. Note, however, that $(5, 3) = \{5, \{3, 5\}\}$. Therefore $(5, 3) \neq (3, 5)$ since $5 \in \{5, \{3, 5\}\}$ while $5 \notin \{3, \{3, 5\}\}$. Note, also, that $(3, 3) = \{3, \{3, 3\}\} = \{3, \{3\}\}$. Thus $3 \in (3, 3)$ and $\{3\} \in (3, 3)$.

Product Sets. If A and B are sets, not necessarily distinct, then the *product set* of A and B, denoted by $A \times B$, is the set of all ordered pairs (a, b) where $a \in A$ and $b \in B$. Thus if $A = \{1, 2\}$ and $B = \{2, 3\}$, then $A \times B = \{(1, 2), (1, 3), (2, 2), (2, 3)\}$.

Mappings. If A and B are sets, not necessarily distinct, then a correspondence which associates with each element of A one and only one element of B is called a *mapping* of A *into* B. If m is a mapping of A into B such that every element of B is matched with some element of A, then m is a *mapping* of A *onto* B. If m is a mapping from A onto B, and if each element of B is associated with only one element of A, then m is a *one-to-one correspondence* between A and B.

Examples. Let $A = \{1, 2, 3\}$, $B = \{8, 9\}$, $C = \{10, 11, 12\}$. If m_1 is the mapping which associates 1 with 8, 2 with 9, and 3 with 9, then m_1 maps A *into* B, but also m_1 maps A *onto* B. If m_2 is the mapping which associates 1 with 10, 2 with 11, and 3 with 11, then m_1 maps A *into* C, but m_2 does not map A onto C. If m_3 is the mapping which associates 1 with 10, 2 with 12, and 3 with 11, then m_3 is a mapping of A onto C in which every element of C is matched with only one element of A; hence m_3 is a *one-to-one correspondence* between A and C.

Relations. A *relation* R on a set S is a subset of $S \times S$.

Example. Let $S = \{1, 2, 3\}$ and $R = \{(1, 1), (2, 2), (3, 3)\}$. Then R is a subset of $S \times S$. This is the relation commonly known as the *equals relation*. Note that $(x, y) \in R$ if and only if $(x, y) \in S \times S$ and $x = y$.

Example. Let $S = \{1, 2, 3\}$ and $T = \{(1, 2), (1, 3), (2, 3)\}$. Thus T is a subset of $S \times S$; T is the "less than" relation on S. Note that $(x, y) \in T$ if and only if $(x, y) \in S \times S$ and $x < y$.

Equivalence Relations. Let R be a relation on a set S. R is a reflexive relation if $x \in S$ implies $(x, x) \in R$. R is a *symmetric* relation if $(x, y) \in R$ implies $(y, x) \in R$. R is a *transitive* relation if $(x, y) \in R$ and $(y, z) \in R$ imply that $(x, z) \in R$. R is an *equivalence* relation on S if it is reflexive, symmetric, and transitive.

Example. Let E be the equals relation on the set R of all real numbers. Then $(x, y) \in E$ if and only if $x \in R$, $y \in R$, and $x = y$. E is reflexive since $x = x$ for every real number x. E is symmetric since $x = y$ implies $y = x$. E is transitive since $x = y$ and $y = z$ imply that $x = z$. The equals relation on the set R of all real numbers is an equivalence relation.

Example. Let L be the less than relation on the set R of all real numbers. Then $(x, y) \in L$ if and only if $x \in R$, $y \in R$, and $x < y$. Since it is false that $2 < 2$, it follows that $(2, 2) \notin L$, and therefore L is not reflexive. Since $x < y$ does not imply that $y < x$ (for example, $2 < 3$, but 3 is not less than 2), it follows that L is not symmetric. Since $x < y$ and $y < z$ imply that $x < z$, it follows that L is transitive.

Example. Let S be the set of all segments in Euclidean geometry. Let C be the congruence relation on S. Thus $(x, y) \in C$ if and only if $x \in S$, $y \in S$, and $x \cong y$. Since $x \cong x$ for every segment x, C is reflexive. Since $x = y$ implies $y = x$ for every $x \in S$, $y \in S$, it follows that C is symmetric. Since $x \cong y$ and $y \cong z$ imply that $x \cong z$ for $x \in S$, $y \in S$, $z \in S$, it follows that C is transitive. Hence C is an equivalence relation on the set of all segments.

Equivalence Classes. Let R be an equivalence relation on a set S. If x is any element of S, then there is a set $[x]$ whose members are x and all members y of S such that $(x, y) \in R$. This set is the *equivalence class* determined by x and R. If x and x' are any two elements of S, then $[x]$ and $[x']$ are either the same set or they are disjoint sets, that is, either $[x] = [x']$ or $[x] \cap [x'] = \emptyset$. To prove this suppose $[x]$ and $[x']$ have an element in common, say y. Let z be any element of $[x]$. Then $(z, x) \in R$ and $(x, y) \in R$ imply that $(z, y) \in R$. Also $(z, y) \in R$ and $(y, x') \in R$ imply $(z, x') \in R$. It follows that $z \in [x']$. Hence if x and x' intersect, then $[x] \subset [x']$. Similarly, if $[x]$ and $[x']$ intersect, then $[x'] \subset [x]$. It follows that if x and x' intersect, then $[x] = [x']$.

Example. Let S be the set of all segments and let C be the congruence relation on S. Then C is an equivalence relation on S. Each equivalence class determined by C is an infinite set of segments all congruent to each other. Every element of S belongs to one and only one of these equivalence classes. Note that there are infinitely many equivalence classes in this example.

Example. Let S be the set of all integers and let R be the relation defined as follows: $(x, y) \in R$ if and only if $x \in S$, $y \in S$, and $x - y$ is an integral multiple of 4. Thus $(1, 5) \in R$ since $1 - 5$ is an integral multiple of 4; $(1, 6) \notin R$ since $1 - 6$ is not an integral multiples of 4. It is easy to show that R is an equivalence relation. S is partitioned into four equivalence classes by the relation R. They are $[0]$, $[1]$, $[2]$, and $[3]$. If x is any integer then one and only one of the following statements is true: $(x, 0) \in R$, $(x, 1) \in R$, $(x, 2) \in R$, $(x, 3) \in R$. Hence every integer is a member of one of these classes. And no number is a member of two of these classes. Suppose, for example, that $y \in [0]$ and $y \in [1]$. Then there are integers k and h such that $y - 0 = 4k$, and $y - 1 = 4h$. Then $2y - 1 = 4(h + h)$. Since the left side is an odd integer and the right side is an even integer, this is a contradiction. Therefore $[0] \cap [1] = \emptyset$. Similarly, it may be shown that every pair of these equivalence classes are disjoint.

Index